Congratulations to
Clare Beams
Winner of the
2020 Bard Fiction Prize

⹌

Clare Beams, author of *We Show What We Have Learned and Other Stories*, joins previous winners Nathan Englander, Emily Barton, Monique Truong, Paul La Farge, Edie Meidav, Peter Orner, Salvador Plascencia, Fiona Maazel, Samantha Hunt, Karen Russell, Benjamin Hale, Brian Conn, Bennett Sims, Laura van den Berg, Alexandra Kleeman, Karan Mahajan, Carmen Maria Machado, and Greg Jackson.

⹌

The Bard Fiction Prize is awarded annually to a promising emerging writer who is an American citizen aged thirty-nine years or younger at the time of application. In addition to a monetary award of $30,000, the winner receives an appointment as writer in residence at Bard College for one semester without the expectation that he or she will teach traditional courses. The recipient will give at least one public lecture and meet informally with students.

For more information, please contact:

Bard Fiction Prize
Bard College
PO Box 5000
Annandale-on-Hudson, NY 12504-5000

COMING UP IN THE SPRING

Conjunctions:74
GRENDEL'S KIN:
THE MONSTERS ISSUE
Edited by Bradford Morrow

When darkness fell, monsters arose. When nightmares first drove us from peaceful sleep, monsters lingered in daylit memory, denizens of the liminal. Monsters have tormented, provoked, and inspired the human imagination from earliest times. Dating back to the dawn of myth and folklore, these representatives of otherness and terror have roamed our narratives, inhabiting countless forms and displaying endlessly weird proclivities. Grendel and Gorgon, Kraken and Snallygaster, Wyvern and Wendigo, Tokoloshe and Chupacabra—each has different cultural origins and geographies, and each horrifies in different ways. If Frankenstein's monster, the Golem, and androids were fabricated by human hands, are not the elusive Yeti and shape-shifting Ryūjin, the thirsty vampire and bellicose Martian equally fashioned from human ingenuity, the mind's eye seeing beyond the ordinary? And what of Jekyll and Hyde, where monster and man share one body?

We bring our monsters to life through art and science, through projection and dreaming and madness. We animate and battle them. We encourage them to battle one another. We are drawn to them and fascinated by them, yet also loathe them. We find them where they don't even exist. It may be that we *need* monsters in ways we can scarcely begin to fathom.

Conjunctions:74, Grendel's Kin: The Monsters Issue, explores, through innovative fiction, poetry, and essays, the many ways in which monsters are sublime and horrifying and an important part of the human legacy from one generation to the next. Contributors will include Julia Elliott, Elizabeth Hand, Madeline Kearin, and many others.

One-year individual US subscriptions to *Conjunctions* are only $18 (two years for $32) for today's most innovative fiction, poetry, and narrative nonfiction. To read dangerously, subscribe or renew at conjunctions.com, or mail your check to *Conjunctions*, Bard College, Annandale-on-Hudson, NY 12504. For e-book editions of current and selected past issues, visit openroadmedia.com/conjunctions. If you have questions or wish to request an invoice, e-mail conjunctions@bard.edu or call (845) 758-7054.

CONJUNCTIONS

Bi-Annual Volumes of New Writing

Edited by
Bradford Morrow

Contributing Editors
Diane Ackerman
Martine Bellen
Mei-mei Berssenbrugge
Mary Caponegro
Brian Evenson
Peter Gizzi
Robert Kelly
Ann Lauterbach
Norman Manea
Dinaw Mengestu
Rick Moody
Fred Moten
Karen Russell
Joanna Scott
David Shields
Peter Straub
Quincy Troupe

Published by Bard College

EDITOR: Bradford Morrow
MANAGING EDITOR: Nicole Nyhan
SENIOR EDITORS: Jedediah Berry, Benjamin Hale, J. W. McCormack, Edie Meidav, Michael Sarinsky, Pat Sims
COPY EDITOR: Pat Sims
ART EDITOR: Jessica Fuller
ASSISTANT EDITOR: Evangeline Riddiford Graham
PUBLICITY: Darren O'Sullivan, Mark R. Primoff
EDITORIAL ASSISTANTS: Michael Blackmon, Emily Giangiulio, Jamie Gray Gillette, Danielle Martin, Nohan Meza, Nik Slackman

CONJUNCTIONS is published in the Spring and Fall of each year by Bard College, Annandale-on-Hudson, NY 12504. This project is supported in part by an award from the National Endowment for the Arts and from the New York State Council on the Arts with the support of Governor Andrew M. Cuomo and the New York State Legislature.

SUBSCRIPTIONS: Use our secure online ordering system at conjunctions.com, or send subscription orders to CONJUNCTIONS, Bard College, Annandale-on-Hudson, NY 12504. Single year (two volumes): $18.00 for individuals; $40.00 for institutions and non-US. Two years (four volumes): $32.00 for individuals; $80.00 for institutions and non-US. For information about subscriptions, back issues, and advertising, contact us at (845) 758-7054 or conjunctions@bard.edu. *Conjunctions* is listed and indexed in JSTOR and Humanities International Complete and included in EBSCO*host*.

Editorial communications should be sent to Bradford Morrow, *Conjunctions*, 21 East 10th Street, 3E, New York, NY 10003. Unsolicited manuscripts cannot be returned unless accompanied by a stamped, self-addressed envelope. Electronic and simultaneous submissions will not be considered. Do not send work via any method requiring a signature for delivery. If you are submitting from outside the United States, contact conjunctions@bard.edu for instructions.

Cover design by Jerry Kelly, New York. Cover art image of Antelope Canyon, Arizona, courtesy of hikersbay.com.

The contribution by Sabine Schiffner was translated from German by Helena Van Brande in 2019 and originally published in the following: "The Anchorite" ("der anachoret"), from *Male. Lyrik Edition Band 23* (zu Klampen Verlag, Springe 2006); "With Great Delight," "Tordo," "Linné," and "Silver Firs" from *Djinn* (S. Fischer Verlag GmbH, 2007).

Conjunctions e-books of current and selected past issues are distributed by Open Road Integrated Media (openroadmedia.com/conjunctions) and available for purchase in all e-reader formats from Amazon, Apple, B&N, Google, Indiebound, Kobo, Overdrive, and elsewhere.

Retailers can order print issues directly from *Conjunctions*.

Printers: Maple Press, GHP

Typesetter: Bill White, Typeworks

ISSN 0278-2324

ISBN 978-0-941964-20-3

Manufactured in the United States of America.

TABLE OF CONTENTS

EARTH ELEGIES

Edited by Bradford Morrow

EDITOR'S NOTE

EVEN BEFORE THE BRAZILIAN RAIN FOREST became engulfed in flames, we knew that the evolving worldwide ecological crisis was one of existential magnitude. Vast territories of arctic glaciers melt, while huge swaths of earth's permafrost continue to thaw, discharging methane, Pleistocene corpses, and microbes from millennia past. Hurricanes and typhoons are counterpointed by drought, against a backdrop of steadily escalating temperatures across the globe. Our oceans, choking on plastic and myriad chemicals, are rising up as if in protest. Populations of insects, birds, fish, mammals, flowers, trees, coral—living beings of every kind—are increasingly endangered as their habitats suffer, ushering them toward extinction. It is inarguable that our planet and all of its denizens, both flora and fauna, humans among them, are imperiled. *Earth Elegies* addresses this essential theme and celebrates our fragile, sublime, indispensable world.

Contributors included here range from poets and naturalists to fiction writers and essayists. Some are elegiac, others incensed. Some envision Anthropocene apocalypse, others offer historical and scientific perspectives. The Fukushima Daiichi nuclear disaster is invoked, as are the Agbogbloshie e-waste dump in Ghana and the Great Pacific Garbage Patch's toxic cousin in the Atlantic. Cases of deadly *Naegleria fowleri* are contracted by innocent swimmers in a Catskills lake. The Brazil nut foragers and eco-martyrs Maria do Espírito Santo da Silva and Zé Cláudio Ribeiro da Silva are remembered here, having been assassinated for their activism in the Amazonian state of Pará, where for years they had subsisted in harmony with their natural surroundings. Even a phantasmagoric Moby Dick resurfaces with Ahab in tow to engage in combat with multinational corporations shipping products across the ocean that are harmful to the ecology.

All of these writers have approached our theme from unexpectedly different angles, but no matter how diverse their narratives, the many voices and visions in this issue emanate from a single concern: the survival of our planet.

—Bradford Morrow
October 2019
New York City

Fallen Martyrs, Felled Trees
Rob Nixon

> *The days stand like angels in blue and gold, incomprehensible, above the ring of annihilation.*
>
> —Erich Maria Remarque, *All Quiet on the Western Front (1929)*

EXIT WOUNDS

ONE FALL EVENING, I was driving through Wisconsin's soya fields, drifting along in the half dark, listening to the BBC World Service, when a voice emerged from the ether to galvanize my attention. The voice started strongly in Spanish then faded as the interviewer translated the man's words.

He had survived the massacre, he said. No, he did not want to give his name. Yes, he feared for his life. Yes, they will come for us again. They always do.

Beneath the translator's dispassionate delivery, the faint voice of the unnamed man quavered as he spoke of the fallen—four indigenous Asháninka from the Peruvian Amazon, forest defenders, murdered by an illegal logging gang.

Then the Asháninka survivor said something that stopped me in my tracks: "Those people were dead to the eye before they were killed."

Their apparently sudden deaths had been a long time coming. Before bullets pierced their flesh, before exit wounds wrenched them from their rain forest and from this earth, the killing of the four Asháninka men was already underway.[1] For some time, those forest defenders had been "dead to the eye," shrouded in obscurity, consigned to a political and existential purgatory, hovering between life and the sustained threat of an always imminent assassination.

---

[1] We now know the names of those men: Edwin Chota Valera, Jorge Ríos Pérez, Leoncio Quinticima Melendez, and Francisco Pinedo.

In the global resource wars, "those people" appear as expendable shadow beings, weighing almost nothing in the grand scheme of things. In the global resource wars, the going price for tropical hardwoods—and the land beneath—is higher than the going price for the lives of the indigenous and the poor. In the cold calculus of the global resource wars—which are always also local—the Asháninka were barely visible, barely audible cost-effective casualties.

THE ENVIRONMENTAL MARTYR BELT

We are witnessing an epidemic of environmental martyrdom, particularly in earth's vital but embattled tropical forests. Front-line forest defenders reside primarily in what we might call the environmental martyr belt that girdles the globe, the tropical midriff of the earth: Honduras, El Salvador, Guatemala, Costa Rica, Mexico, Peru, Columbia, Brazil, Nigeria, Congo, Gabon, Sri Lanka, Myanmar, Cambodia, Laos, Vietnam, Indonesia, Malaysia and the Philippines. In the contested forests of these lands, adhering to the values that make life feasible can expose inhabitants to the risk of murder. The environmental martyr belt is pocked with shallow graves and traversed by ghosts; it is full of shadow places to which we're all materially bound.

Activists invoke the idea of environmental martyrdom, but they do not invoke it in isolation. A chorus of other terms recur: environmental assassination, targeted killings, cold-blooded execution, murder, persecution, massacre, carnage, ecocide, the green murder epidemic, eco-criminal hot spots. Each word or phrase inadequate on its own, all necessary, as people reach for ways to give voice to an intolerable, ambient terror.

Martyrdom is direct action in extremis. Martyrs put their bodies on the line, risking, for the sake of principle and survival, not just a weekend in jail, but burial in the dead of night in a shallow grave. Some environmental martyrs remain anonymous, vanish unheard of outside their villages. But others achieve in their earthly afterlife a complex rallying power and an enduring force. For we are witnessing a pushback from endangered forest communities against unregulated plunder by men wielding guns and chain saws, men whose actions jeopardize local life and, incrementally, our planetary prospects.

Rob Nixon

To be a martyr is to become larger than life after your life has ceased. To be a martyr is to die for a cause in a manner that confers on your being posthumous power and purpose. When repressive regimes have shut their eyes and closed their ears to suffering, the martyr's body—by shocking insensate senses back to life—demands that the inattentive pay attention. Where words no longer serve, the corpse silently conscripts witnesses.

Martyrdom is a resonant word, but it carries certain risks. The risk that the singular figure who ascends into the firmament of memory may become uncoupled from the broader social movement. The risk of sanctifying suffering and forbearance. Yet, amidst the current spate of forest martyrdom, one is struck by the recurrence of ordinary martyrs, people whose lives and deaths attest to the quotidian violence against their communities, both human and ecological.

The corpse personifies a raw brutality—directed against the individual body, against the body politic of besieged communities, and against the living body of the forest itself. The environmental martyr thus mediates between systemic injustice and specific suffering.

Over the past decade, we have seen environmental assassinations soar. According to Global Witness, between 2008 and 2018 some 1,427 environmental activists were murdered.[2] That's nearly three every week—more than twice the rate of journalists killed, which has itself reached appalling levels. Hit men, security guards, private contractors, ranchers, and timber gangs—often abetted by the military or police—continue to murder defenders who try to hold the line against illegal logging, forest arson, unregulated mining, agribusiness, mega-dams, and associated land seizures.

All this while earth is hemorrhaging ten billion trees a year. The rate of deforestation has doubled since 2000 and the planet continues to shed trees like early autumn leaves. A forest the size of Italy goes under annually. As Global Forest Watch reports: "If tropical deforestation were a country, its emissions would be greater than those of the European Union." In destroying forests, we're destroying the planet's most significant terrestrial carbon sink—only the oceans

---

[2] The real figure is likely to be much higher: in some regions, like the Central African rain forests—subject to acute resource wars—no reliable statistics exist on the murder rate of activists.

store more carbon. However we strive to rein in this runaway process, community-held lands—many in the environmental martyr belt— are vital to any solution. A survey of thirty-seven tropical countries found that community lands sequester fifty-five million tons of carbon, four times the world's annual emissions.

Intrepid NGOs like Global Witness, Not1More, and Brazil's Pastoral Land Commission play a critical role in keeping tally of green murders of indifferent interest to the corporate media. In mapping the distribution and scale of the killings, such NGOs do essential work. Global Witness, for example, insists on naming all the dead and, where possible, excavating their stories. Such stories are vital, for statistics in isolation can only get us so far as we seek to transform public attitudes and policies in the exacting pursuit of an elusive justice.

Metrics are indispensable. Yet metrics alone are insufficient for the task at hand. To bring numbers to life, we need ever more inventive forms of testimony that can infuse disembodied data with a bodily immediacy. How can story and image complement statistics with the quite different powers of nondata-driven knowledge? How can we summon the creative energies of witnessing to bring to the metrics of environmental suffering a granular specificity?

Ta-Nehisi Coates, writing against the backdrop of Black Lives Matter, makes this observation:

> Racism is a visceral experience, that dislodges brains, blocks airways, rips muscle, extracts organs, cracks bones, breaks teeth. You must never look away from this. You must always remember that the sociology, the history, the economics, the graphs, the charts, the regressions all land, with great violence, upon the body.

Coates's words apply with equal force to the indigenous communities and microminorities inhabiting the environmental martyr belt, where to take a stand for cultural and ecological survival can be a life-ending experience. The fate of such communities is twinned to the fate of the great rain forests in our age of climate breakdown, twinned to the future of forests where the economics, the graphs, the charts, the regressions all land, with great violence, upon the soon-to-be martyred body.

Rob Nixon

Through the gravity of stories and images, artist-activists can bring a corporeal intimacy to the global environmental murder rate. And so we turn to them—these writers, photographers, filmmakers, street artists, oral historians, bloggers, video artists, and podcasters—in our quest to bring a vital urgency to a bloody epidemic. We depend on such witnesses to make visceral the algebra of a diffuse mass murder. For the dead deserve the vital specificity that is their due: names and faces and flesh to body forth the bare bones of graphs and charts. The suffering may be systemic but it's never general.

Behind the numbers, people are living there. People are living there: behind the numbers, beneath the trees.

Maria do Espírito Santo da Silva and Zé Cláudio Ribeiro da Silva.
Felipe Milanez.

IF THE FOREST HAD FEET TO WALK

Before Maria do Espírito Santo da Silva and Zé Cláudio Ribeiro da Silva were ambushed near their home, the couple—Brazil nut foragers and artisans—had enjoyed a long, nonviolent relationship with the forest.

Before two men ambushed them on May 24, 2011, beside a narrow bridge, the couple had spent twenty-three years together. Year in, year out, they proved—to themselves and others—that it was possible to

12

live off and with the rain forest, rather than treating the forest as an enemy hostile. This belief made them dangerous.

Before the two gunmen, strangers, unknown to the da Silvas, ambushed them around seven thirty on a Tuesday morning, the couple had borne witness to a life of possibility. They were agroforesters and small-scale farmers who forged a path of hope. They were idealists and pragmatists, who lived adaptively. They drew on customary knowledge of forest food ways, but were cognizant of a world of shifting values, in which Brazil nut products traveled to other continents, gathering value as they went. The couple was committed to surviving. They believed their survival and the rain forest's survival were perfectly compatible if they approached the forest in a spirit of respectful inventiveness. They consumed and sold a smorgasbord of forest products, including brazil nuts, nut oils, nut creams, nut flour and bark, not to speak of produce developed from myriad other Amazon plants.

Before the ambush, the couple lived peaceably with the rain forest's nonhuman communities. Humans were another matter. Maria and Zé Cláudio's commitment to forest life and forest law made them a multitude of enemies. Zé Cláudio, in conversation with his friend the journalist, filmmaker, and scholar Felipe Milanez, struggled to enumerate all the people who wanted the couple dead: illegal loggers, illegal charcoal burners, illegal miners, beef and soya-bean barons, land-hungry settlers, politicians and police officers up to their necks in graft.

Before the ambush, near Marabá in the Amazonian state of Pará, the couple had no illusions about the region they were living in. They and their families before them were from around there: Maria and Zé Cláudio had first harvested Brazil nuts as children. Pará was now in the grip of such lawlessness that "extrajudicial"—including extrajudicial killings—covered almost everything.

Before the gunmen fired the first shot, the couple had learned to live with a sense of being shadowed. They explained to Milanez how you had to inhabit the mind of your as-yet-unknown would-be killer. You had to outwit this all-too-real imaginary enemy. You had to learn to vary your routes, traveling this way and that. If you dropped your guard and let a rhythm shape your days, it would be that much easier for your murderer to set a trap.

13

Before their killers had plotted the ambush, the couple had gained—depending on your perspective—local notoriety or local renown for seeking to uphold the law. Their method was intrepid. They lay in wait for logging trucks transporting their illegal bounty of hardwoods, including lumber from the much-coveted Brazil nut tree, which was officially protected. The da Silvas liked to position themselves on the crest of a hill, where they knew a logging truck would have to shift to a lower gear, laboring up the slope. Zé Cláudio would step forward, accost the driver, and inform him he was breaking the law. In the background, Maria would pull out her small camera and photograph the truck, the license plate, the driver. Then they would present their evidence to local authorities and demand action.

Before, just seconds before the hitmen fired the first shot, Zé Cláudio was on his motorbike, Maria riding pillion, hugging him tight from behind. They were negotiating a rutted road a few miles from their home. The gunmen had chosen their spot carefully. The road was terrible: full of potholes, deep puddles, and wandering cows. Any motorbike would have to slow to a crawl.

Before, over two millennia before that first shot entered Maria's body, the Greeks coined the word μᾰρτῠρέω (marturéō). The English word "martyr" and the Portuguese "martírio" owe a shared debt to the Greek term, which means "to testify or bear witness."

Before a rancher dreamed of turning their rain-forest reserve into clear-cut cattle land and before he hired two hitmen, Maria and Zé Cláudio bore witness. They bore photographic witness to crimes against the forest. They bore witness to the possibility that existing laws could be actively enforced. They bore witness to a civic ideal by turning their reserve into an island of legality amidst a sea of lawlessness. They bore witness, through the arc of their lives, to the possibility of human and biotic communities successfully cohabiting. But through all of this they bore witness in a state of anticipatory martyrdom.

Six months before the hitmen completed the contract killing, Zé Cláudio traveled to an environmental conference in Manaus. There he declared: "I will protect the forest at all costs. That is why I could get a bullet in my head at any moment." The strain was near constant. How do two people dwell in the present, pottering about on their daily tasks, while being thrust forward into a kind of hovering afterlife, observing themselves retrospectively after their near-certain murder?

Before the ambush, in interviews with Milanez, Maria and Zé Cláudio speak openly of their fears. Her mental health is starting to suffer. Yet neither is prepared to forgo their principles. Zé Cláudio puts it this way:

> If I say I'm not afraid, I'm lying, right? Because the almighty knew he was going to die, but he was coming back on the third day and he was afraid. I am afraid but I have obligations as a citizen: when I see an injustice, it takes away my fear. . . . It's better to die trying than to die indifferent.

Before the ambush, a quarter of a century before, stands the figure of Chico Mendes. Maria and Zé Cláudio are intensely conscious of Chico's fate, of the events leading up to his assassination in 1988. How could they not be, as they go poking sticks into those twinned hornets' nests of rain-forest conservation and Brazilian land reform?

Six months before the ambush, Zé Cláudio declares: "The same thing they did to Chico Mendes in Acre, they want to do to me. Because I aggressively denounce the loggers and charcoal producers, they think I shouldn't exist. I'm here talking to you today, but in a month you may get the news that I'm gone." Asked if he and Maria should consider hiring an armed guard for protection, Zé Cláudio gives an emphatic no. Look what happened to Chico, he says. An armed guard, who accompanies you everywhere can easily be bribed and become a paid informer, increasing your risk of being murdered. For protection, Maria and Zé Cláudio choose to go everywhere together so that when death comes it will not separate them.

Before the ambush, Maria says: "The foundation of my whole story was inspired by Chico." Like Chico, they believe that a more just system of land and labor rights, the defense of forest-dependent people, and the health of the rain forest are all facets of a single struggle. Chico is more than a personal inspiration. He has passed down to them a sense of structural possibility. For they're living his greatest legacy: the extractive reserve, a notion Chico championed and helped institute. Under this system, the reserves are publicly owned but cooperatively managed, allowing customary inhabitants to harvest

15

rain-forest produce and practice subsistence farming, tending the forest without exhausting it. Extractive reserves continued to gather force after Chico's murder and they now comprise 13 percent of the Brazilian Amazon, creating a buffer against private development. The da Silvas see themselves as beneficiaries—but also custodians—of the system Chico has made possible. There he dwells, behind and ahead of them. From the afterlife, this is his bequest.

Fourteen years before their joint murder, Maria and Zé Cláudio had helped found an extractive reserve. Initially, four hundred families signed up for territory covering twenty-two thousand hectares. At that point, 85 percent of the rain forest in the reserve remained intact. But by the time of their deaths, only 20 percent of the native forest was still standing. And only a handful of families continued to practice agroforestry. Over time, Maria told Milanez, a collective, viable dream had become downgraded into a utopia.

A few months before the hitmen dragged Maria and Zé Cláudio into the forest and executed them beneath the canopies they adored, Maria reflected on the region's history of foul play and land theft. Newcomers would offer cash for forest and logging rights. At first, many locals, Maria explains, dismissed individual land ownership as an exotic, improbable fiction. They'd never thought the forest was theirs to own; after all, the forest owned them. Thus, people found themselves dispossessed without grasping the principle of possessive individualism that underpinned the "sale." Land barons intimidated locals into signing documents—with just a thumbprint—that in their illiteracy they couldn't remotely understand. Land barons brought in indigent outsiders, promising work but then docking the workers' entire salaries for board and lodging, trapping them in a kind of modern slavery.

But before the ambush, Maria and Zé Cláudio stood firm. With the help of the forest, they sidestepped the threat of peonage. After their testimony shut down illegal sawmills, some locals angrily dismissed the couple as "backward people, people from the past." But they kept the future steadily in view. They had figured out that—if you were patient—a standing Brazil nut tree was worth far more, even in market terms, than a logged tree reduced to a one-off wad of cash. The da Silvas were in it for the long haul.

Before the ambush, in a series of lyrical interviews that Milanez conducts, Maria and Zé Cláudio make one thing clear: they won't be bought. They're emphatic on this point: the unfragmented parcel of forest in their custody won't ever be for sale. They're not budging, but sometimes they wish the forest had the power to move away from there. Zé Cláudio recalls a song that the rubber tappers used to sing: "If the forest had feet to walk, it would no longer stay, when it sees the danger it would speed away."

Before the ambush, Maria and Zé Cláudio were not locally obscure: four thousand people turned up for their funeral. But the wider world would have known little of their philosophies of forest consciousness, environmental time, and social justice were it not for the prescience and persistence of a singular figure, Felipe Milanez, who became a fast friend. He recognized something special in their story of interspecies love, justice, dignity, and persecution. Something special but also something powerfully ordinary that spoke to the broader struggles of people pushed to the edge. So—in essays, on film, in podcasts, interviews, and TED talks—Milanez bore witness to their witnessing. And gave volume, a priceless volume, to the voices of these rain-forest martyrs and the values they upheld.

Zé Cláudio Ribeiro da Silva and Majesty. Felipe Milanez.

Before the gunmen murdered the da Silvas, Milanez had known the couple for just over a year. On their first meeting, Zé Cláudio invited him on a pilgrimage to pay homage to Majesty, "the pride of our forest," the most gigantic, munificent Brazil nut tree in the reserve. As the two men walked, Zé Cláudio offered a running commentary on the ecological matrix of the rain forest—on edible plants and botanical medicines, on creatures, like the coatimundi, that are vital for dispersing Brazil nut seeds. When they reached Majesty, Zé Cláudio stood at her feet and flung out his arms in a posture of unjaded amazement and ecstasy.

Before the ambush, Milanez struggled to place his story of these agroforesters in the media. He weathered rejection after rejection. But he continued to believe. Finally, *Vice* gave him a venue. Then something happened that seemed almost preternaturally coincidental. On the morning of the assassination, Milanez posted the grim news on the *Vice* blog, including excerpts from the vibrant interviews he'd conducted with the couple. By fate or chance, that very day the Lower House of Brazil's congress was debating some devastating cuts to the forest code, changes that would weaken the protection of the rain forest and the people it sustains. In protest, a member of the Brazilian Green Party got up and announced in front of the assembly: "Unfortunately, I'm standing here now to speak of a tragedy that happened today. I would like to read an excerpt from an interview conducted by Felipe Milanez." What he read included these words, which went out to the nation:

> Felipe Milanez: "When a tree is cut down does its sap remind you of blood?"
> Zé Cláudio: "My friend, it exudes a smell when it's being cut down and you can smell it. When it's about to fall, you can hear it groan."
> Felipe: "Do you feel as if someone has died?"
> Zé Cláudio: "I do. If you kill something it had to be a living being first."

The ruralistas in parliament—the lobby of ranchers, loggers, soya overlords, charcoal barons, and property speculators—booed at these words. Their boos continue, echoing down the halls of history.

*

That was before the funeral, where a woman held up the placard "Majesty Has Been Orphaned." Before a second woman shouted: "They've killed another and another. But they will resurrect, will resurrect, will resurrect."

Before the ambush, Maria speaks to Milanez about her fears. The greatest one is this: if deforestation continues in a headlong rush, nothing will remain except the consequences—"And the consequences are very large." As the rain forest recedes, a distance opens up between people and the little miracles of nature. Maria is aghast that at the local festival of flowers they're now celebrating with artificial plastic blooms. What's next? she asks. Here, in the Brazil nut heartland, children reconstructing the giant nuts out of Play-Doh because they have no access to the real thing? How can you put a market price on the loss of such small, sacred intimacies? Maria's concerns are not hers alone. Kapka Kassabova, walking through the beleaguered forests of her native Bulgaria, frets over the pace of estrangement:

> What remains sacred if a sacred mountain becomes a super-dump? I felt strongly that within my lifetime, we may all become exiles. That we may all be robbed by devouring demons disguised as policy and industry, that we may all walk down some road carrying in plastic bags our memories of forests and mountains, clean rivers and village lanes.

Immediately after the murders, one of the hitmen pulls out his hunting knife, saws off Zé Cláudio's right ear, and puts it in a plastic bag. Now he has evidence that the contract killing is complete. What stories that ear holds. It has listened to the groaning of great trees as they fell. It has heard the shrieking of macaws, the mewling of marmosets, the soft tread of feet moving across forest moss. It has listened to the wind rearranging leaves. It has listened to the thinning dawn chorus as the forest fractures and birdlife attenuates. It has listened as a new silence arrives, the silence not of peace but of environmental pain. It has listened for the vroom of illegal chain saws, ready to intervene. That ear has lived so long on the qui vive, in a constant state of readiness, awaiting, in the dead of night, the footfall of would-be killers. As Zé Cláudio tells Milanez: "I live with my ear standing on alert. We can't sleep properly. When the dog barks you get vigilant."

19

Tell me, when an ear finds itself severed from life, all bloodied in a plastic bag, how long can it hold on to the sounds it loves and fears?

THE BONFIRE OF REGULATIONS AND THE RING OF FIRE

Enter stage right—stage far right—Jair Bolsonaro, known to his detractors as Captain Chainsaw. An ex-military man, he fans—speech by speech, tweet by tweet—the flames engulfing the Amazon, the Cerrado, the Pantanal, and beyond. He boasts of his slash-and-burn mentality, as he wields a machete against the safety nets vital to environmental and human health.

Bolsonaro: a swaggering misogynist given to raw racism and xenophobia while possessing a passion for "opening up" public lands and native reserves to unregulated plunder. Like a president closer to home, Bolsonaro exhibits an anti-native nativism. He tramples on indigenous rights and territorial sovereignty while denouncing foreigners and native communities alike as threats to his sovereign nation. The sprawling fires of 2019 were likely set, he suggests, by frustrated left-wing NGOs.

Like many misogynists, he is eager to protect hymens: "Brazil is the virgin that every foreign pervert wants to get their hands on" (that sentence warrants an essay in its own right). When the G7 nations offered to help mitigate the Amazonian conflagration, Bolsonaro excoriated them for their "colonialist" mentality. His reasoning exemplifies what Anne McClintock calls the "victor-victim reversal." For by condemning "colonial intrusions," foreign and indigenous, into a sovereign Brazil, Bolsonaro suppresses a genocidal and near-genocidal history against native peoples. He hides from view the internal colonialism that has seen fires, yet again, weaponized for the purposes of pillaging native lands.

Bolsonaro presents native communities as inauthentically Brazilian, as devious aliens, as paradoxically less than native. They are the beneficiaries of land theft: "They don't speak our language, but they have somehow managed to get 14 percent of our national territory," he protests. "One of the purposes of this is to impair us." By this logic, two sets of invaders—meddling foreign colonial "perverts" and internal colonialists aka the indigenous—are scheming together to subvert a sovereign Brazil's right to raze the Amazon.

"The Amazon is ours not yours," Bolsonaro insists. But his proprietary statement raises all sorts of questions. Who holds sway over the rain forest? Where does sovereignty reside? How much of the forest belongs to the species, to the nation, to the tribes who predated the nation-state by millennia? Is the forest the property of the ruralistas, the powerful landowners' lobby? Does it belong to the agrobusiness mafia that views the rain forest's infinitely complex biological cornucopia as an inconvenient roadblock on the march toward more monocultures, be they beef ranches fattened on deforestation or soya megafarms for feeding Chinese pigs?

What percentage of the Amazon belongs to the living, to the dead, to all those unconceived and inconceivable people yet to come? What claims to the forest can its more-than-human inhabitants exert? And how do we reconcile incompatible notions of what it means to belong to the forest and own—or be owned by—it? For Raimundo Mura, watching invaders set fire to his community's protected lands in 2019, the fate of the forest and his people's fate are one and the same thing. Standing amid the smoking relics of the Mura reserve, he laments the martyrdom of trees: "All of these trees had lives. They all needed to live, each in their own place."

A rival politician described Bolsonaro as "the exterminator of the future." Brazil's president is certainly equal to our own as the would-be-exterminator of scientific facts, with a strong prejudice against evidence. He fired the head of Brazil's National Institute for Space Research after he made public satellite-derived deforestation statistics that Bolsonaro found unpatriotic. Bolsanaro has a habit of sacking government scientists whose positions hew too faithfully to the data—on everything from forest fires to climate science, which he disbelieves. Taking a leaf out of Trump's playbook, Bolsonaro appointed a minister of the environment dedicated to dismantling both the ministry and the environment.

Between them Bolsonaro and Trump hold sway over a huge swath of this planet's environmental future. But it would be a mistake to read their traducing of justice as mere expressions of their personalities. Both men are largely epiphonema, symptoms of a global trend toward blurring the boundaries between democracy and autocracy, a trend enabled by neoliberalism's winner-takes-all-and-takes-it-now mind-set. The world's most populous democracies and quasi democracies—from Brazil and the US to India, Indonesia, the Philippines, Russia, Turkey, and beyond—are sliding toward authoritarianism; to different degrees, yes, but in ways that profoundly damage the integrity of environmental and human communities. Ecological erosion is twinned to the erosion of democracy.

We are witnessing the rise of strongmen within putative democracies, men hell-bent on expanding their executive powers, while weakening the civic sphere. They suppress voter rolls, rig elections, fire and hire judges at will, disenfranchise citizens, shrink the space for dissent, create politically expedient "states of emergency," demonize, imprison, and even murder activists and journalists as agents of hostile foreign powers, while casting the shadow of paramilitary terror over everyday life. Their political bases are skewed toward rural communities where religious fundamentalism—be it evangelical Christian, Hindu nationalist, or Islamic—is wielded against minority communities vilified as national threats.

Deforestation, in this context, is inseparable from a broader dispossession. Deforestation becomes collateral damage in the paramilitary war against the poor. A neoliberal ideology that holds the managed commons—and the common good—in contempt has opened a chasm between the ultrarich and the uberpoor. Environmental suffering and economic pain get outsourced, off-loaded onto communities who are "dead to the eye before they are killed." Indigenous reserves and public lands get converted, through burning, occupation, and assassination, into hot cash, free land, and speculative property. The cumulative wisdom of past practices, the empathetic constraints of future lives, be damned.

Rain-forest communities depend on thin margins of survival. As the forest fragments, such communities become vulnerable to fracture, are at risk of sliding into a divisive, degrading race for atrophying resources. A ploy used by one autocrat after another is branding as terrorists the very people most terrorized by the lawlessness of the law. Take the Philippines, another hot spot where environmental martyrdom and rain-forest destruction converge. President Rodrigo Duterte rules with an iron fist from beneath a semidemocratic veneer, shredding environmental laws and civil liberties while green-lighting extrajudicial killings. Nonviolent indigenous protesters (who often double as forest defenders) and dissenting journalists alike have found themselves in Duterte's crosshairs.

Among those persecuted by Duterte's regime is Victoria Tauli-Corpuz, UN Special Rapporteur on the Rights of Indigenous Peoples. Tauli-Corpuz, a member of the Philippines' Kankanaey-igorot tribe, has emerged as a globally significant defender of the kind of agroforestry that Maria and Zé Cláudio da Silva exemplified. She attests to the incalculable value of rain forests as carbon sinks. She denounces the fatal misperception of nature "as inert, dead manipulable matter that has value only as a commodity." She berates governments around the world for "indigenous criminalization"—for how, to facilitate murdering and dispossessing tribal communities, regimes denounce them as backward, as squatters, as illegals, as terrorists. After Tauli-Corpuz condemned logging concessions that threatened Filipino rain-forest communities, the Duterte regime added her name to the national registry of terrorists.

Following this designation—and the regime's incitements—Tauli-Corpuz has suffered full-spectrum digital persecution, including rape and death threats. Nonetheless, she continues to testify against the forces of forest anarchy and the looting of indigenous lands. She testifies against "huge land concessions that come in with the 'legitimacy' to log, stripping us of our very culture and sustenance." She testifies to the folly—the ethical, political, and biological folly—of shrinking rain forests to targets of short-term "market efficiencies." She testifies against asphyxiating contractions of the idea of rain-forest worth—both metaphorically and physically asphyxiating when it comes to "the lungs of the earth."

Bolsonaro is a huge fan of efficiencies, including the genocidal kind. Lamenting that "indigenous land is an obstacle to agribusiness," he adds this (historically inexact) regret: "It's a shame that the Brazilian cavalry wasn't as efficient as the Americans, who exterminated their Indians." Who can fault Brazil's Indians, nine hundred thousand strong, as they hear such utterances and watch their reserves go up in smoke; who can fault them for suspecting that the ring of fire around their lands is a noose about to throttle the very possibility of indigenous existence?

Rob Nixon

Some years ago, writing of the Zapatistas, John Berger made this prescient prediction:

> Neoliberalism disguises itself as the defense of a sovereignty which has been sold in dollars on the international market. . . . These indigenous people irritate the modernizing logic of neo-mercantilism. Their rebellion, their defiance, their resistance, annoys the powers that be. The anachronism of their existence within a project of globalization, an economic and political project that, soon, will decide that poor people, all the people in opposition, which is to say, the majority of the population, are obstacles.

In society after society—across the environmental martyr belt and beyond—the time Berger foresaw is coming to pass.

If Maria and Zé Cláudio are philosophers of environmental time, so too, in his way, is Bolsonaro. He cheers on neoliberalism's rush toward monopoly, reducing the time that matters to the profitable instant, discounting ancestral time and the long, long time to come, neither of which is a meaningful source of wisdom or policy. To shrink time in this way is to devalue the ecological rhythms of retreat, recovery, and replenishment, rhythms that have proven vital to human survival, rhythms that we disparage at our peril. To shrink time so radically is to risk triggering, in the words of Cristiana Paşca Palmer, executive secretary of the UN Convention on Biological Diversity, the "cascading collapse of natural systems." Such systems don't have an "outside"; they don't offer *Homo sapiens* the option of purchasing a special exemption from the cascading effects.

Research by Carlos Nobre projects that if the 2019 spike in deforestation persists, the Amazon is at risk of flipping from being earth's largest terrestrial absorber of CO_2 to a net emitter. If the current trajectory continues, the Amazon Basin's rainfall will enter a downward spiral. As dry inflammable grasses invade fractured forest, and as thinning forest morphs into savanna or is burned for ranches, the hydrological cycle will be further destabilized. Fifteen percent of the Amazon is currently deforested. According to Nobre, we're now only twenty to thirty years away from reaching the 20 to 25 percent rate of deforestation that will tip the Amazon irreversibly into savanna, with drastic repercussions for the global climate.

To say that neoliberalism discounts past and future is to give the word "discount" a double valence. For discounting means dismissing past and future as sources of deep value, but it also implies discounting them in the sense of shortchanging, selling off past and future at the dollar store for cutthroat prices. One is reminded here of words from *The Overstory*, Richard Powers's soaring, searing tree novel: "We're cashing in a billion years of planetary savings bonds and blowing it on assorted bling."

In our age of mergers, monopolies, and martyrs, we are witnessing the breakup of nations through what Arundhati Roy calls "the vertical secession of the rich." Driving this secession is the dream of a pure realm untainted by the indignities of participatory democracy.

Bolsonaro salivates at the prospect of sweeping democracy aside: "I am in favor of dictatorship." Not only does he favor it, but he has a precise nostalgia for the twenty-one years of military dictatorship that, from 1964 to 1985, squeezed Brazilian society in its iron fist, a period that saw hundreds tortured to death or assassinated or disappeared, a period that saw fifty thousand civilians detained and ten thousand Brazilians driven into exile. Bolsonaro's fondness for that era, though, is not unqualified: "The only mistake of the dictatorship was torturing and not killing." Expressing skepticism that elections can ever deliver the kinds of changes Brazil needs, he adds: "this country will only change on the day that we break out in civil war here and do the job that the military regime didn't do: killing thirty thousand."

Brazil's indigenous peoples, its *quilombolas* (descendants of rebel slaves) and its *ribeirinhos* (who, like Maria and Zé Cláudio, have lived off gathering forest produce, off swiddens or fishing or tapping rubber), all of these groups may reasonably feel that the civil war has already begun, or has never fully ended, this war conducted in large part by environmental means.

We see this process unfold in the 2016 documentary *Martírio* (*Martyrdom*), which traces the plight of the Guarani-Kaiowá in the Brazilian south. Historically, the tribe has ricocheted from one violent displacement to another, returning and returning only to be evicted over and over. In the era of Bolsonaro-fanned fires, the Guarani-Kaiowá are raising their voices again. As one unnamed spokesman puts it: "If indigenous peoples become extinct, the lives of all are threatened. . . . Without forest, without water, without rivers, there is no life, there is no way for any Brazilian to survive." Contra Bolsonaro, they are apt to take the long view: "We resisted 518 years ago, we fight in victory and defeat. . . . As long as the sun still shines, and while there is still fresh air under the shade of a tree, while there is still a river to bathe in, we will fight."

Similarly, the Xikrin tribe of the northern Amazon—like other embattled communities—is refusing to accept the commandeering of their lands through the torching of ecosystems and the murder and starvation of ecosystem people. In Pará, the state in which Maria and Zé Cláudio resided, Xikrin warriors swept through charred lands in August 2019, expelling fire-emboldened invaders, and seizing their chain saws and machetes.

Always, the odds are stacked against them. But as the ranks of the excluded swell, Brazil's rulers underestimate, at their peril, indigenous resolve and the resolve of all the besieged who refuse to disappear obligingly into some zone of nonbeing.

In Pará and elsewhere, 2019 saw farmers organize coordinated "fire days" for setting forest and brush alight. These festivals of fire celebrated the farmers' sense that they were the beneficiaries of a systemic shift. What they were burning was more than vegetation. They were burning the very idea of limits, of regulations, of environmental finitude. They were writing in the sky, in hot orange lettering, personal permits to live without government oversight.

The journalist George Monbiot once questioned neoliberalism's assumption that we can survive infinite unchecked growth, can survive what he called "the bonfire of regulations." Monbiot meant that phase metaphorically. But in these incendiary times of jubilant fire days and choking air his phrase takes on a prescient materiality. Something has to give. Or beneath banners of progress, development, and growth we will reduce mighty forests to stumps and turn whole biomes into charnel houses of combined but uneven suffering.

*

THIS BRANCH WE'RE SITTING ON

Before two gunmen ambushed Maria and Zé Cláudio da Silva near their home—nine days before, to be specific—Arundhati Roy published a book about a very different forest conflict at the other end of the earth. *Walking with the Comrades* recounts Roy's journey through the densely wooded states of central India, home to millions of indigenous people. She bears witness to a brutal contest over sovereignty: over who owns the forest's wealth; over logging, land, mineral, and human rights; over who gets to dictate the terms of development; over the right of the forest itself to persist alongside the stigmatized cultures that the forest shelters. The story Roy tells is of a struggle that has spiraled into intractable violence.

On the book's final page, Roy adopts a more philosophical mood. Her words are worth summoning at length, because they achieve a far-reaching resonance:

> If there is any hope for the world at all . . . it lives low down on the ground, with its arms around the people who go to battle every day to protect their forests, their mountains and their rivers, because they know that the forests, the mountains and the rivers protect them. The first step towards re-imagining a world gone terribly wrong would be to stop the annihilation of those who have a different imagination—an imagination which has an altogether different understanding of what constitutes happiness and fulfilment. To gain this philosophical space, it is necessary to concede some physical space for the survival of those who may look like the keepers of our past but who may really be the guides to our future. To do this, we have to ask our rulers: Can you leave the water in the rivers, the trees in the forest? Can you leave the bauxite in the mountain? If they say they cannot, then perhaps they should stop preaching morality to the victims of their wars.

Roy had never heard of Maria and Zé Cláudio. Before their murders and before Milanez took up their cause, they were little known outside their region. Yet Roy's words speak uncannily to the couple's "different imagination," to the ideals they inhabited.

In their sylvan redoubt, in their disparaged "backwardness," Maria and Zé Cláudio held to the *longue durée* of tree time, a time that encourages us to flex our imaginations and extend our ethical sight lines. They refused cul-de-sac definitions of development that paid little heed to past practices or future safeguards. They refused a neoliberal ideal of prosperity that is a kind of poverty. They refused to bow to a deified market that doubles as a looting spree. They rejected notions of individual sovereignty so fiercely self-interested that they become a suicide trap. They saw that the only survival possible is collaborative, one that acknowledges—and responds with creative vigor—to the rain forest as a community of being.

Their voices assume a special resonance in the world of 2019. The year not just of fires sweeping the Amazon, but of new research calculating that planting 1.2 trillion trees could cancel a decade's worth of global CO_2 emissions. The year when ecologist Thomas Crowther declared trees to be "our most powerful weapon in the fight against climate change." The year when Crystal Davis, director of Global Forest Watch, called forests "the forgotten climate solution . . . We're always searching for these great technologies that will do it on a megascale, but the most efficient way you can pull CO_2 out of the atmosphere is with trees." The year when Greta Thunberg said: "We're sawing off the branch we're all sitting on."

"Free Yourself." Pejac.

Front-line green defenders—who are always also more than that—enjoin us to heed the bodies buried beneath scorched canopies of hope. Enjoin us to heed the violence in the smoke. Enjoin us, through their example and their exorbitant suffering, to honor the possibilities that remain amidst the precarious plenitude. They enjoin us to make common cause with the biological congregations to which our fates are bound. And to refuse the dynamics of desecration that threaten to sunder both the social fabric and the great web of life.

NOTE. For my reflections on Maria and Zé Cláudio, I have drawn on the films *Toxic Amazon* (2011, directed by Bernardo Loyola and Felipe Milanez) and *The Crying Forest* (2011, directed by Gabriel Elizondo). I have also drawn on writings about the lives and deaths and afterlives of Maria do Espírito Santo da Silva and Zé Cláudio Ribeiro da Silva available in English.

But my primary, abiding debt is to the work of Felipe Milanez, above all the long interviews—by turns uplifting and wrenching—that he conducted with the couple during his friendship with them. Milanez transcribed and appended those interviews to his PhD dissertation, *A ousadia de conviver com a floresta: uma ecologia política do extrativismo na Amazônia* (*The Audacity of Living with the Forest: A Political Ecology of Extractivism in the Amazon*). Milanez's book on this subject is forthcoming from Editora Elefante in Brazil, while the interviews will be included in a volume on Maria and Zé Cláudio's work from Iguana.

I was eager to read the couple's words, to channel their voices, once Milanez described them to me as "containing a kind of poetry." Although fluent in English, Milanez resisted hazarding a translation of the interviews: "even one phrase because of their Amazonian Portuguese." When I asked Beatriz Oikawa Cordeiro whether she would attempt an English translation, she responded positively, but with a similar caveat: that she couldn't hope to capture the depth and richness of the Amazonian Portuguese. Nonetheless, she generated a moving, creative (and as yet unpublished) English translation.

This process reminds us what else is at risk when rain forest goes up in flames: whole languages and deep dialects and the cultures that sustain them.

The third section of my essay claims to be nothing more than a set of reflections on an approximation. I have written it from a place of impossibility. That said, I wish to thank Felipe Milanez for his vision, his great generosity, and the integrity of his witnessing. I also wish to honor the necessity of attempting, amidst all the inevitable misapprehensions and failures, to reach boldly across barriers of meaning.

After Maria

Yxta Maya Murray

In our survey, interruption of medical care was the primary cause of sustained high mortality rates in the months after the hurricane, a finding consistent with the widely reported disruption of health systems.

—Nishant Kishore, MPH; Domingo Marqués, PhD; Ayesha Mahmud, PhD; Mathew V. Kiang, MPH; Irmary Rodriguez, BA; Arlan Fuller, JD, MA; Peggy Ebner, BA; Cecilia Sorensen, MD; Fabio Racy, MD; Jay Lemery, MD; Leslie Maas, MHS; Jennifer Leaning, MD, SMH; "Mortality in Puerto Rico after Hurricane Maria," *The New England Journal of Medicine*, May 29, 2018

I WAS EXCITED TO HELP. The response here, officially, was bad. A lot of us knew we needed to react to that somehow. We wanted the victims to know that not everybody here felt like he did. But also, yeah, that's the word for it, excited.

I applied to go through my union. I'm a nurse in San Bernardino Memorial's critical care unit. My union had asked for names of people who were willing to go there and do first aid, public health, whatever was needed. Our representative didn't say anything outright political, but a lot of us didn't like the president's tone. He'd said, "They want everything done for them." We knew that you can't talk like that about patients, victims. I signed up right away.

My husband looked bashful with pride when he saw me packing my bags. He told everybody at his work that I had been chosen to do triage in a crisis zone. He said he'd get his mom to help with our daughter and that everybody at home would be OK without me for a little while.

"You're an amazing woman," he said. That made me feel good.

Two days later I left.

*

We landed in Luis Muñoz Marín Airport in San Juan. A bunch of girls and guys from all over California, not just San Bernardino, were on the flight. We were very geared up on the trip over. Nobody drank anything and we discussed how serious the situation was. But there was also a lightness about it, people glowing and speaking loudly and quickly, like they were on a date.

At the airport you could see the beginnings of the real damage. The lights were out. Hundreds of people lived in the hangars. Families sleeping there, eating there. We did first aid on many children. It was not clean. It was wet, there was a smell. We hiked up our bags onto our shoulders and ran out into the crowds. One mother cried as I cleaned her daughter's foot, which had been cut by falling branches. Another old woman came up to me and asked in English for penicillin. I had a few small bottles on me and I gave her two, which I later knew had been a stupid mistake. At the airport, it was a populated area and those people had some care; there were doctors and nurses. The older woman was really grateful, though, you know. I told people at home about it later. I said her reaction was the real story of the people there, and gave a picture that folks in the States—I mean, in our parts of the US—weren't getting over the news. Anyway, she was thankful. She kissed my hand.

The government sent us cars to take us to the city, the capital. It's a little over seven miles to get there on the 26 Expressway from the airport. The sky by that time had turned blue again but power lines and tree branches were still scattered on the freeways. We weaved back and forth on the road. Our driver had seen some bad things already. He was tall and nervous, sort of zany. He acted serious when the advisers assigned him to our group and told him where to take us. But once he got on the road he zipped back and forth through the power lines, smiling at us through the rearview so that we could see his spaced-apart teeth.

"The fast and furious!" he yelled, I guess like the movie. He kept laughing.

We'd been in good moods on the plane but we smiled at him with closed lips like we were being empathetic but didn't think it was funny.

*

31

San Juan. At first I thought, *Oh my God, this is terrible.* Some of the buildings were crushed and people milled around, asking for food and supplies. That's when I first saw the huge lines. FEMA had set up shop in the middle of the city and victims were lined up to get an application for hurricane relief, if that's what you call it.

The nurses gathered into groups of ten or so. The FEMA officer in charge of our quadrant assigned my group an attaché, Brian, from Kansas City. I pegged him at forty years old, with a Bluetooth that he talked on constantly. He wore glasses and he had to clean them with his shirt every five minutes because of the humidity. He wore the blue FEMA slicker. He gave us rubber pants and boots and our own FEMA ponchos for the rain, even though we weren't government employees. He was getting pulled in every direction but would click his Bluetooth off to listen to our questions.

"Where's the deepest impact?" one of our group asked.

"Have you segmented by pathology?" another inquired.

"Is there a geriatric unit around here?" is what I wanted to know, as I'd had some experience with the elderly.

"Well, we'll see what kinds of trouble we can get into," Brian joshed. He brought us to the Coliseum. There we did a little triage again like before at the airport. The hundreds of victims made the space dirty, hot, and steamy, but guards and nurses and doctors had been stationed there. From what I could tell, the Coliseum wasn't like the Superdome in Katrina where people did die.

After a couple of days, Brian took us to the historical district, with the romantic pink and blue colonial buildings. We saw more flooding. Trees and a couple of cats floated in one of the streets. The police kept people clear of them. We passed by the state capitol, a white building with marble or concrete steps that had been covered in sludge. Three men washed the steps clean with huge hoses. Brian then brought us to a clinic at the San Jorge Children and Women's Hospital, where we showed a mother how to breastfeed and treated four children for dehydration. The power had all switched over to auxiliary. We walked around the plaza and saw other groups from our union walking around too, and waved at them. We saw Mayor Yulín Cruz running across Avenida Juan Ponce de León. She had this blue sweater on her shoulders that dropped on the street and she just left it there, racing to wherever. She had this totally fierce look on her face, just furious.

The people had no power, no reliable power. The grid had gone out the first day the storm hit, on September 20. In the capital, people used generators. You had to come to the main city mostly to get help. FEMA didn't really go to you. A lot of people had traveled. I don't know how the folks from the mountain towns got to San Juan without any juice up there. Maybe the army? And they'd traveled all that way just to stand in line. They stood in long rows, and I saw a lot of people falling asleep, just like that, on their feet.

The most FEMA investigators I saw were in the capital. I didn't see them anywhere else. In San Juan, they sat at tables and gave out the applications in one section and the water and beef jerky and cookies in another. Everybody spoke English. FEMA made their announcements on Twitter, though bilingually. At first I didn't question it, because I use social media constantly. But then, later, I wondered.

"What the hell are we doing?" Craig asked after a week of this. He was one of the nurses in our group, a big, tall guy with a red beard from Chicago. He'd just put a Band-Aid on a man with no mobility issues.

"Yeah," I said. "Let's get out of here."

"I'm in," Latisha said. She was a girl we had met from Oklahoma, an emergency RN.

Another girl, Ranee, wanted to tag along too. She came from New York.

"I didn't come here to be a tourist," Ranee said.

So we looked around and scrounged food, medicine, water, batteries, and a satphone that we thought we'd need. Finally we also got ahold of a Rambler. We split.

We went to the mountain areas. We had the rubber gear—rubber boots and pants and gloves, and our FEMA slickers. We ate power bars. We cursed and swore when we looked out of the Rambler's windows and saw the smushed cars and ripped trees. Meanwhile, we also talked some about the political scene, but then Ranee wound up saying she liked the president fine and so I kind of kept all that to myself.

The thing is, these people are Americans. They are United States citizens. That's what a lot of people didn't understand back home at the time.

I felt better once we left. I had that feeling again on the road, that this was new and I was doing something important and big. Like it was war. I mean, it looked like warfare out there, past the city. The roads were

33

just destroyed, often impassable on account of live electrical cables, cracked surfaces, and huge palms that had been pulled from their roots. Boulders toppled from cliffs or mudslides and landed in the highways. Utility poles had tipped over. The mud ran thick and filled with rocks and our car skidded out of control over the slick parts. Trash spread out everywhere in huge piles—plastic, torn furniture, hazardous materials like asbestos and electronics, chemicals, batteries, televisions. Aluminum hung on the standing utility poles and dragged down the cables, which shot sparks. About ten miles out we had to physically pick up the cables to let the car squeeze in beside the piles of trash, a big mound made up of what looked like a broken sofa and plastic bags and gas cans that spilled everywhere.

The worse part was the flooding. We saw dead animals, dogs and cows. The water stood sometimes two feet up on the road, three feet, as we splashed through.

About twenty or thirty miles out of town we saw a man walking through a passable part of the current with his little girl on his back. We stopped and yelled at him to get out of the water. When we got them into the car we freaked because he had a cut on his arm and the girl had one on her stomach. We stuffed them with Cipro and cleaned the wounds as best we could and then drove them to shelter on higher ground.

"Don't walk in the water," I told him in English. I swear to Christ none of us spoke Spanish; it was stupid. A lot of nurses have some medical Spanish but none of us did. We'd tried to get ahold of a translator in San Juan but they were all doing administrative tasks and didn't want to go to the mountains. I told the man, "There's sewage, chemicals, viruses, mold. Don't touch the water. Don't let your daughter touch the water. If you need some water, clean what you get from a tap with bleach or chlorine tablets. Don't get near it otherwise."

"Thank you," he said. He had streaked dirt all over his face from where he'd rubbed it with a cloth.

"Do you understand what I'm telling you?"

"Thank you, thank you," he said.

"Thank you," his daughter said. She was like six, with light brown hair and wrapped up in my sweatshirt. My daughter at home is four years old so it was like, you know.

"Yeah, you're welcome," I said.

But at least we saved them.

After we dropped them off we zoomed through the flooding and the water splashed into the Rambler from a crack I'd idiotically left open in a back window.

What was he doing at this point? This was, like, October 3. I think he was throwing paper towels to rich people in Guaynabo. But the people in the mountains didn't know about that. They didn't know where anybody was or what was happening.

I don't know why the people in the mountains stayed so long. I'm talking about the ones that the army for some reason didn't get out. Mostly, it might have been because they just couldn't walk or drive out under their own steam. But I think other people got confused by how smooth things went down in Houston earlier—when, oh, Hurricane Harvey happened those last weeks of August 2017.

I think the people in the mountains thought that if they stayed put they'd get the same kind of help that folks in Texas got.

We saw a woman standing on top of her house in Camarillo. She was a large, heavy lady, really broad, wearing a mud-covered dress and waving her hands. She was crying. The flooding had come up halfway to her house and when she saw us she started screaming about her dogs. Latisha in our group knew the word for dogs, *perro*, and when I thought about it, I knew the word too.

"Here we go," Craig said.

"She's in trouble," I said.

We ran out to save her. We pulled on our rubber pants and wandered through the water, trying to figure out how to get her down. Latisha found a ladder sticking through a smashed window and we pulled that up and propped it against the roof of her house. I climbed up first.

The woman's eyes looked strange, but I'm a nurse and so I'd seen that before. A real spaced-out look, like an animal's. Maybe I shouldn't say that. It's just a human thing, though. You get animal when you get that scared, we all do.

She fucking gripped onto my legs, yelling about her dogs, and I thought she was going to pull me down.

"Wait, wait!" I yelled at her. Craig came climbing up and he's got a way with the ladies, I guess. He knew how to use his voice to calm her. She clambered up on his back and kept slipping down, so I held her up by her bottom, like to support her. We lugged her down the ladder somehow. Then we carried her over the water, the whole team did. She kept crying. She yelled at us about her dogs. We finally hauled her to higher ground and she sat down in the mud, exhausted and talking excitedly in Spanish.

I ran back to the house. Climbed up through the smashed window where Latisha found the ladder. The house smelled awful. Black mold. Gets in the lungs. The woman had been stranded for a week, maybe, but I think more. The ceiling curdled or buckled or something. The walls had cracked with water damage. I tried not to breathe. I went wading through the kitchen, the water up to my stomach, pushing past floating plastic forks and spoons and cups, until I got to the bedroom.

Two of those little itty-bitty types of dogs looked straight at me. Soaked and trembling. They stood up on a bureau, just above high water. Those pop-eyed dogs. Chihuahuas. They started howling with their poor little mouths. I chugged through the water and grabbed them and hauled ass out of there before the ceiling came crashing down.

I don't know how I got through the window with a dog under each arm. One of them started biting me. I was like, laughing, I guess from fear. I gave the dogs to Ranee, and she ran over to the woman and gave them to her.

The woman stuck her face into the dogs and just cried and cried. We all started crying.

We looked at her feet and asked her, "Are you diabetic?" The word for diabetes is almost the same in Spanish. She said yes. She didn't have her medicine. Later I learned that a lot of people didn't know that it could go unrefrigerated, and they threw it away.

We cleaned her wounds and bandaged them. We gave her insulin and Cipro and water and some food. We treated the dogs too, even the bitey one. They had sores.

After a while some girls from higher ground showed up and all of them starting talking really fast in Spanish. Then the girls spoke English and said that the woman was very thankful. The girls said that they knew the lady, and she could come stay with them because their house was undamaged.

We dropped everybody at the girls' house. The parents came out and wrapped up the woman in a blanket.

I felt like a hero.

*

36

Toa Baja sits on the northern coast, about twenty-five kilometers from San Juan. It's a smallish city, maybe eighty thousand people. It looked deserted. It got really ripped up. A lot of the little houses there didn't have roofs. It's a tourist place because it's by the water, which wasn't perfect when the storm came. Later I learned that the army had come and evacuated a lot of people. But they didn't get everybody.

We found a man on the outskirts of town. He waved at us from the top of a small apartment complex, trying to yell, but his voice didn't work anymore. He looked to be about eighty years old. I couldn't see that then, exactly how old he was, but I've learned the general look of geriatrics. We stopped on the side of the road and yelled back up at him that it was OK and we were going to get him.

His apartment complex had been crushed on the side and was not stable. It was only two stories. The ceilings had come crashing down on the interior and blocked the staircase. I don't know how it was still standing. We couldn't get up through the inside of the building.

I could hear him trying to yell at us for help. *Heeeeehhh Heeeeehhhh.* His voice had just been completely thrashed.

"Call San Juan," Ranee said.

Craig called on the satphone. He got through to Brian, but Brian said there was nothing he could do right then. I said to Craig, Call Brian's boss at FEMA. I said, Call the army. We didn't know who the hell to call. We just dialed Brian again and nobody answered.

"What are we going to do?" Latisha said. She looked really tired and wiped her eyes with her hands, until she remembered about infection.

I looked over at the much taller, four-story stucco building next to the one where the guy was. It was crushed too. But it had some black metal balconies sticking out from the side. These balconies were so close to the old guy's apartment complex that they were in almost jumpable distance. I thought that maybe I could climb up those balconies and then somehow scramble to the other building's roof. It would only be two or three stories to be level with it. It'd be like Spiderman. Like parkour. You had to be creative out there.

"No," Craig said, when I told him my plan. You know, a man. But the victim was still trying to scream at us and I said, Fuck it.

I ran over to the side of the building with the balconies and started to climb up, from floor to floor, from the outside. I'm in good shape, thankfully. I lift weights and I do trail running. I do yoga. Not that it helped me much.

I climbed up to one of the first-floor balconies. It was wrought metal, black, and very slick from the water. I clambered up and jumped down into it. It was fine. And then it turned out that there was a little fire exit extending from the second floor's balcony to the first, and so I climbed up that, even though it had been broken in the storm. I grabbed onto the little steps, but the fire exit swayed almost all the way out and I thought I'd come crashing down.

The nurses below were all yelling at me and I thought, *Yeah, maybe not a great idea.*

But I hooked my foot onto the second-balcony railing and swung the fire exit back. I hopped into the little balcony. It didn't feel very stable. It creaked. But from there I had a good view of the roof of the two-story building where the old man was stranded. I could see that he needed immediate crisis care. He had this old shriveled face. His hair came down over his eyes. He was hurt.

His whole left side was just red. I couldn't tell exactly what was going on. But from the position of the leg I could see it had broken. And he had some serious hematomas and lacerations. Exterior wounds of that size mean a good chance of internal bleeding too. He must have fallen or had something topple on top of him. I don't know how he made it to the roof. He had crawled over it to scream at us from the edge.

I could see him pretty close. I could see his eyes. He didn't have animal eyes like the lady. He had the kind of eyes that terminal patients get when it sinks in and they know they have to get ready. The light goes out of them.

I yelled when I saw that. I said, "Hey! Hey! Hey! Hey!"

He nodded and laid his head down on the ground.

"Hey! Hey! Hey! Hey!" I'm yelling. "I'm coming to get you!"

I couldn't hop to the roof from the second balcony. From that height, there was a good chance I'd just hit the wall and have to grab the edges with my fingers. The third balcony up rose higher than the top of his building. I could do a long jump down from there, maybe. But when I grabbed up at the third balcony's ironwork, it shook loose from the stucco. Then it just collapsed. It popped out from the top, swung all the way down, and then hung toward the ground from one rivet. I had to duck because it almost knocked my head off. I started trembling then. I knew I was a complete tool with no idea what I was doing.

"Sindy!" they're all yelling down there.

"It's fine!" I yelled back. It wasn't fine. I couldn't jump from building to building. I'm not Spiderman and I don't do parkour. Also the balcony I stood on was creaking and shaking.

I looked across at the other building, at the man, who still lay down on the roof by the edge, trying to raise his hand at me. I looked at his eyes, at the red on his skin and clothes all down the left side. On the part of his rooftop I could see, there was a red stain around his body. I didn't know how long he had been there but the bone can get set wrong and there is a serious problem with bacterial infection, septicemia, in those conditions.

He looked at me again and shook his head. I could see him really well, that's how close I was. But not close enough to get to him. We looked at each other for a long time.

Then he started shuffling. He tried to scream, I guess from the pain, but couldn't. He was rummaging through his pocket with his good hand. He took something out of his pocket and dropped it from the roof into the shallow water below. I heard it plop.

"He dropped something!" I yelled.

"I got it," I heard Ranee say.

"I have to get down," I said to the man.

He didn't say anything to me. He laid completely flat on the roof and then I couldn't see him as well.

"Just wait here," I said. "We'll send someone for you."

He still didn't say anything.

"We'll send somebody," I said.

I climbed down.

We got back in the Rambler and drove away. Craig drove and Latisha sat in the front. Ranee put a blanket over me.

"What did he throw down?" I said.

Ranee had put it inside her rubber pants and now fished it out. It was a small soaked square object. She handed it to me.

It was his wallet. I opened it up and saw his identification cards. He was smart. It had his address, his location.

His name was Antonio Hernandez.

As soon as we got to San Juan I tracked down Brian and I was like, this guy needs our help. He lives here. I showed Brian the address. We need to call the army, I said. We need FEMA. We have to get the police.

Brian took the wallet that I handed him. He said he'd write the guy's name down. "I'll let our team know," he said.

"No, you don't understand. We need to get him now," I said. I explained about the hematomas and the balconies.

Brian took off his glasses and cleaned them with his shirt, from under his FEMA slicker. He tilted his head at a line of people who were waiting for I don't know what. The line was so long I couldn't see where it ended.

"We'll do what we can do," he said. "But we have our hands full."

"You need to listen to me! This is an emergency!"

Brian walked away.

Later, that night, in our hotel, I got so mad. I realized that if I could just somehow get ahold of rescue equipment or some people myself, I could go save Mr. Hernandez before he died. I could get a ladder, like the one I'd used to help the woman and the dogs.

I just lay there all night thinking of his whole left side that had been turned red from the hematoma and the cuts. I thought of his eyes. Thought how stupid I'd been to just give his information to Brian and then expect a miracle. I had to do it myself.

Thing was, I couldn't remember exactly how to get back to the apartment in Toa Baja. I tried to track it in my mind, but couldn't. I called Craig about it, in the middle of the night. He said that he didn't know how exactly to track back either, because we'd been going all over the place without a plan. So I called Latisha and Ranee but they didn't know either.

"Didn't Brian say they'd get him?" Ranee said into the phone, sleepy.

What I needed was that wallet. With the wallet and an ID card, I'd plug in the address using GPS.

I got up the next morning and it was raining. I prepared by putting on my rubber pants and my slicker, so when I got Mr. Hernandez's information I could just get a car and go. After that, I started running everywhere looking for Brian. The mother and child clinic, the Coliseum, the historical district. When I found him, around three o'clock in the afternoon in the cantina, I started hollering at him that I needed the wallet. He was like, What are you talking about? Then he remembered. He said, "I gave that to so-and-so." A supervisor. He said, "They'll take care of it when they can."

I said, "Just give it back to me and I'll get a car and a ladder. I'll get supplies. I'll go up there myself."

Brian looked at me sort of sympathetically. "I can see this is getting to you," he said.

"Just give me the wallet back," I said.

He put his arm around me and gave a little tug on the FEMA slicker I wore. "You've done really great work here, you've been such an incredible part of the team."

We stood by a pile of sandwiches wrapped up in plastic, but in my mind I saw the long lines with the people sleeping standing up, and the FEMA guys handing out applications. I said, "No, I'm doing something different. We went up to the mountains."

"Every little bit helps," Brian said.

"I'm not part of *this*," I said. "We went up to Toa Baja, and I have to get back."

Brian looked at me and said, "Sorry, I'm coming. I'll be right there."

"What?" I said.

"I have a meeting," he said, getting suddenly busy. He'd been talking to his Bluetooth.

"His name's Antonio Hernandez," I said.

"I know, thank you, good," Brian said. He took off again.

He never got back to me about the wallet. I must have called him six or seven more times, but he didn't answer.

Two days later it was time for us to leave.

I heard that the president said that the death toll was sixteen. He was like, This is a really impressive number.

Later there were some studies by Harvard and George Washington Universities.

Those estimates said that eight hundred to eight thousand people died in Puerto Rico, mostly from "interruptions in medical care." That just means that they didn't get seen by surgeons or doctors or nurses. Less people died from drowning, or direct impacts.

So I went home. I went home to my husband and my daughter.

They looked so crazily happy to see me that at first it was OK. At the airport, my daughter crawled all over me and got too excited, so I had to sing to her so she'd stop screaming. My husband wrapped me up in his arms and then drove us all back to the house. I slept in the car and when I woke up we were there.

Our place looked like a palace, I swear.

I slept in our bed. It was good to be back. Like the other wasn't real almost. My husband cooked me eggs and pizza. I was just so grateful

41

to have my family. My daughter showed me some pictures she'd taken while I was away. They were of flowers and grass.

I told my family about the woman with the little dogs, and how I'd held her by the butt and saved her Chihuahuas by basically swimming through the house. My daughter liked that. I told my husband, later, at night, about the man and his daughter in the floodwater and how we'd treated their wounds and given them Cipro. I talked about how FEMA stayed in San Juan while we went to the mountains in that Rambler, and how we'd had to pick up the fallen cables with the electric sparks. I drank a lot of wine and went on and on about it. How the old woman at the airport had kissed my hand and blah blah. I told my husband all of the stories except for the one about the man on the roof. And he, my husband, was really, really proud of me.

The problem was that after a few days I started to feel like just lying down on the floor and not getting back up. I got this idea that Brian had been right when he'd said that I was *part of the team*. He'd hinted to me that I didn't count as some special superhero. I hadn't wanted to hear that at the time, when I was yelling at him about Toa Baja. But after a few days of telling my stories and eating my husband's cooking, I saw that he had a point.

Because I didn't speak Spanish. I let myself feel all puffed up when that old lady kissed my hand just because I gave her a couple little bottles of penicillin. Me thinking that I'm righting some wrong, sort of resisting the political crap. But the truth is I never even thought about Puerto Rico until the union emailed us about the opportunity. I'll just say too that I didn't realize they were citizens until the rep explained it all to us. And then, even though I knew he was still out there, might be dead already, I'd just gone home when the time for our trip was over.

I tried to call Brian again but I just got dumped into voice mail.

The way he'd dropped the wallet into the water, hoping. Just hoping to live.

About a month later I was crying into the sink in our kitchen and my husband found me.

"Honey, baby." He hugged me and kissed me and rocked me back and forth. "What's wrong?"

Disputed Site Sestinas
Kate Monaghan

SHIPBREAKING

You would not go there. Mountainous
ships gather in at the beach
of Alang. Each will feed 100 mouths
broken down into elements
by the young. Sent out between the places
we have scoured so now our harbors push it past

five countries, rusting, heaving a passage
along the sky—the man-made mountain
rubs against eternity. The hull displaces
water as the tanker rides in, beaches
at last in the shipyard: lot flooding when dark elemental
water runs over the workers' legs into the small mouths

of the mud and scattered metal, then flows out the mouth
of the harbor, settling. After its final passage
past the cape this ship becomes scrap elements.
No more a merchant vessel. The captain
drops anchor, cuts power, steps down to the beach
and goes. The buyer's offshore money displaces

these now: multiple million dollars, a loan, and workers displaced
from poorer regions. Who cover their mouths
with cloth while one journalist climbs up from the beach
in blue body suit and full gas mask. He passes
into the bridge and points out the small mountains,
whitish piles of asbestos, each shred's harm an elemental

certainty. And iron. All around, the element's
ore mined from far grounds, forged into steel, displaced
in welded sheets and sent floating in the tumbling mountain
of tanker made steady with its great cavities of cargo. Tank mouths
sealed with 10 miles of pipe and valves—the tons of oil that pass
sustaining nations, their corporate bodies held in the reach

of these cold quiet arms. But here where toxins leach
through oily mud workers run in this element
each day the tooled heat pours while summer passes
and hull sections crash—pulled apart in this place
where some still tower, announcing themselves like oaths
to bring distance up close, undissolved. Mountains

of want and labor. As the master gas cutter braces in this place
a country where the live gas line opens its small mouth
now his torch may cross igniting a mountain.

STOMA

Spring changes what it's made of, the air
loosening, tree fibers warming while new
light frequencies press brimming over the root zones
damaged in winter. The trunk holds but its axis
tilts tipping a canopy that dandles leaves
to inhale over troughs of rich chemical

air. Inside each leaf, flights of swirling-in chemical
carbon dioxide—fast and thin. Wisping into the airy
underside stomata cells of these leaves
that entertain, allow access to interiors newly
awakened when earth tilted its old axis
curtailing the night. Then within this temperate zone

the phytochrome—sensitive to far-red zones
of the visual spectrum—presses chemical
fingers into the small branches, triggers a praxis
of bud building that spins sugars shaken out of the air
and folds them into tiny bud-newspapers
wound up, bound, bundled, soon to become leaves.

Flooded with blossoms—is this how nature leaves
us? The tree all in heat, blustering into the warm zones
of the airspace, demonstrating a readiness in its sinews
for reproduction it fizzes up pink like some chemical
toxin. These limbs are as delicate as ever, debonair
though laden, arraying their plunder out from that axis

the trunk whose seed fell down here like a taxi
passenger deposited by accident. The leaves
regrow. They don't know how to despair
as now the branches with their flailing arms emblazon
the sky, claiming the air where new chemical
compounds waft over a property whose contract renews

while its prospects decay. I am newly
infused with boundaries this spring, watching the tree's axis
slant, crossing the land, spreading its earthy alchemical
vision. A villain says, nobody leaves
until I say so, but this time his interzone
of ownership extends into but one cross section of airspace.

The tree is dying. I know. Still pressing new buds up
from its axis, its leaves catch at vitreous air.
The stoma tugs at clear space. The chemical sky divides.

Kate Monaghan

DISPUTED SITE
(Agbogbloshie E-Waste Center)

Listen. "It is the world's largest e-waste dump site."
Plastic encloses what men and kids patiently
dig for, scraping and burning what's brought
to this stretch in the center of Accra. Wiry
smoke rises from the mounds of the dump—
churns up and turns into soot clouds that pose

available for photographers to expose
this trash as our own. How best to see the sight
we're told is mostly our discarded monitors, the dump's
legal basis and central element, patented
cube seats and material drifting, inner wires
still unstripped. From containers brought

out of Europe, Australia, the US, often not bought
but gifted—"secondhand"—a practice now exposed
by journalists who tell us that our old wires
can be found here. But some say they're local. The site
shifts, sifts, while photos make their own patently
slanted stories. And the city's ordinary dump site

surrounds it all, showing us the wasteland dump-
scape we've imagined—as produce is brought
at dawn into the market next door. Where patient
sellers mind their stalls, abundance exposed
to air and ground and the long seep of this site
at the center of the city. As men gather wires

into bundles they guard all day then light into fires
that sear through the haze of the dump:
blossoms beckoning to those still rapt at the sight
of combustion and burn. Hydrogen chloride. Bought

for free like so much trash sorted and exposed
in this community improvising, at work, impatient—

attacked by some governments and important
media outlets—entities reaching out for the wires
in which user names are coiled sometimes exposed
then passed on to scammers who use what's dumped
in material no one thought to destroy. Stuff bought
and password protected. Sent out of sight

from its source nation. Brought here now exposed
where the formerly unburdened consumer finds
his wires alive in a site of unmeasured impact.

PERDIDO SPAR

It's out there, somewhere, staring from a horizon
200 miles offshore, in water too deep for conventional
tension legs. They call it lost as if from men,
from ourselves—from Dido? A gamble on breaking into currents
deeper below wet crusts of rock: this floating case of steel,
air, ballast, pressure, measured exactly—the welded chambers

channeling oil into the pipelines, pulling deep-chambered
algae and plankton from million-year mud: a time horizon
too far to follow but drilled open, cracked by steel
and by explosive charges. The method is unconventional—
imagined through three billion dollars in currents
of desperate technology that radiate agency out from men's

minds. Here master-slave arms uncouple from the men
who made them move uranium through glass chambers.
Now a sub-aqua rover glides, telemanipulated, between currents
as it tends to the wells: one video eye on the dark ultradeep horizon

Kate Monaghan

it returns lit images up to the platform where 150 conventional
bodies maintain a cramped equilibrium inside epoxy-painted steel,

held for 2-week sessions within this coating ready to steal
heat from burning metal. The paint absorbs temperatures men
can't withstand—it bubbles and chars towards where conventional
bonds break and unstable electrons cut the layer-cake chambers
down, melting. And whatever tropical disturbance covers the horizon
even then it is 2 hours' flight 24 hours by boat through the currents

to any shore. How do I see this? Floating within the current
frame of cable grids, invisible but embedded, I am made in habits of steel
I have never seen. I have sensed some tremor past the horizon
where flames follow the lines down—where creatures cluster like men
and drink chemosynthetically what wafts up from the oil chambers.
Fire follows, crossing into the subsea system, and conventional

sentiments are announced on the website, our conventions
of interests mount, their appetites pressing like the currents
that bring a shark far too deep—looking for food at our chamber's
very door—he rises inside the matrix of sub-aqua steel
installed over the submerged mountains: ranges that men
might never have seen, might have left dark, unbuilt upon, a horizon.

Acequias as Quipus, Quipus as Poems
Arthur Sze

1.

FOR THE LAST FORTY-FIVE YEARS, I have lived in northern New Mexico; during this time, I've been involved with two acequias: the Ancon de Jacona and the Acequia del Llano. The word acequia is derived from the Arabic *as-saquiya* and refers to the irrigation ditch, as well as the association of members connected to it, that transports water from a river to farms and fields. For eighteen years, I was involved with the Ancon de Jacona, twenty miles north of Santa Fe, and, for the last four years, I have been actively involved with the Acequia del Llano.

The Acequia del Llano is the youngest of the four acequias that run through the city of Santa Fe. It is 1.5 miles long and begins at Nichols Reservoir and runs eventually into the Santa Fe River. Fourteen members are in this ditch association, and the acequia irrigates about thirty acres of gardens and orchards. In this environment, some of the endangered and threatened species that draw on this watershed include the southwestern willow flycatcher, the least tern, the violet-crowned hummingbird, the American marten, and the white-tailed ptarmigan. Other wildlife in the area include deer, black bears, coyotes, turkeys, and quail.

As a *parciante*, or voting member of the acequia, I am actively involved in the maintenance of this ditch. Just last week, all of the members came, or hired workers who came, to do the annual spring ditch cleaning. This involves walking the length of the ditch, from reservoir to river, cleaning, with shovels and clippers, branches, silt, and other debris that has accumulated over the late fall and winter.

The ditch association is organized with a mayordomo, ditch manager, who oversees the distribution of water according to each *parciante's* amount of water rights and also verifies that each parciante follows the strict days and times of the watering schedule. The current mayordomo, Mike Cruz, drives periodically up and down Canyon Road and monitors the usage to make sure no water is being wasted

Arthur Sze

and spilling into the street. The rules of the acequia are that if someone upstream is not using water during their allotted time, someone
downstream can draw on that water. However, one cannot draw on
water when someone downstream has the right to that water. The
mayordomo resolves any conflicts about water usage, and he also has
the authority to fine landowners who do not abide by the rules. For
our land, we have two days a week when we can draw water: from
Thursday at 6:00 p.m. to Friday morning at 7:30 a.m. and from Sunday
at 6:00 a.m. to Monday at 6:00 a.m.

The acequia runs at a higher elevation than all of the land held by
the parciantes, so the flow of water is gravity fed. On Thursdays and
Sundays, I walk about a quarter of a mile uphill to the ditch and drop
a metal gate into it. Water then backs up, and as the level rises, water
goes down two pipes. Two large green holding tanks fill, and then
water runs into a complex system of pipes set with timers, so sprin-
klers water grass, a garden, a few hundred-year-old apple trees, and
flower beds around the house, according to the different zones and
times. I manually turn on and move a secondary set of rotating sprin-
klers to water the orchard that has apple, peach, and pear trees.

New Mexico has a very dry landscape, and this year, due to climate
change, the drought is particularly damaging. By July 1, the annual
rainfall is normally 4.5 inches, and, as I write today on July 5, the
annual rainfall is an astoundingly low 1.25 inches. Severe water-
conservation measures are in effect throughout the city, and everyone who has the right to draw water off the Acequia del Llano is
aware how precious this resource is, and the sharing of this irrigation
water actively promotes community needs over a single individual
need. It also serves as an important reminder and contrast to our consumer culture, in which, as Ezra Pound once observed, "[Nothing] is
made to endure nor to live with / but [. . .] to sell and sell quickly."
During the Depression, there were stories of impoverished families
sharing sheep bones to flavor broth. Just like the water that was
passed along the irrigation line, bones were passed from family to
family to flavor subsistence soup.

Each year the irrigation season runs from about April 15 to October
15. In April, as I get up in the dark in the early morning and walk
uphill to divert water from the ditch, I notice Venus, Orion, and other
constellations of stars. I see lights from a dozen houses on the far side
of the Santa Fe River, flickering in the darkness. As it moves toward
summer, I notice the constellations shift in the sky, and by July 1, when
I walk uphill, I am walking in early daylight. By mid-September, I

50

will again be using a flashlight to head uphill in the dark and will be listening for deer or coyote in between the piñons and junipers. Connected to this seasonal rhythm, I am in biweekly contact with flowing water and recognize, as a steward, it is a privilege to use it to irrigate the land. This liminal awareness sparked my poem "First Snow":

FIRST SNOW

A rabbit has stopped on the gravel driveway:

> imbibing the silence,
> you stare at spruce needles:

>> there's no sound of a leaf blower,
>> no sign of a black bear;

a few weeks ago, a buck scraped his rack
> against an aspen trunk;
> a carpenter scribed a plank along a curved stone wall.

>> You only spot the rabbit's ears and tail:

when it moves, you locate it against speckled gravel,
but when it stops, it blends in again;

> the world of being is like this gravel:

>> you think you own a car, a house,
>> this blue-zigzagged shirt, but you just borrow these things.

Yesterday, you constructed an aqueduct of dreams
> and stood at Gibraltar,

>> but you possess nothing.

Snow melts into a pool of clear water;
> and, in this stillness,

>> starlight behind daylight wherever you gaze.

51

2.

If you take an aerial view and visualize the acequia running along the hillside as a primary flow and then locate the many subsidiary or secondary flows running downhill, perpendicularly, from the main flow, to irrigate various orchards and fields, you will see a quipu composed of water. In Inca culture, a quipu is made out of spun fiber and is defined in the *Merriam-Webster's Collegiate Dictionary* as: "a device made of a main cord with smaller varicolored cords attached and knotted and used by the ancient Peruvians (as for calculating)."

The word quipu has two spellings: the older version, quipu, is based on the Spanish spelling for the Quechua word that means "knot." It is more often spelled "*khipu*" today. In either case, the quipu is usually made of cotton; it is lightweight, portable, and encodes information. There are two kinds of quipus: numerical and nonnumerical. The numerical ones record accounting information. Researchers have examined the knotting in quipus, and they are able to read the numbers, one to nine. The location of knots on the numerically based cords follows a base-ten decimal system, so a quipu can easily incorporate ones, tens, hundreds, and thousands. For instance, a quipu that accounted for containers of potatoes in a mountainside storage vault would be invaluable during a famine. The rulers could pull potatoes out from storage, feed people, and retie the knots, so that inventories of food could be kept up-to-date. Numerical quipus track numbers of sandals, gold, census numbers of people living in villages, and so on, so these quipus provide essential day-to-day information that helped the Inca rulers respond to crises and rule the kingdom.

Interestingly, poet and translator Brenda Hillman has mentioned that water usage in the Sahara was tracked by tying and untying knots. And there is also evidence of ancient Chinese quipus, composed of silk, that predate Chinese characters. In the next-to-last chapter of the *Dao De Jing*, there is a passage that says, Let people go back to communicating through knotted cords. In the poem "Thoughts," by Du Fu, in the Tang dynasty, the speaker sits on a porch at night and muses how people struggle futilely for glory, and then the speaker considers how someone started communicating by knotting cords and now there's the mire and endless bureaucracy of government! So the use of knotted cords as a vehicle for communication can be found in many ancient cultures.

Focusing on the nonnumerical quipus, the possibility that they encode language is tantalizing, but so far no one has been able to "read" or decipher them; the knotting does not follow a linear base-ten accounting system. Nevertheless, several important historical accounts provide evidence that quipus incorporate narrative information that encodes the myths, legends, and histories of the Incas. One important historical account describes an Inca runner who arrives at a remote mountain village. He pulls out a quipu, and a *quipucamayoc*, a specialized reader of quipus, looks at it. The village then begins a revolt against the Spanish. Here, then, is evidence that the quipu must have contained narrative information.

As a poet, the nonnumerical quipus interest me most. I like to think of the knotting in a quipu as a physical and visual reminder of the way a word or phrase may be repeated and turned in a poem. Robert Fitzgerald once remarked that repetition in Homer utilized elegant variation, that each time the repeat occurred, the word was enriched and deepened in meaning.

In composing my book *Quipu*, I looked at all the dictionary definitions of the word "as" and noted ten different meanings. In the title poem, "Quipu," a sequence of nine poems, I took it upon myself to keep using the word "as" and, over time, allowing different meanings to accrue. This was an organic way to layer, deepen, and simultaneously enrich the meaning of the poem. The poet Cole Swensen has noted that repetition frequently involves casting a spell. I agree and would add that repetition can also become a form of insistence. The knots can refer to repeats of words, and they can also refer to repeats in syntactic patterns; moreover, as in a quipu where the spin of fiber in secondary cords can shift from clockwise to counterclockwise, I envisioned a shift where nouns could turn into verbs. The sequence "Quipu" is too long to reprint here (the complete poem was first published in *Conjunctions:35, American Poetry: States of the Art*), but some of these thematic currents are clearly initiated in the opening section:

QUIPU

I try to see a bald eagle nest in a Douglas fir
but catch my sleeve on thorns, notice blackberries,

hear large wings splashing water in a lagoon.
I glimpse a heron perched on a post above a tidal flat,

remember red elderberries arcing along a path
where you catch and release a newt among ferns.

And as a doe slips across the road behind us,
we zigzag when we encounter a point of resistance,

zigzag as if we describe the edge of an immense leaf,
as if we plumb a jagged coastline where tides

wash and renew the mind. I stare at abalone eyes,
am startled at how soft a sunflower star is to touch,

how sticky a tentacle of an anemone is to finger.
When we walk barefoot in sand, I sway

to the motion of waves, mark bits of crabs
washed to shore, see—in an instant a dog wrenches

a leash around the hand of a woman, shatters bones—
ensuing loss salamanders the body, lagoons the mind.

3.

The flow of water is also the flow of language: water and poetry are
essential movements that affirm and shape life. Water can be conceived of as beginningless beginning and endless end; if water has no
shape of its own, it can take any shape and has infinite possibility. In
poetry, I am interested in a finite thing that has a multiple or poly-
semous range of expression and meaning. Poetry utilizes a finite set
of words and yet has the possibility of reaching into the infinite, and
it calls our attention to the mystery of existence. I am reminded of
Dōgen's dictum "Water is the koan of water." If water is a riddle
of itself, then all of creation is mysterious and marvelous. It is astonishing life exists and that there is anything at all.

In looking back over my time in New Mexico, I realize that the
scarcity of water has helped me pay close attention to living details
and the profoundly changing landscape. This realization is embodied
in a poem of mine set in Jacona:

Arthur Sze

RED BREATH

Shaggy red clouds in the west—

unlatching a gate, I step into a field:
      no coyote slants across with a chicken in its mouth,

      no wild asparagus rises near the ditch.

In the night sky, Babylonian astronomers
      recorded a supernova
      and witnessed the past catch up to the present,

      but they did not write
            what they felt at what they saw—

they could not see to this moment.
From August, we could not see to this moment

      but draw water out of a deep well—
      it has the taste of

      creek water in a tin cup,
            and my teeth ache against the cold.

Juniper smoke rises and twists through the flue—

      my eyes widen
      as I brush your hair, brush your hair—

      I have red breath:
      in the deep night, we are again lit,

            and I true this time to consequence.

Another time, walking in the ditch of the Ancon de Jacona before spring cleaning, I marveled at the landscape around me and, in imagination, moved across space and time. The village of Jacona is in an agricultural valley fed by the Pojoaque River, and Los Alamos, the birthplace of our atomic age, sits visibly on a mesa to the west. The following poem is in an invented form. Starting with the title, each line picks up a word or words from the previous line, and at the end, a word is picked up again, in the title, so my form embodies line and circle. In a similar way, an irrigation ditch in northern New Mexico that carries water to the fields forms a line and circle; it marks the seasonal beginning and end that supports and sustains life here.

SIGHT LINES

I'm walking in sight of the Río Nambe—

salt cedar rises through silt in an irrigation ditch—

the snowpack in the Sangre de Cristos has already dwindled before spring—

at least no fires erupt in the conifers above Los Alamos—

the plutonium waste has been hauled to an underground site—

a man who built plutonium triggers breeds horses now—

no one could anticipate this distance from Monticello—

Jefferson despised newspapers, but no one thing takes us out of ourselves—

during the Cultural Revolution, a boy saw his mother shot in front of a firing squad—

a woman detonates when a spam text triggers bombs strapped to her body—

when I come to an upright circular steel lid, I step out of the ditch—

I step out of the ditch but step deeper into myself—

I arrive at a space that no longer needs autumn or spring—

I find ginseng where there is no ginseng my talisman of desire—

though you are visiting Paris, you are here at my fingertips—

though I step back into the ditch, no whitening cloud dispels this world's mystery—

the ditch ran before the year of the Louisiana Purchase—

I'm walking on silt, glimpsing horses in the field—

fielding the shapes of our bodies in white sand—

though parallel lines touch in the infinite, the infinite is here—

NOTE. This essay is based on a talk presented at *Writing on Water*, Brown University, April 12–13, 2018. The two-day conference was part of a larger conference, *Water's Edge*, held from April 3–13, 2018.

A Theory Pre-Postmortem
Joyce Carol Oates

NAEGLERIA FOWLERI HAS TRAVELED through their nasal passage-
ways and into their brains.

Burrowed deep into the marrow of their bones.

Riding the crests of tiny waves, warm-coursing arterial blood.

Fresh water heated by the sun, aswirl with muck and teeming with
microbes emboldened in recent years by rising temperatures, fewer
prolonged periods of subzero weather.

Ravenous *Naegleria fowleri*, devourer of brains.

An adventure!—they'd thought. Swimming in the sun-warmed
mountain lake in the Catskills, invited to spend a weekend at the
country home of old friends in Margaretville whom they hadn't seen
in several years.

If the genre is romance, then it is their (genuine) love for each other
in the warm-water shallows of late middle age that should be emphasized. If the genre is didactic nonfiction, it is the folly of their behavior in a rapidly changing climate that should be emphasized. If
the genre is tragedy with a satiric edge, or satire with a tragic edge, it
is the (ironic) ignorance of intelligent, intellectual, highly educated
individuals (PhD, MFA between them; both "educators") that should
be emphasized.

If the genre is allegory, it is their *representative nature* that should
be emphasized, for M_____ and G_____ are more than simply individuals for whom personal catastrophe is imminent; indeed, it isn't
their *individual selves* that concern us since we scarcely get to know
M_____ and G_____ before their story is abruptly and rudely ended.

Knowing to avoid landfills, notorious "Superfund" sites in which
poisoned soil might be habitable again only after three hundred million years yet swimming in the lake at Margaretville without a
qualm—why not? G_____ swam longer in the lake than M_____.

Consequently, G_____ has become more infected than M_____. This is the theory.

Possibly M_____ isn't infected at all or if she is, it is not with brain-eating *Naegleria fowleri* but with another microbe, which accounts for her raging fever. (This is another theory, unproven.)

(Until there is an autopsy, or autopsies, nothing can be proven definitively.)

Of nearly seven thousand languages in the world, approximately one-half have fewer than three thousand speakers, which classifies them as *endangered*.

If a majority of speakers of a language are elderly, the danger of extinction is compounded.

If a language is written, it will endure (to a degree). If a language is primarily spoken, it can endure only as long as there are living persons who speak it.

G_____ is the founder and director of the Brookline Center for the Study of Endangered North American Languages. G_____is the custodian, caretaker, curator of endangered North American languages. He has also been a tireless fund-raiser, a writer of grants—indeed, G_____ has been called by admirers the Tolstoy of grant writers: his proposals are masterpieces of erudition and persuasion, bolstered by meticulously footnoted statistics. Yet, in recent years, G_____'s requests for grants from federal agencies have been frequently denied. The budget for the Brookline Center was halved in 2018, and has been halved again for 2020; soon, the center will exist primarily as a letterhead, an address. Now that funds are evaporating, the building is being taken over by the more robust, younger-staffed Brookline Community Center for Diversity Initiatives.

The languages for which G_____ has been a dedicated custodian are all aboriginal—"indigenous." M_____, who speaks no more than one language with any facility, is in awe of her husband, who can speak such languages as Comanche, Hopi, Blackfoot, Arapaho; G_____ can read even more languages including the near-extinct Mandan and the "severely endangered" Cherokee (Oklahoma). There are languages spoken by as few as 250 people, as few as twenty, even eight (at last count). But a factor in assessing languages is the age of the primary speakers; if there is a majority of young speakers, as with Hawaiian sign language, or any language that has been adopted into a public school curriculum, the language will have a chance of survival.

Many speakers of endangered languages are not themselves literate in those languages and have little interest in preserving them. Especially if they are elderly, and if they are ill, or what is called *socially marginalized*. Small, diminishing populations on reservations in Wyoming, Utah, Oklahoma, Nevada, North Dakota, where other problems (alcoholism, sexual abuse, poverty) are more immediately urgent.

Preserving a unique and irreplaceable language is often a matter for outsiders to fuss over, not native speakers. These outsiders are likely to be white scholars with degrees in linguistics and anthropology; G_____ has advanced degrees in linguistics, anthropology, cognitive psychology. He has lobbied in Washington, DC, on behalf of endangered languages and has been confounded by shoulder shrugs from native speakers themselves—*Who cares?* Other remarks are untranslatable except as epithets—*Who gives a damn/shit/fuck?* Profanities in other languages strike the ear as quaint but sometimes a remnant of their original force remains like a trace radioactive element in minerals.

G_____ doesn't let such apathy dissuade him. He can understand that Native Americans distrust white academicians anatomizing their cultures, appropriating their problems as their own, assuming a position of authority, patronage. It's analogous to pressing charges against an abuser even when the victim denies that there has been a crime—sometimes you have to protect victims for their own good. Whether they give a damn or not.

M_____ fell in love with G_____ because he so loved these rare languages. Though he was nine years older than she was, and often distracted and disheveled, not a man to whom many women her age would give a second glance, yet M_____ had never met a man like G_____, who spoke with such passion of his work that tears shone in his eyes.

Because the languages are beautiful and will pass away into oblivion without the effort of people like me.

Because beauty must always be preserved.

Because someone has to care.

Because time is running out.

Their hosts in Margaretville, older than M_____ by a decade or more, longtime friends of G_____'s, explained apologetically that they rarely swam in the lake any longer, too much seaweed close to shore, too many damned gnats, though certainly the lake was still beautiful, especially at dusk. Also apologizing, they rarely hiked in the woods any longer, too many ticks, Lyme disease, many friends had been infected but if you were careful, as surely G_____ and M_____ would be, there was no grave danger.

Also—*We're not so young any longer! Can't keep up with you.*

M_____ and G_____ are made to feel subtly flattered—though younger than their hosts they are hardly *young*.

M_____ and G_____ have planned their future(s) carefully. They have savings, investments. Medical plans, insurance. They will have paid off their mortgage within a few years. Their children are grown and gone and independent—financially, emotionally. (Thank God! M_____ jokes that empty-nest syndrome gave her no more trouble than hot flashes—which is to say nil.) Each has projects, plans for books: a memoir for M_____, a study of the Comanche language (now spoken by less than thirty persons) for G_____. When G_____ retires, they will spend a year in Tuscany. Planning the future is second nature to them, a habit cultivated as (gifted, ambitious) schoolchildren of educated parents.

M_____ will remember with a shiver of love G_____ emerging from the lake: water streaming down his bare chest, arms, legs, flattening dark hairs against his skin like an animal's pelt.

M_____ will remember with a shiver of love how standing in the lake with water lapping to their waists they'd kissed. Not usual for them in a quasi-public place yet for some reason, who knows why, G_____ had been affectionate, playful. Such moments of happiness, cherished because inexplicable. The skin about G_____'s eyes was unusually pale, and his eyes unusually naked, without glasses.

You know, I love you. My dear wife.

Hope you know that.

Rare for G_____ to utter such words. For though G_____ was fluent in a half dozen "endangered" languages he was shy in the language of intimacy. But now G_____ spoke gravely as if (somehow) gazing back upon the moment.

M_____ laughed in delight of her husband, his fatty-muscled body, folds of flesh at his waist, gut-heavy, though with hard, muscular legs, ankles.

Faint with love for her husband. Oh!—she adored G_____, who was so kind to her, overlooked her failings as other men had not done, and still believed, evidence to the contrary, that she was beautiful, desirable. Smiling to think, with the dark wit for which, in her small circle of friends, she was famous: Who could hope for a more abiding love than a folie à deux?

Though not liking it how, when they swam together in the lake at Margaretville, G_____ frequently pulled ahead, oblivious of her. As sometimes he did when they were hiking together. Even walking together, unless M_____ managed for them to hold hands. As if something in the future tugged at G_____, he was helpless to resist. Oblivious not of *her* (she thought) but of the presence of another. A kind of trance overcame the man as if drawn by the gravitational pull of private thoughts (a future? but what future? did it include M_____?) in the languid sun-warmed Catskills lake in which splotches of light winked and shone like teeming life, though alien and not their own.

An Interview with Robert Macfarlane

Conducted by Diane Ackerman

ROBERT MACFARLANE IS THE AUTHOR of books about landscape, nature, people, and place, including *Mountains of the Mind*, *The Wild Places*, *The Old Ways*, *Landmarks*, *The Lost Words* (with artist Jackie Morris), *Holloway*, and *Underland*. He's an ever-alert and dynamic traveler, a deft mountain climber, spelunker, and interlocutor. A collector of lost words for landscape, he's especially fascinated by the power of single words to provide a vivid sense of place. I was first enchanted by his climbing sojourns in *Mountains of the Mind*, and since then have followed much of his wayfaring on earth, sea, and ice. Most recently, I've been delighted by his new book, *Underland*—which won the 2019 Wainwright nature-writing prize— where his climbing takes a turn as he inserts himself right under the earth's skin to explore what lies beneath our feet. I couldn't resist talking with him about words, wandering, climate change, the fate of the planet, and the solace of nature.

DIANE ACKERMAN: I found *Underland* beautifully written and wise, a haunting book, a treasure, both as personal memoir by one of nature's keenest celebrants, and as an eye-opening odyssey into parts of the planet we recoil from, or never knew existed, or thought we'd safely hidden from view. It reads like a seamless dive, crawl, and trek through deep time, in sense-rich landscapes, while watching the human saga soar and unravel all around you. I understand you began this book nearly ten years ago, in the midst of many Anthropocene "unburials," as you refer to them—in which "forces, objects, and substances thought safely confined to the underworld are declaring themselves above ground with powerful consequences." What are some of the disturbing unburials that caught your attention?

ROBERT MACFARLANE: The idea for *Underland* first arose in 2010, a year when four differently catastrophic "surfacings" occurred: the Haitian earthquake in January, the Deepwater Horizon blowout in the Gulf of Mexico in April, followed a few days later by the explosion of the Icelandic volcano Eyjafjallajökull, and then in August the trapping of thirty-three Chilean miners deep in the San José gold and copper mine, far beneath the Atacama Desert (all of the men were eventually brought back alive to the upper world, after sixty-nine days in the dark, in a rescue capsule codesigned by NASA). It was impossible to me, that year, *not* to think of what lay beneath the surface—and of the traumas, disruptions, and disclosures that occurred when the boundaries between above and below were breached.

The Deepwater blowout and the Chilean mine collapse laid bare what it is in the interests of both the extractive industries and most consumers to keep hidden from view: that is to say, the largely invisible infrastructure and "slow violence"—to human and more-than-human communities—inevitably generated by the staggering extent of our extractive activities as a species. Humans have drilled more than fifty million kilometers of oil borehole alone. Humans have removed the tops of entire mountain ridges to get at the coal they contain. Humans have warrened mines deep into massifs and far out beneath the sea. Technology has amplified human capacities such that we (that is to say, some of "us") have become immense geological agents, terraforming the underearth at vast cost, incurring largely unmeasured externalities. Haiti and Iceland, by contrast, were declarations of the earth's own unbiddable, restless powers; a reminder that we exist, as a species, in a slender boundary layer beneath vaults of turbulent air and above seething depths of shifting crust and molten mantle. All four of these events spoke to me of precarity and volatility, and of illumination and ignorance, and I became determined to discover more about what the underland *knew*, if I may put it like that. It felt a subject that was both urgent and ancient, and so it proved to be.

I made the first sparse notes towards what became *Underland* in that year, sure that I would write at length on this subject, but without any sense of how to shape or explore all that it held. I began work in earnest on the book in early 2012—and wrote the last paragraphs in June 2018, in the very days when billions of people worldwide were gripped by yet another underworld story—that of the thirteen young Thai footballers and their coach, who on the afternoon of 23 June, after football practice in their home province of Chiang Rai, decided to explore the Tham Luang Nang Non cave complex, drawn into the darkness by curiosity and a sense of adventure. Shortly after they had entered the cave, a cloudburst occurred and water levels in the system rose rapidly, trapping all of them around two and a half miles inside the mountain.

And in the intervening years, yes, I found my writing overtaken by Anthropocene circumstances, as what I came to think of a master trope of our epoch—*things that should have stayed buried, rising to the surface*—recurred across the world: ancient methane deposits released by melting permafrost, the eerily preserved body of a fifty-thousand-year-old wolf pup found by gold miners in the Yukon, the bodies of soldiers killed in conflicts over a century previously yielded up by fast-melting glaciers, the marks of long-vanished prehistoric structures (Neolithic enclosures, Bronze Age barrows) showing themselves as cropmarks on the land's surface during summer heat waves; aridity as X-ray, drought as hauntology.

ACKERMAN: Climate change unburials have become increasingly visible, and not just to Arctic and Antarctic ecotourists, or climate refugees, or those prone to viewing the whole human saga, swiveling from past to future, elsewhere and elsewhen, dizzying as that can be. Most people can no longer ignore climate change, because it is now happening in their own backyards. They may notice that geese have stopped migrating, or that their annual plants are overwintering, or that Lyme ticks and other "pests" are finding their winters bearable, or their traditional fishing holes are barren, or their seasons are hotter or stormier than ever before. We used to talk about going into the wilderness and leaving only our footprints behind. In the Anthropocene we realize that's no longer possible, that we've touched every inch of the planet, left our neon fingerprints everywhere, and are not only altering the evolution of other species, but tinkering with and imperiling our own evolution as well. You write fervently about climate change, and refer to the sense of claustrophobia it's created in everyday life. Why is the Anthropocene a time of claustrophobia?

MACFARLANE: This is brilliantly put. Yes—these are all versions of the experience that Glenn Albrecht has memorably named as solastalgia, which he defines as the psychic distress brought about by watching an environment or landscape change towards the point of unrecognizability around oneself, brought about especially by the effects of climate breakdown, big corporate actors, or other large-scale anthropogenic change. Where nostalgia is the pain arising from moving away from a loved place, solastalgia occurs without you going anywhere; it is the landscape that "leaves" from around you. The last decade—and especially the last two or three years—have seen an intensification and a globalization of this distinctive Anthropocene effect, from Californian wildfires to Hawaii's plastic-saturated shorelines, the diminishing of birdsong or the decline in insect populations, and the many unsettling phenological shifts you describe.

As to claustrophobia, well, it came to fascinate me in the course of writing *Underland*. I first had to reckon with claustrophobia as a sheer physical force, and to determine whether or not I could withstand its claims upon me during the journeys I anticipated making. So I asked a friend of mine, the photographer, climber, and caver John Beatty, to take me on a challenging day's caving in the limestone underworld of the Peak District. He did—so challenging, in fact, that he ended up turning back at a spatially parsimonious point of the system called the Vice. I made it through the Vice, and went on and down into the earth, and found myself both exhilarated and mostly unfrightened by the experience.

Claustrophobia also interested me greatly as a writer, for its power to affect readers vicariously, in their bodies. More so than vertigo, reading about claustrophobia is gripping. It compels what William Golding once called sympathetic kinesthesia: people's limbs start to twitch, their heart rates rise, their breathing gets faster. All writers want to move people, in one way or another; writing about claustrophobia enables that in a way that can approach the sinister.

And lastly, yes, claustrophobia came to seem to me the phobia of our crisis-stricken, endgame age; the sense of time and space running out, of a narrowing down of opportunity for amelioration or escape. The Holocene was the postglacial period of climatic stability in which the flourishing of *Homo sapiens* occurred; the Anthropocene is the period of stricken ecologies, resource exhaustion, slow violence, and scarcity in which the species is now floundering. Yet—primarily because of the systemically entrenched nature of the problems—we seem unable to organize against these self-produced confinements. Or, as in a story I tell early in *Underland* of Neil Moss (the victim in surely the most notorious British caving death of all time), the more we struggle to free ourselves, the more stuck we seem to become. Moss was a twenty-year-old student of philosophy at Oxford University, who in 1959 took part in an exploratory eight-person trip into the famous Peak Cavern system in the limestone of Derbyshire. Descending an unfathomed and near-vertical shaft, Moss lost his footing on the light caving ladder he was using, and became wedged in the shaft. "I say, I'm stuck!" he called up to his friends. "I can't budge an inch." Nor could he, and despite the immense rescue attempt subsequently mobilized to free him, Moss died there, suffocated by the carbon dioxide he produced with his last hours of breath.

ACKERMAN: In your writing about the Wood Wide Web, you focus on how behaviors we attach human virtues to—altruism, compassion, affection, tending the sick, etc.—are performed not only by other animals, but by life-forms we don't think of as conscious, emotional, fearful, loyal, or loving. Would you talk a little about the seamless web of nature, the social nexus of a forest, for instance, and the mutualism of species and how you believe trees communicate as a metaphor for the nature of love? Share a little of that personal vision, please.

MACFARLANE: I'm glad that these aspects of that chapter—which is called "The Understory," in reference to the term of art in forest ecology for those aspects of arboreal and woodland life which exist above the woodland floor and beneath the canopy—stood out to you. That chapter forms part of a deeper subtext in *Underland*—a word wide web, perhaps—that recognizes and celebrates mutualism both biological and social. I found myself returning again and again to this subject and in the end decided, reflexively, to bury these moments in the book rather than explicitly relating them, thereby allowing readers to perform their own conjoinings. One of the best public moments I've had with *Underland* came while I was on book tour in the US in June 2019. I was in Point Reyes, California—placed right on the San Andreas Fault; those people know all about the earth's restlessness!—in conversation with the great Rebecca Solnit. Rebecca suddenly produced two pages of notes and began to read out parts of many of the passages in the book concerning mutualism, symbiosis, and reciprocity. It was exciting to me to see the pattern perceived, as it were; those apparently isolated examples standing, reflexively, in mutual meaning-making relation to one another, and together becoming an ethic when encountered in association.

There are, perhaps, two leitmotifs at the heart of *Underland* (or at the core, perhaps I should better say): one is of the network, the web, and the other is of the opened hand or the handprint. The hand stencil is one of the very earliest extant marks made and left by human beings—created by placing the palm against the rock and then spitting a mouthful of paint powder against it, thereby staining stone and hand back, such that a negative trace is left on the rock once the hand is removed. I take that gesture—the hand opened in greeting, in offer of help, in communication—to be a resonant sign, and modern as well as ancient versions of it are embedded throughout *Underland*, right down to the very last line of the epilogue, "Surfacing."

So much of our current crisis—which Jason Moore names not as the Anthropocene but as the Capitalocene—is born of a system that structurally embeds profit above all other kinds of ethos or "good" (cf the obligations of "fiduciary duty"). Yet within the confines of capitalism we still prove ourselves capable of remarkable kinds of giving, trusting, and loving; those forms of open-handed interaction which reach outside the compulsions of proportionate reciprocity or unequal betterment conditioned by capital. "We must love one another or die. / Defenseless under the night," wrote Auden in his great poem on the eve of World War II. That is the idealized or epigrammatic version of mutualism. Jedediah Purdy, in his superb book *After Nature: A Politics for the Anthropocene*, unfolds it towards practicality:

> People are best able to change their ways when they find two things at once in nature: something to fear, a threat they must avoid, and also something to love, a quality . . . which they can do their best to honor. Either impulse can stay the human hand, but the first stops it just short of being burnt or broken. The second keeps the hand poised, extended in greeting or in an offer of peace. This gesture is the beginning of collaboration, among people but beyond us, in building our next home.

ACKERMAN: Speaking of mutuality, there's no doubt we humans have created a lot of planetary chaos. Mainly *accidentally*, which is important. Not always accidentally—some exploiters know exactly what they're doing, and don't care. But for a long time, we didn't realize how much we were altering the climate and ecosystems. Now we do. Just think how much we could achieve if we worked together as a species, on purpose this time, to undo our worst mistakes and safeguard the planet's future. How likely do you think that mutuality might be? The theme of this issue of *Conjunctions* is "Earth Elegies"— do you feel elegiac about the earth? What hope do you see? What do you tell your children about the state of the climate, the planet?

Robert Macfarlane

MACFARLANE: My children are scared. Deeply scared. No ambiguity about it. My students too. When I was growing up in the 1980s, my future horizon, probably like yours, was foreclosed by the possibility of nuclear conflict. Theirs is foreclosed by climate breakdown and mass extinction, an incremental but still calamitous vision. I have frequent conversations with students who have almost normalized this prospect; they feel themselves involuntarily to be entering what E. O. Wilson calls "The Age of Loneliness," in which our depletion of more-than-human communities results in an emptied, echoing earth.

Personally I am, one might say, more hopeful of our visions than I have ever been before but more despairing of our futures. By which I mean that I think we now see the difficulties more clearly than ever before, and we know better than ever before what must be done, but the window of opportunity to act is closing frighteningly fast. Incidentally, I dislike the tendency to singularize Anthropocene circumstances into a single "wicked problem." The current conditions were produced by the work of many hands over much time, and they will be turned, if they are to be turned, by the work of many hands too. To fall into binaries of "collapse" and "salvation" is irresponsibly soteriological to my mind. Vulnerability in and culpability for the present mess are unevenly distributed; the solutions too are granular, partial and effortful in nature. No rapture here.

ACKERMAN. I find all of your books eye-opening, and keenly attuned to the landscape in delicious, appreciative, at times almost forensic detail. They're full of a physical awareness of what it feels and thinks like to be a life-form here on earth, how intricately one's mind and body interact with the landscape. It doesn't matter if the locale is exalting, terrifying, mucky, painful, or deadly—it's as if the land inks itself onto your body, dot by dot, and later, in the plaintive calm that nature writers also crave, you translate its sensations and ineffable lure into words. Those words are eloquent, often poetic, and you're frequently driven to widen our lexicon by including antique or rare (but richly precise) words for the land. If one has a hundred words for snow, one understands snow differently. I love how vividly imaginable your landscapes become.

I know from my own experience that making one's travels replay in a reader's mind takes hard work, and in my case at least, a glaciation of revisions. Others would probably find that tedious. But I love

69

trying to net something in words, however long it takes, because finding a way to make the world sayable feels minerally, viscerally satisfying. I know you know what I mean. Those two modes of being—fingering the world, reading it with the senses, and then being at a monk-like remove while writing about it—both require intense presence, though the first may include hair-raising dilemmas and frights. As a result, nature writers sometimes live contradictory lives. A lengthy cyclone of intense alertness that's punctuated by moments of uncertainty, loneliness, discomfort, or danger may be followed by work at the keyboard, with long hours of contemplation, verbal problem-solving, and obsessive research. The writing may happen in attention gulps, while taking part in family life. There's also the strange circadian transition between seasonal time while on expedition and domestic chronicity at home. Do you find your life divided in that way? You write "Time feels differently reckoned" after going underground: "further deepened, further folded." In *The Wild Places* you wrote that "the wild prefaced us, and it will outlive us. Human cultures will pass, given time, of which there is sufficiency. The ivy will snake and unrig our flats and terraces, as it scattered the Roman villas. The sand will drift into our business parks, as it drifted into the brooches of the Iron Age. Our roads will lapse into the land." How has going underground changed your ideas about time? Could you talk a little about living in "deep time" as opposed to the more comfortable flatlands of everyday life?

MACFARLANE: Your questions are essays in themselves, Diane, and quietly unfold responses in their course that are likely better than any I may be able to offer. The "monk-like remove," the "glaciation of revisions," the "mineral" and "visceral" work of "making the world sayable." Yes, yes, yes! Let me pick up if I may on the invitation to reflect on craft that is tacitly extended above, especially the means by which language might be charged with some version of the "palp and heft" of the given world, and also the means by which human and geological timescale might be brought not into alignment with one another, but at least into sharpening relation.

Language first: I revise obsessively. The first sentence of the book—"The way into the underland is through the riven trunk of an old ash tree"—took weeks to hear and catch; the first fifteen pages or so probably took as long to rewrite and get right as all forty thousand words of the Greenland and Finland chapters. I'm fascinated by rhythm and sound pattern in prose, and am committed to at least *trying* to give my sentences—even across the course of a 130,000-word book—the same kind of prosodic attention and acoustic life that one would without hesitation give a sonnet sequence. That takes time. A lot of time. When I had a rough first draft of *Underland* done, I read the whole thing aloud to myself, annotating the pages as I went, wanting to hear the sentences as they will be read in the mind's ear of someone who is not me; trying to see where slips and trips occurred, or where—as, perhaps, in the description of a "black-star" calving of vastly old glacial ice in Greenland, or some of the "surfacing" scenes after time spent below ground—the rhythms and tempo of the language as it moves might work on the reader in ways that exceed purely propositional content. It doesn't always succeed, of course, and God knows sometimes I can sound arch or awkward or overtorqued. Finding a way—in the revision stages of a big book, with which you have lived for years—to encounter your own writing as a stranger seems to me a hard but necessary thing for a writer to do. When I'd finished a second draft, I let it sit for a few weeks, then picked it up and read it through one evening and night, in one sitting, waiting for what Nabokov once described as "the tell-tale shiver down the spine." Whenever that came, I knew the writing was working. When it didn't come for pages at a time, I tried to figure out why and fix it.

As for time—well, it was quite late in the book that I realized I wanted to tell all of the first-person sections in the present tense. A person at a reading during the Q&A recently put her hand up to say that she'd taken a vow to hurl against the wall the next book she read that was written in the conventional or historical present tense, or both; she asked me why I wrote parts of *Underland* in that way. My answer was that—while I was sorry for triggering her readerly allergy—this wasn't done for trivial reasons of vividness or modishness. It was done because the book's principal chronology is deep time; that is to say the geological expanses of past and future that stretch behind and away from the present moment, and that are both humbling and crushing to consider. *Underland* argues for a "deep time ethic," in which contemplating ourselves within a deep-time context should have the effect not of inducing a flat ontology (whereby all things are equalized in worthlessness and transience by this immense perspective), nor of ethical abrogation (on the grounds that "it will all be all right in the end"), but rather of ethically charging us with a sense of responsibility *now*, minute by minute, for the legacies we are leaving behind as communities and as polities—and also of pristinating the present moment into greater clarity and wonder. Implausible as it seems when viewed within epochs and eons of our billion-year-old earth, we *do* exist. You do, I do, somehow, now. So the present-tense sections became the knife-edge on which the book's telling walked, while to either side plummeted away the anchorless fathoms of deep time.

ACKERMAN. I love *Mountains of the Mind*, in which you find the allure of mountains intensely gripping—literally—as you hold the planet in your arms and grip its pinnacles, ribs, and crevasses.

In *Underland* you continue that spartan, perilous climbing odyssey, to the summit (or nadir) of otherness, where a climber is as likely to die as to return fleeced in fame. This time it's crawling down labyrinthine caves, unpeeling strata of civilizations, exploring the convoluted and murky warrens below metropolitan streets, roaming vertical tunnels under the ocean, or abseiling into a glassy, glacial melt shaft in Greenland. Humans have always lived on and off the land, and yet we've obsessed about what lies beneath, sending our heroes underground on legendary quests. Why do you think that is? Do you have favorites among such classic stories? Please talk a little about your journey of "deep mapping" the world and what that means to you. Will you ever feel like you've completed that personal cartography? Which of your *Underland* expeditions stirred you the most?

MACFARLANE: I am "north-minded," as I once wrote in a book called *Landmarks*. I'm drawn by acculturation and decades of mountaineering and walking to high altitudes and high latitudes; to snow, ice, and rock. It so happens that these places—the thawing poles, the deglaciating peaks—are now also among the front lines of climate breakdown, as the cryosphere thins, the "eternal snows" of the Arctic are shown to be decidedly mortal, and the word "permafrost" seems increasingly absurd. All of which is to say that the last third of *Underland*, which takes place in Arctic Norway, East Greenland, and Finland in deep winter, is the part of the book I'll never forget writing, traveling, or thinking. The summer of 2016, when I was in East Greenland, was at that date the summer of most intense melt on record; temperatures in Nuuk, Greenland's capital, topped 22°C, meltwater began flowing on the ice cap a month earlier than ever before. Icebergs sweated in the fjords, polar bears starved or were shot.

Robert Macfarlane

It was a shocking, indicting time to be in that place—and to understand that the fate of ice is the fate of us.

Despite and in addition to the historically particularized contemporary experiences that are retold by me in parts of this most recent book, I did also have the sense often that I was merely adding a further iteration to—twist in the tunnel of—a very ancient story form. As you imply, another of the peculiar doublenesses of the underland is that it has long been a realm that compels both aversion and attention. One of the oldest known stories of them all, *The Epic of Gilgamesh*, written around 2100 BC in what we now refer to as Sumeria, contains among its variant passages the story of the servant Enki's descent into the "netherworld" to retrieve something that is precious to his master, Gilgamesh. Enki endures an arduous and hazardous journey through hailstone storms and violent sea tempests (extreme weather events of ancient Mesopotamia!), only to be imprisoned on arrival in the netherworld. He is eventually freed and carried back to the surface on a lofting breeze. Upon surfacing, he and Gilgamesh embrace, kiss, and talk. Enki has not retrieved the lost object, but he has brought back valuable news of vanished people. "Did you see my little stillborn children who never knew existence?" Gilgamesh asks him desperately. "I saw them," answers Enki. On first reading that exchange, I came close to tears; Gilgamesh's longing—his need—for news of his lost children from beyond the pale of life spoke so clearly across more than four thousand years, as did Enki's calm compassion. It echoed, to me, so many of the stories of parents awaiting news of their children from below the ground or through the veil, right down to the parents of the Thai footballers who waited day after agonizing day by the mouth of the Tham Luang Nang Non cave system, as rainstorms gathered and the waters rose and fell. . . .

In *Mountains of the Mind* I was concerned with tracing—mapping, if you like—the revolution of perception that wild landscape, especially mountainous landscape, underwent in what might loosely be called "the Western imagination" between the later 1700s and the present day. Though the break or turn is not absolute, it is largely true to say that through the medieval and early-modern periods in Europe and, subsequently, colonial America, mountains were regarded with trepidation, awe, and fear, but were not perceived as secularly transcendent spaces, or as structures to be climbed to their summits. Then a combination of economic and cultural forces, beginning with early Romanticism—including Edmund Burke's popularization of "the sublime" as, really, a driver of the tourism industry in his 1757 treatise *A Philosophical Enquiry into the Origin of Our Ideas of the Sublime and the Beautiful*—helped bring about the transformation that now sees, this year, more than two hundred climbers in a queue on the summit ridge of Everest, dying slowly from exposure and altitude, in order to have their photographs taken on the earth's highest point.

What struck me early on in my research into the underland was how very *young*, historically-culturally speaking, this mountain love is, and how very, very ancient, by contrast, the draw down into the darkness of the underworld is. Recent advances in thorium-dating techniques have allowed researchers to establish that the earliest "artworks" on cave walls in western Spain—a hand stencil, a red circle or dot, a rough red ladder—are around sixty-four thousand years old. That predates the estimated arrival of anatomically modern humans into the region by around twenty thousand years. Neanderthal artists went into the dark to make those marks.

As for cartography: well, yes, I have for a long time been interested in practices of "countermapping," most particularly associated as a practice with indigenous or suppressed cultures who seek to disinter and reinscribe forgotten or overwritten toponymies and modes of perception. I first encountered this idea in Hugh Brody's magisterial *Maps & Dreams*, and have pursued it ever since. Mapping is always partial, and for that reason is always an expression of priority—and often an expression of power. The countermappings I have undertaken—explicitly figured as such in *The Wild Places* (2007), which set out to offer a rebuke and alternative to the road atlas—seek to invite revisions of the world. In *Underland* that has meant making visible those aspects, psychological as well as geological, that we have sought to bury, suppress, hide, or render obscene. Such things have—in trauma theory as in geomorphology—a tendency to resurface. "What we excrete comes back to consume us," as Don DeLillo grimly puts it in his epic 1997 novel *Underworld*.

ACKERMAN: Most readers probably think of you as a writer, a walker, an explorer, an academic, a climber, a caver, an open-air thinker. It may surprise them that, in *Underland*, you're drawn both to urban exploration and wild places. Equally? You've said that *Underland* is "a book about death, disposal, darkness, trauma, harm, killing, mass graves, and nuclear waste," and that it's probably the "strangest thing I've ever written or ever will write." I don't doubt it feels that way to you. But as a reader, I find your books all part of a single mosaic that, could it ever be completed, would reveal us to ourselves fully, with perfect clarity, along with every other facet of the earth we have the privilege to briefly inhabit. That's an impossible quest, I know, but each book adds more interlocking pieces to the mosaic. I wonder what you're tempted to write about next, what glistening shards of that mosaic now tempt you?

MACFARLANE: It would indeed be an impossible quest, a Borgesian pursuit of the totalizing vision of the habitable earth; a cross, perhaps, between Funes the Memorious and the "Imperial Cartographers" who sought to make a one-to-one scaled "Map of the Empire." And of course as you know and as Borges reminds us, such visions are futile, tending to perilous. The scraps of the imperial map are left rotting in the desert, having destroyed the empire they set out to represent; Casaubon in *Middlemarch* wanders lost in his quest to find the "key to all mythologies." Tim Robinson, one of the greatest living writers of and on place, speaks warningly of the "delusion of a comprehensible totality."

That all said, I do see most of my books as parts of an unfinishable whole; I began on the mountaintops with *Mountains of the Mind*, and have ended up in the darkness of the underland, a trajectory that's taken me seven or eight books and over two thousand pages to complete. I'm sure there are people who hope that's it from me, a gravitational logic resulting in a full stop and silence. Maybe it will be, in terms of long books at least. I have recently completed a book called just *Ness* that may well run *Underland* close for strangeness. It took three years of work on and off, but is only ninety-six pages long. I don't know quite how best to characterize or describe it: an attempt to write an atomic-age version of *Sir Gawain and the Green Knight*, perhaps, or a medieval mystery play for the Anthropocene? It is fictional, but not a novel. There are aspects of superhero/Marvel culture to it, but the heroes are not Captain America and Iron Man— rather, five protean beings—"he," "she," "it," "they," and "as"— who embody different forms and forces of the natural world, and who converge on a shingle spit known as The Ness to prevent the fulfillment of a destructive ritual performed by a technocratic and power-addicted male figure known only as "The Armorer." The book was written in part in the shadow of Trump—though I am rather loath to let his name pollute anything I write—and in part in the shadow of renewed and mutated fears of nuclear war. Climate breakdown has, for good reasons, moved center stage as the eschatological catastrophe of our age—but just offstage continues to lurk the nuclear threat. Anyway, I digress—but *Ness* stands in family relation to *Underland*, a strange kin of a kind.

I might end, then, by speaking beyond the page to other forms of "work" that I see as important, but that have little or nothing to do with writing in the literary sense—and that are nevertheless more broadly part of what you call the "glittering mosaic" to which we all bring tesserae. Returning to the idea of climate breakdown being too often singularized as a "wicked problem," the question I am most often asked by people is: "What can I do?" There is a longing for change and a wish to drive change, mingled with an uncertainty about how best to act for the good. The cultural theorist Sianne Ngai recognizes and names this modern affect as "stuplimity," a modern mash-up of "stupefaction" and "the sublime," characterized by awe at the scale of the problem on the one hand, and a dulled concussion and fatigue arising from relentless exposure to its symptoms on the other. That is to say, one is knocked into a state of paralysis or pessimistic stupor by the sheer, iterated monstrosity of the situation—and ends up either failing to act or "consuming" the virtuous actions of others (what Robert Pfaller calls "interpassivity") in substitute for taking action oneself.

There is of course no easy solution to this recognizable feeling—but I can say that nothing makes me despair like resignation. The crises of the Anthropocene exist across the scales, from vast systemic global injustices to tiny losses of habitat and imperceptible biodiversity declines in specific places. This is the perniciousness of the Anthropocene, but also its "weakness," as it were. What degrades across scales can be remedied across scales. Some of the most important "writing" I take myself to have done in the past five years has been drafting website copy for the young charity Action for Conservation, of which I'm a founding trustee; some of the most important "reading" I take myself to have done has been scrutinizing its policy documents along with my fellow trustees. This is hard, mostly thankless work: but what it results in is, it seems to me, vital—young people between twelve and seventeen, many of them who find nature hard to access, taken on free summer camps to the Welsh coast or the South Downs, conservation workshops delivered in

Robert Macfarlane

schools, local environmental projects devised and driven by young people, and—just launched—the world's largest youth-led landscape-regeneration project, beginning in South Wales last summer, and due to run for an unlimited time into the future, seeking to transform the biodiversity of thousands of acres over dozens of years—all of it properly steered by teenagers. In September 2018, while finishing *Underland*, I co-edited *The People's Manifesto for Wildlife*, which detailed two hundred implementable ideas for change in the structural, political, and cultural relations between humans and the living world in Britain. Young people delivered it to Whitehall at the head of a march of ten thousand people, and though its ideas ended up being largely ignored by government (sigh . . .), it has been taken up by NGOs, individuals, and communities in heartening ways. I see these versions of engagement—enabling people to come together as communities rather than driving onwards only as individuals—as thriving alongside, rather than in tension with, writing challenging five-hundred-page books!

Donna Haraway's justly famous phrase for the task that faces all of us is "staying with the trouble." There is no prelapsarian state of nature to be returned to, or even briefly accessed. It is impossible now to write from outwith a context of damage, decline, and injustice. The trouble needs to be clearly seen, and organized against up and down the levels, from local to global. But—and—keeping hope, love, wonder, and the belief in possible betterment in view; this too is part of the work of staying with the trouble.

The Entanglements: A Representation
Rachel Blau DuPlessis

I am writing amid it, same sentences again,
    parallel reportage, little
        shifts of tone
dipped in gray literature (diagrams, stats),
    again tracking pitiless sites
        piled in a midden of raggedy detritus.
The issue being how to represent
    our ecologies, the second issue powerless
        to represent them. We know some already.
Information has got out.
    We are writing each other's
        obituaries while tripping on
edges, off known paths and down
    the multiply teeming earths
        that earth offers. Offered.
These are // We are
    "multitudinous beyond imagination, tangled, muddy,
    muddy, painful, and perplexed."   [1907]

*

I don't fit into life anymore.
    Night-kits pile their plotless loops,
        scare upon score.
Headlines suction
    air from the room
        when it gets light.

If my blood is saturated with plastic, if my water with danger, if my food
with hormones; if I take this photo of the monarch (one), flown through
the city (here), landing on the third-floor deck (mine) because I planted a
few asters this year,

and celebrate its making it here,   [2016]
    then it's clear this is an archive where
        sorrowful anger lurks under the surface.
            The in-bloom pom-pom cherry a delight, and sorrow,
            a book (oh, look, a book amid   [2015]
            Styrofoam flat packs), a delight, and sorrow.
A bizarre rhythm, step after step and at every step (at every stone and stalk),
the wonder saddens, stains, strikes.
        But living amid these pocky stacks of harm—
I am bound to this space
        and cannot either fit or get away.
So the mode is mourning?
        Does it change to "morning" via the poem?
Can writing represent these mists of toxicity
        with the subtle sounds of elegant syllables?

                    *

I've not evern heard or evern seen
        so much talk
about the end of earth as now, not
        even ever.

SUCH HAP IS MADE,
and wherevern HAP IS MADE
BY THE POWERS OF OTHERS
my HAP arrives

        Rescuers cradled it in a shallow canal, their arms
        wrapped around its slick, shuddering body. It
        could not eat and struggled to swim and breathe. . . .
        It died Friday after a five-day fight. . . .
        An autopsy revealed dozens of plastic bags jamming
        its stomach. . . . Thai officials said they believe
        the whale mistook the floating plastic for squid.   [2018]

my happenstance   what? am I a whale?
having once been your profit and
always forever here before that,
can our memories look forward to

Rachel Blau DuPlessis

the absolute absence of whales
which will make us die,

and thus I try to wiggle hap
as best I can, but all that seems to happen
is a hard push, body check,
slammed against a glistening machine
that makes things ring and flash, racks up the points, me
                    het up by the distraction. the binging.

                                    *

Dear W——
We are playing games. We need to try to get control of the situation out of
control, almost out of gasp, out of grasp, out of reach. It's finding fastness
moving along every vector in and out of the entanglements. Fast or
fastness? What do we have? Sheer acceleration versus us holding tight?

There's talk of superheated deep-sea vents, the postulates that organic life
therein might rebegin, after us. Heard talk of colonizing space (though
sources for food, water, air, and fuel are under discussed). (And is that
where the fantasy of buying up Aotearoa-New Zealand comes in?) (Sea
vents, you're generally to the left. Colonizing Mars, you're generally the
right.) Everything of this presentation is parenthetical deflection.

Where will we actually be without ourselves,
        would we, world we,
        entangled with what's made us *as* ourselves.
        We are each other's gloss.
The as such. To be felt as such.
        With sensing selves already formed by it, inside of it,
            and pulses activated by its weathers and its tides.

                                    *

Do we evern get the sense of that "it" to which we owe and have always
owed our living. I don't mean the owning-owed of economics. I mean our
very Being. And still it looms, not unspoken, but precisely the spoken
unspeakable. This is the "It" that we are discussing.

Earth as we know it. Our entangled consciousness, and consciousness of this Thing—earth, life, our time, "this in which," this-as-such, the pileup of engagements that we know. Our demonstrative conjunctions, our clotted kenning-stuff all tries to "tell it." Make a representation. We hardly believe our individual deaths. How to credit the deaths of earth, one animal and one place, and one water course and one butterfly at a time? Then multiplied and compounded.

*

So this "now"
now emerges, shadows be-fallen here,
          and we debate
               how vast the eulogy we need.
                    What ears to hear the hap?

What has occurred within
the lurching zones of
our own befallen "fate" is
that fellest branch now has the force to fall.
More than "happenstance"—not
by accident or chance.
Must thus unfix this "fate."
By what politics—fixed-up zones and stay-dead zones?
Thus "We" still try to rule.
          And the problem of representation
               is still not solved, but some wordplay,
                    Fall, befallen and so forth
                    has happened,
                    as too the puns on mourning,
                    morning, fast and fast,
                    glossed over, glossed, rag and rage.
                    Doubling words.

*

What is the task at hand? Multiple, beyond doubling.
To represent, to tell.

Rachel Blau DuPlessis

But we are told already; we are alive in this Tell.
Nomadic allegories—will that hap help?—
remembering words like toll or tolled,
excavating the midden—
it's so—Contemporary Purgatorio!
     There's fuzz and buzz.
Trucks in the video perpetually back up, beep, beep.
     Rough hark, all round.

I followed, slo-mo and suspicious,
into this daily underworld, entering a narrative arc
that used to be called the "nekuia," which

                    ENGLISH ONLY
                    OR GET OUT   [2006]

means a "search for ghosts," at least for shadows with names,
who may perform a fancy necromancy
if appeased beforehand with a good-looking animal
(like a goat or something), and thus will get
shriven of their guilt for your forthcoming future,
leaving you with only yours (guilt, that is; future, also).

Perhaps these "hungry ghosts" will in fact appear—
yet be unintelligible.
Perhaps like animals and plants, they do not "speak." To us.
     Intensities wailing incomprehensible findings.

This scene is titled "untitled"; it's constructed
of syntax, keening, and fragments—
     a contradiction   only on the surface

given that
the dead among us
include bees, the birds, other mammals, etc.
also inside us,
and all that we are now, and what we were and
what we'll come to be
have them as witnesses.

*

So
"The World Wildlife Fund released a report Monday saying it has found an 'astonishing' 60 percent decline in wildlife populations globally over the last 40 years, mostly due to human activity, including climate change and habitat loss." . . . "'From rivers and rain forests, to mangroves and mountainsides, across the planet our work shows that wildlife abundance has declined dramatically since 1970,' said Ken Norris, director of science at the Zoological Society of London, which provided one of three indexes used to write the report."   [2018]

I cannot represent this sheer cellular entanglement. The things happening on the side, are the things happening! It's another kind of "plot," this thing demands:
"not 'realism,' but reality itself."   [1923]

*

What is the normal? If you say "Don't rebuild there" or "—there was a reason people didn't settle there," or "the waters from wetlands (estuaries, marshes, coastal creek beds) have no place to go but here, so if you pave it, or try to channel it . . ."—few want to hear. We were talking about place, property, and propositions.
That's it. No more. Money and proposals. Your item does not figure on the agenda.

Program to defuse 100 tons of plutonium is too costly. [2001]

Or try the Newspaper for a week. Representation decorating power, preventable death, fuckup of resource allocation, embittering malfeasance— just roll along, with occasional zooms of irony (aha) or cleanups or preventions until suddenly it's your wreck, your child, your house, your loss, your pile of toxicity, individuated one by one by one. Do "we" learn only one by one by one? Total "revelation" will occur with the last person's "aha!"? Simultaneous with total destruction? I can't hardly wait.

83

Rachel Blau DuPlessis

This dream was evidently
"up to no good" but rife and rich
enough to colonize us gleefully
with a bullying intimacy.
"Managers, program heads, where have you been?"
"I've been to Place-Name to visit the queen.
"Officials and bureaucrats, what said she there?
"'I don't really care,
do U?'"   [2018]

                                            *

                    The world is constantly in tears.
But worse,
a person
might get used to those tears.

                                            *

If the permafrost melts, the carefully framed Global Seed Vault
will be undermined, destroyed.   [2008/2016]

Do "we" get a choice?

Poetic realism lets the mark go down

no matter how distraught and unpromising,

no matter how inchoate, how unstrung,

to represent the damage we are tortured by.

                                            *

                    So I've joined with you and
answered something
that I cannot answer wholly

being so baffled (not puzzled, really,
but shut off, shut out. With "a baffle.")

and yet in hope that there are openings for the world and these can be
found and made to happen.

Not without vertigo, not without the vertiginous, not without antic
radicalism. The poem is always a curved diagonal, a matted compost of
representation. O dizzy dizziness, there's no rest here. We need to spring up
like grass.

> "The statistics are scary, but all hope is not lost. . . .
> Our report sets out an ambitious agenda
> for change . . .'"   [2018]

*

Thin consolation but some—
      "SCARY"!
        but a less domestic word choice
          might paralyze with terror.

Will it begin : has it begun?
has it will have begun?
is the future perfect
available? What are the conditions
under which? Could will /could would?
Has the past passed?
What future can, when come?
It's a tense problem.

What we lack is representation: do "we" evern get a choice?
or rather representation, what rhetoric speaks for us, to us on this ground?
How can destruction on this scale be turned?
I mean who represents us
at this stinking table;
what legislative-executive-judicial-human-popular
will to effect or affect, could stop the
downward momentum of this moment?

85

Rachel Blau DuPlessis

Sometimes the real

is so stark that one wakes up stunned

and tries to undo paralysis by a writing

awkwardly direct.

The mend of the vessel was once in gold.

Now the mend of the vessel is already blood.

Do we really want to give up on the world?

Earth Is Just as Alive as We Are. Its life is ours. Entangled inside it are our lives.

[2019]

This is the end of the representation.
    Though here it's not the end.
    Here it will go on.

86

The Great Trash Vortex: Dispatch from Fuerteventura, Islas Canarias
Matthew Gavin Frank

WHEN IN CAPTIVITY, the mynah bird, in what naturalists believe to be an act of desperation, reproduces, in panic, the sounds it hears, including human speech. We have come to expect, even demand, that it mirrors our voices. Some species of mynah, though, have larger, more unwieldy tongues, which their owners often cut to match the shape of the human tongue in miniature, in order to allow them our version of speech. When the captive mynah sings us to sleep in our own language, that is the mutilated mynah slowly going mad.

Here, in the Hotel Atlantis, I speak to the endemic geckos of wickedness; how on the Canaries, in ancient times, before the African and European mariners introduced species like the mynah, the waxbill, the ibis, and the stilt, the Holocene-era Gran Canaria giant rat would regularly tear the viscera from the Holocene-era giant goliath lizards—progenitors of the geckos to be sure; how King Juba II of Numidia and his first wife, Cleopatra VIII (sole daughter of Greek Ptolemaic Queen Cleopatra VII of Egypt—*the* Cleopatra—and Roman triumvir Mark Antony) dispatched naval ships to search for far-flung island civilizations, whom they could overpower, kidnap, and enslave to the dye-production sweatshops at Mogador (now western Morocco).

Juba landed at Fuerteventura, sometime around 1 AD, and likely trapped some of the early populace, though he claimed, according to Pliny the Elder, that all of what we now call the Canaries was uninhabited, ornamented only with exotic flora, giant animals, abandoned temples of stone, and "some traces of buildings" of unknown purpose, but admirable stability. Of course, Pliny, having been born only in 23 AD, the very year King Juba died, heard of these accounts only secondhand. Still today, Spain and Morocco argue over which country owns which portion of the seabed over which the islands float, each government differently interpreting the territorial boundaries as laid out by the Law of the Sea. So where I am can be variously interpreted.

If I spoke of this to the mynah rather than the geckos, the mynah would repeat it back to me, *Juba-Juba-Juba*—or to the names of Louisa and my ever-insomniac infant ghosts, inscribed on the first pages in this spiral notebook I keep on the nightstand in the Atlantis—with a ruined and scabbing tongue. So far from home and Louisa, unable to sleep on this pillow-top queen, I review our old list of potential baby names, and I'll be damned if Mynah isn't on it.

Because the mynah bird is seen as invasive here, it's seen also as a plague. It is aggressive and omnivorous, and gorges on local insects and arachnids, reptiles and crustaceans, fruits, grains, seeds, and the edible waste we humans are fond of leaving. Local wildlife divisions trap the birds and put them down—about a thousand per year. Their carcasses are heaped into an unofficial dumping ground on a sandy beach on Fuerteventura's southwest shore, amid plastic bleach bottles, Pepsi cans, amputee rag dolls, and rusted drums filled with mysterious liquid waste. The dump is patrolled by the island's large populations of wild dogs (after which the archipelago was named by King Juba, Canariae Insulae—Islands of the Dogs) and cats, along with swarms of the endangered Canarian Egyptian Vulture (itself at least as old as the Bible, where it's known by its Hebrew name, *rachamah*). The mynahs that are not eaten by the scavengers will be swept up into the ocean along with the rest of the junk cocktail, becoming part of what scientists have come to call the Great Texas-Sized Trash Vortex of the Atlantic.

Canaries—the birds—are in fact named after the islands to which they are endemic. Though the birds are endemic—and dogs are not—still, if in name only, the birds are shape-shifters. The birds are dogs in the bellies of the vultures.

The vultures themselves may be transmogrified gods, having once made their cameos during the denouement of a Greek cautionary myth of incest, jealousy, and revenge, wherein two young boy gods (Neophron and Aegypius) are each interested in sleeping with the other's mother, but each is also secretly jealous of his own mother's attention spent on the other boy. Eventually, in a proverbial (or mythological) "dark chamber," Neophron tricks Aegypius into fornicating with his very own mother, Bulis. Upon this revelation, Bulis gouges out her son's eyes before committing suicide. The newly blind Aegypius calls on Zeus to exact revenge for the deception on Neophron, but Zeus, fed up with these shenanigans, turns both boy gods into Egyptian vultures, doomed to circle the Fortunate Isles, touching down only to feed on the trash left behind by the other deities.

In addition to Neophron's and Aegypius's scavenger descendants, the ancient Greek mariners reported finding on the Canary Islands a population of dog-worshipping "aboriginals," who prayed to dogs and mummified dogs, and were otherwise so devout that they evolved to be dogheaded demigods, though the remainder of their bodies was of the human variety. Some historians believe this population to have been somehow affiliated across time and ocean with the Egyptian cult of the dogheaded god, Anubis, god of cemeteries and embalming, who safely ushered souls into the afterlife.

Plutarch, affecting the first-person voice of one of the tale-spinning Greek mariners, says of one of these alleged demigods, "When I saw a dog on board ship, since the sailors were away, putting pebbles into a half empty jar of oil, I was amazed at its knowing that lighter substances are forced upward when the heavier settle to the bottom." Whether this is a metaphorical treatise on the ushering of a soul into the afterlife, Plutarch does not say.

This beach dumping ground—patrolled by dogs more mangy than godly—has become a strange tourist site of the ironic and kitschy roadside-attraction variety. People take pictures of dead animals and the emaciated ones who survive on their bodies, of dirty diapers, of oxidized boat motors, of banana peels, paper plates, traffic cones, cyanide. I am not immune to its allure or to the need of a hot shower after paying my filthy visit. The shampoo in the shower is BASiC brand. It's a clear tube the size of a C battery, printed with purple ink. It's slippery in the hand. It feels good in the hand. Its ingredients include sodium chloride, cocamide DEA, citric acid, and methylchloroisothiazolinone, the latter of which, if ingested, has the power to inhibit the growth of bacteria, including maternal symbiotic bacteria, which greatly contribute to a baby's well-being in utero.

*

89

Matthew Gavin Frank

In his *Life of Sulla*, Plutarch writes of the debauched and blood-thirsty Roman general who launched a campaign of capital punishment, executing all those whom he arbitrarily (and seemingly for his own amusement) deemed enemies of the state. "Sulla," Plutarch writes, "now began to make blood flow . . . There was therefore no counting of the slain, but their numbers are to this day determined only by the space that was covered with blood. For without mention of those who were killed in the rest of the city, the blood that was shed in the market-place covered all the Cerameicus inside the Dipylon gate; nay, many say that it flowed through the gate and deluged the suburb . . . The marshes were filled with their blood, and the lake with their dead bodies . . ."

And the gods, or, as Plutarch refers to them in *Sulla*, "the heavenly powers," having had their Fortunate Isles–bound leisure disturbed by Sulla's hematic wrath—a wrath that they perceived as within their dominion alone, this silly psychotic man trespassing on godly territory—responded with a kind of retribution that could be called mythologically biblical. From the shores of Fuerteventura (then blissfully free of mynah corpses and golden cans of Cerveza Dorada Especial), the gods compelled great fires to break forth and consume Rome, "which they had much ado to extinguish; and three ravens brought their young forth into the street and devoured them in the sight of so many surprised people, and afterwards carried the garbage they left of them back into their nests; and after mice had gnawed consecrated gold in a temple, the keepers caught one of them, a female, in a trap, and in the very trap she brought forth five young ones and ate up three of them . . ."

Once again, in response to masculine transgression, the gods compel the mothers of the animal kingdom to do violence against their instincts to their offspring, to render the body of the baby to its "garbage," to make of the homeland (the "nest") another sort of dumping ground, to decorate it with the havoc we wreak, and the detritus we leave behind. This is the charge of the gods, Plutarch tells us, and as I peruse the intricacies of what will become yet another microcolony within the Great Trash Vortex, this aerie of trash nestled into such powdery white sand, I can't help but sense a kind of ancient holiness in it, born precisely of its grossness, its flagrance, its ability to do so much of the world so much harm.

*

During antiquity, Fuerteventura was called Planaria (due to the then plain-like flatness of some of its terrain), a name that we now lend to a species of flatworm that inspires the research of so many dreamy geneticists. The worm seems to defy our version of the life cycle with its limitless regenerative capacity, making it, according to physiologist Thomas C. J. Tan, "effectively immortal," the stuff of myth made real, and—as this worm thrives in humid soil—literally terrestrial. Of course, our primary interest in this worm involves uncovering the anatomical engine of its immortality, harvesting it, and eventually mimicking "[its] ability to replace aged or damaged tissues and cells, to regenerate indefinitely by growing new muscles, skin, guts, and even entire brains over and over again," so we too can one day live forever like the gods, lunch with the likes of Sulla and Plutarch.

Fuerteventura, like the planaria worm, has many meanings and contains within its unlucky thirteen letters the mundanely elemental, the fortitude of some paradisial opulence, the juvenile blueprints for what would become manifest destiny, that barbaric ideal. Of the Canaries, it's the most ancient of the islands and, therefore, the most eroded. Still, the indigenous Majorera goats find enough nourishment to produce more milk on average than any other goat species, resulting in the strong export economy of the local Majorero cheese. And it's a hell of a place to stargaze: there are two professional observatories on the island. The word Fuerteventura itself is variously translated by linguists as strong winds, strong fortune, or great adventure. The first translation is justified by the frequent dust storms of Saharan sand that sometimes plague the island. Sometimes the wind is so strong, it blows masses of African locusts to Fuerteventura, along with the sand and ocean-riding microplastics, in a multifaceted, sort of vaguely biblical plague.

No plague strong or great has yet blown away the ancient goatskin shoes known as *mahos*, believed to have been worn by the original cave-dwelling inhabitants of the isle. These shoes have been found in subterranean depressions (ancient bedrooms?) and sea caves, and tangled into the dense tubercled statice bushes amid tatters of plastic grocery bags and Milka Huesitos candy-bar wrappers, where the local *haemorrhoa* mining bees effortlessly couple with the purple flowers, make hives in the hollows of the *mahos*, and raise their young gently, hiding from the territorial gods. Some things the wind can't blow away. Some things even fortune can't crush.

*

91

I'm trying to get a handle on the size and shape of things—the homes we make of hollows, the stories we tell ourselves of those homes, and how we got there. Like Crassus, we are all, so to speak, "reared in a small house," as Plutarch said, inevitable "observers of how natural and familiar . . . were such fatalities as the conflagration and collapse of these buildings," of which we must take measure before the Sullas of the world kill us and sell our homes, "considering it and calling it spoil of war."

So: I buy the tape measure from the Minimarket Buenavista on El Greco Street in Puerto del Rosario. The distance from the bottom of my hotel-room door to the hard emerald carpet is three centimeters. The distance from the lower hem of the yellow shower curtain sewn with stylized black and white bees to the sloppily mortared baby-blue tile is seven centimeters. The distance from the underside of the bed's box spring (elevated by the steel frame) to the floor is a full ten inches. Respectively: the same measurements pertaining to the dilation of the cervix during early labor, active labor, and the end of labor's transitional phase. This room is preparing to give birth to something. There's a portal to a new world under the bed. There, the more wrathful of the gods enjoy their vacation disguising themselves as dust bunnies, as I measure the tissue box, end to end.

On the dump, at the beach, the endangered vultures care not to speak with a human voice. They eat the dead mynahs and become a little less endangered.

It's night, and the ocean swells, accepts into itself more of our garbage. This does not mean that it is a Plutarchian raven's nest. This does not mean that the holy can't be bad for us. In bed, fetal, I envision Louisa's left earlobe—my favorite one. In this vision, the lobe appears longer than it actually is. A couple of centimeters at least. I breathe into the belly of this hotel pillow—itself toxic with atomic fungi, formaldehyde, and polybrominated diphenyl ether, the latter an ingredient in a flame-retardant spray that can accumulate, atomically, in the placenta, increase the chances of miscarriage, and contaminate breast milk. I know that, outside, so many strange hemispheric stars are falling. I can feel it. Great chunks of fire screaming across the cosmos among our satellites, on their way to terrestrial graves, oceanic graves, or else destined to tumble, dead, among the sort of universe we ache to raise awareness, and hope, and wealth, and children, within. The stars fall still, over the isles, as we try to rest on soft little pillows that conspire to undo us. Still, the pillows here remain silent, fire-free.

If we're to believe the satellite images, the Great Trash Vortex is beautiful, a rainbow-colored spiral whirling in the blue water, fluttering wishfully like a video of some infant heart. Most seafarers avoid it, as the vortex forms a kind of wall that blocks the wind, stalls sailboats in place. The fact that it contains parts of the SS *America* (a former warship and ocean liner that gained odd prominence for its onboard dog-kennel facilities) and other shipwrecks does little to slake mariner superstition.

It is soupy, and mostly plastic, and in 1992, 6 shipping containers of bathtub toys were lost to the seas during a storm, and the crews of subsequent passing vessels claimed to witness schools of curious flying fish, and solitary sea turtles swimming amid the 95,000 lost-at-sea rubber duckies. Five years later, 62 containers of Legos fell into the sea, a cargo that included 353,264 plastic daisies, and, strangely, a disproportionate number of nautical-themed Legos that included miniature cutlasses, flippers, spearguns, seagrass, scuba gear, and sea creatures both actual and legendary, most of which were gathered up into the vortex, some of which are still washing up onto the world's beaches to this day.

"It's the same old things coming in with the tide," says competitive beachcomber Tracey Williams of Perranporth, Cornwall. "These days, the holy grail is an octopus or a dragon." "The mystery is where all of this will end up," says oceanographer Curtis Ebbesmeyer, who is, according to *National Geographic*, "the world's leading expert on flotsam." Since 1997, these Legos could have drifted nearly one hundred thousand miles, and since it's only about twenty-four thousand miles around the equator, if they have indeed washed up onshore, they could be on any beach on earth.

"Theoretically," Ebbesmeyer says, "the pieces of Lego could keep going around the ocean for centuries . . . The most profound lesson I've learned from the Lego story is that things that go to the bottom of the sea don't always stay there. . . . Tracking [them] is like tracking gods or ghosts—you can't see them. You can only see where flotsam started and where it ended up." The stories of their "middle lives" remain invisible and unknowable.

Matthew Gavin Frank

*

The hotel's television remote control is a rectangle comprising three screwed-together pieces of black plastic, plus the little snap cover for the pair of AA batteries. It has sixty-eight rubberized buttons pocking its face—black ones, white ones, ones in every color of the rainbow except purple. One of them says PAUSE. One of them says STOP. Good advice, I think, though I am not sure how exactly to heed it. POWER, I press, expecting the trash vortex to stir up one final wave that will marry the Hotel Atlantis with the actual Atlantis, but no. It's just the TV turning on to the hotel's home page, which bears the image of what appears to be a staticky tight-beaked mynah in the upper-left corner of the screen.

According to Plutarch, well before Cleopatra gave birth to the daughter who would marry King Juba, and well before Juba and his new wife claimed the discovery of the Canary Islands as their own, she suffered a miscarriage following the stressful funeral of Julius Caesar. She reportedly recovered from her grief by spending weeks on a fuchsia fainting couch, weeping into the cushions beneath the swinging cage of a mynah bird. According to the 1891 tome *The Living Age*, "The talking mynah, which lives in the same room, sprang from end to end in its cage with ecstatic hops [as Cleopatra recovered], and whistled and coughed, and gave evidence that it at least was a critical listener. . . ."

Later, after hearing of Antony's suicide, Cleopatra would famously kill herself not by enticing an asp to bite her breast, as the myths tell us, but by overdosing on wolfsbane, hemlock, and opium. The asp in question (an Egyptian cobra), according to Plutarch, was a laboratory subject of sorts, on which Cleopatra conducted experiments with its venom, eventually determining that use of its poison in the execution of condemned prisoners yielded a more dignified death, as it brought on the appearance of sleepiness without visible spasms. As Cleopatra OD'd, the asp was actually a few rooms away, gumming one of the shiny blue eggs of her pet bird.

Some linguists believe that Caesar himself was so named for the cesarean section procedure that predated him, as one of his ancestors was reportedly delivered into the world in this way. The word Caesar

94

relates to the Latin verb *caedere*, "to cut." The Roman Republicans, who viewed him as a Sulla-like despot, often slandered Caesar, uttering, *"a caeso matris utero"* ("cut from the mother's womb") as he marched the avenues.

Other linguists believe that the word Caesar may derive from a pre-Roman cleansing ritual to evict evil spirits from the city. At the base of a holy fig tree, male goats were sacrificed to Faunus, the horned god of the forest. The sacred tree grew over the mouth of the Lupercal cave in which dwelled Rumina, goddess of breastfeeding. In preparation for the subsequent feast, the populace skinned the sacrificed goats and engaged in what they called *februis caedere* (of which Caesar and thereby cesarean may be etymological derivations): the act of striking the land with goatskin whips that literally cut the earth open.

Throughout the festival, Plutarch writes, in his *Life of Caesar*, "many of the noble youths and magistrates run up and down through the city naked, for sport and laughter striking those they meet with shaggy thongs. And many women of rank also purposely get in their way, and like children at school present their hands to be struck, believing that the pregnant will thus be helped in delivery, and the barren to pregnancy."

Julius Caesar's first wife, it must be noted, died in childbirth, resulting in a stillborn son. It was determined, right then at the time, so many years ago, that the performance of a cesarean section would have saved both of their lives.

The capital of Fuerteventura is Puerto del Rosario, population 36,928. Historically, the port was a fertile fishing ground, and a hub for the shipping and receiving of goats. As such, until 1957, when the Spanish government changed the city's name to the more "appropriate and attractive" Port of the Rosary, the settlement was known as Puerto de Cabras, Port of the Goats.

Strangely, some of those "traces of buildings" referred to by King Juba and his 1 AD occupiers are built around Fuerteventura's Caves of Ajuy, one of which is fronted by a Bourjasotte fig tree, and in which a small pyramid of *mahos*—those ancient goatskin shoes believed to have belonged to the island's original inhabitants—was recently excavated. Still today, the people of Fuerteventura refer to themselves as Mahoreros, or Mahos, flesh-and-blood descendants of the actual by-products of ancient sacrifices that may or may not have been purely mythological.

*

Perhaps Juba's recolonization of Fuerteventura in 1 AD—when Christian juju may have been at its most powerful, what with the Virgin Birth and all—laid the groundwork for Christianity's eventual firm foothold on the archipelago in 1392. According to legend, a statue of the Virgin Mary (now known as the Virgen de Candelaria, and depicted as a Black Madonna) floated along the fourteenth-century beach on which now sits the wild-dog-and-vulture-riddled dump, carrying a child by the arm in one hand and an ethereal green candle in the other. Carved into the statue's neck, left sleeve, belt, and robe hem were strings of strange letters of unknown origin and meaning (*OLM INRANFR TAEBNPEM Reven NVINAPIMLIFINIPI NIPIAN*, for example).

Two Guanche "aboriginal" goat herders, walking their animals along the beach, saw the floating statue and, appropriately freaked out, one of them tried to throw a stone at her, but his arm became paralyzed. The other herder pulled out a knife, but ended up stabbing himself. They immediately recognized this power as belonging to their goddess, Chaxiraxi the Sun Mother, and the statue was worshipped as such for one hundred years, until the Castilian conquest enslaved the autochthon Guanche peoples to the canebrake and their beliefs to Christianity. They were forced by the conquerors to forsake their homes, their language, and their gods, and the descendants of those two goat herders who first bore witness to the power of the statue ran into the landscape, and took refuge in their progenitors' caves.

Sometimes, even the Great Trash Vortex of the Atlantic forsakes its own, evicts members of its colony out into the lonely ocean, as if in some ritual cleansing. Sometimes, these lonely bits of spun-out trash, after months or years of solitary bobbing, migrations of impossible distances, magically, magnetically seek out other trash vortexes like, for instance, the Great Trash Vortex of the Atlantic's even larger cousin, the Great Garbage Patch of the Pacific, which itself includes five shipping containers' worth of Nike sneakers and work boots (made of sacrificed cow- and not goatskin), some of which washed ashore onto isles on the other side of the world, where the local residents gathered them up and held swap meets to find matched pairs to sell.

*

With regard to the rubber duckies and Legos that are still part of the Great Trash Vortex, Curtis Ebbesmeyer says, "Ultimately, the toys will turn to dust, joining the scum of plastic powder which rides the global ocean." I close my eyes and see him with a pet mynah on his shoulder. It pecks affectionately at his gray beard, his long left earlobe. It bounces up and down. "Flotsam," it says.

At the hotel window, the gummy rubber window seal is starting to gap. If I put my ear to it, I can hear it gapping via some terrible and terribly quiet sucking sound. Trapped in its gap are insects dead and dying—tachinid flies and barklice and baby ground beetles and a single Hyles moth. In the window's upper-right corner, a *Steatoda nobilis* spider has been lurking for so long its web has become unkempt and messy. It's been so patient. I can see the dust that's built up on its abdomen. To its right, hiding in the fold of the rose curtain, an even dustier gecko waits for the spider to fatten herself before feeding.

And beyond this window, in that trash heap on the beach, all that strong wind, all those dead mynahs. Oh, the treatises they could have spoken on the lice, the spiders, the gecko, on Cleopatra and Caesar and Cleopatra's dead baby, and Caesar's dead baby, stories passed on to them from their progenitors, and oh, the information we could have learned if only we had properly snipped the birds' tongues and asked them the right questions before killing them with pesticide.

Perhaps we can convince ourselves that all sad things, or manifestations worthy of our disgust are beautiful, or holy, when viewed either up close, or from such a great distance. Perhaps it's this middle distance that's inevitably liminal, when we're compelled to contextualize a thing without the sufficient tools. "Then Sulla threw himself from his horse, crying," Plutarch writes, "then he fell back a little distance . . . and his hopes became vague."

Because we're more likely to kill a mynah than a parrot, we're less likely to incorporate the mynah into our language as a verb. Even when repetitious, nobody *mynahs* anything, least of all all those dead mynahs. To us, even the loquacious mynahs, when alive and well, don't *mynah*. They *parrot*.

Sometimes, it's a blessing to be anointed with the identity of another, to crawl, if only in narrative, out of one's own skin for awhile. Other times, though, it means you're leaving your homeland, headed for a lifetime of labor over Juba's steaming dye pots. Tangled in the bedsheet in the Hotel Atlantis, I can't tell quite to what depths I've sunk. Can't quite tell the size and shape of the holiness that I'm seeking. Can't quite tell whom I need to become to feel a little better. If an object has had all of its components manipulated by the elements, or all of its components replaced, does it remain, fundamentally, the same object, or is it a new entity? If one has endured sufficient tragedy, can one safely forsake the old self, forge a new identity in heartbreak? Is this a good thing or a bad thing? *And what does this mean?*, I want to ask, but the mynahs aren't talking anymore.

"The ship on which Theseus sailed," Plutarch tells me, "was preserved by the Athenians . . . They took away the old timbers from time to time, and put new and sound ones in their places, so that the vessel became a standing illustration for the philosophers in the mooted question of growth, some declaring that it remained the same, others that it was not the same vessel."

I'm looking for reasons, Plutarch. Don't you get it? Or *reason*.
And by *garbage*, I mean tragedy.
And by *garbage*, I mean the gods.
And by *garbage*, I mean everything we're forced to leave behind.

*

As ever, we discard the very beings on whom we have forced our voices—our birds, our babies. This does not make our voices holy. In another language, the two-centimeter-by-two-centimeter tag at the end of the Hotel Atlantis bedsheet says *Egyptian*, says *cotton*, says *cold*, says *delicate*.

*

I'm not sleeping so well. I'm hearing at night what I think may be the alarm cries of the mythological Anghiak—the ghostly abortions of Inuit lore who, having been turned into evil spirits in the afterlife, return to the land of the living to exact revenge (via a ravenous devouring) on those who were once their would-be parents. They are shape-shifters, and often take the form of scorned birds who beguile us by speaking with human voices. I can hear them in the dark hallways of the Hotel Atlantis, their mutant calls commingling with the low hum of the soda pop machine.

They score images of the day: my walk along the trash beach and back along Calle Juan de Béthencourt, named after the French explorer (Jean de Béthencourt), who reconquered Fuerteventura for Castile in 1405, renaming himself king of the Canary Islands in the process. Béthencourt led numerous battles to slaughter the "aboriginals," who were themselves descendants of Juba's 1 AD occupiers, the Berbers of the Maghreb, and the indigenous peoples of still-unknown origin who first fashioned those "traces of buildings." Portugal's Prince Henry the Navigator tried to reclaim the islands, but would eventually give in to a treaty acknowledging Castilian control, only if Portugal could claim ownership of the Azores, Madeira, and Cape Verde.

As the original inhabitants of the islands were enslaved to Juba's dye factories, these "aboriginals" were enslaved by the Castilians to the newly sown sugarcane fields. Eventually, competition with other countries sank the sugarcane industry, and after nearly a century of recession and starvation, the Canaries saved themselves with a new cash crop—the cultivation of the cochineal beetle, from which is extracted that lovely carmine dye so favored by the likes of King Juba.

Today, on the street, so much exhaust from so many Mahindra pick-up trucks, the consumptive man traversing the curbside on home-made stilts, houses with flat roofs harboring old rainfall. *Fuck Trump, Fuck Tyranny*, says the graffiti in Spanish against the outside wall of the Estación de Servicio Cepsa gas station.

Louisa and I lost what we told ourselves will be our last one, a week and a half before I came out to the Canaries. I haven't told you this yet: that we had a cremation ceremony back home, that I brought her ashes out here with me, on the three different airplanes, and on the inter-island ferry. On the boat's upper deck, the sound of the Ziploc bag opening. I stored it—the bag and its ashes—burped of its air, for the travel in an A-Team thermos. On its flank, B. A. Baracus, as usual, looked pissed about this, another misuse of a vessel. Louisa helped me to pack it safely, wrapped in clothes, so the plastic wouldn't crack. The consummation of this seemingly dreamed decision to scatter the ashes into the Atlantic, where they could be swept up into one of the largest oceanic trash heaps in the world, and circle the globe, in theory, forever. If Curtis Ebbesmeyer tells us that the ultimate fate of the toys of the Great Trash Vortex is that they will turn to dust, the scattered ashes of our last miscarriage are already there, at that end stage. They are what they are. They are what they will always be. Immortal and floating.

The ferry's metal deck vibrated as tourists and locals alike stepped across it, their bodies suspended like mine over all of this water. Some took photos of distant volcanoes the color of saffron. Louisa and I tried not to name this one.

We had the cremation ceremony back home soon after it had happened, on the periwinkle of the bathroom rug, with the red-and-black butane grill lighter and the blue-and-white spiraling of the out-of-season Hanukkah candles. Sweating in this bed now, I remember then how the murk of winter webbed our panes, and how the frost hardly even melted when we lit the wicks. I remember my recitation of the Mourner's Kaddish there in front of the toilet, and again on the ferry's deck, at the threshold of the Atlantic—all 41.1 million miles squared of it, its average depth of 3,700 feet, shore length of 70,000 miles, its coverage of 20 percent of the surface of the earth, its role as the border between worlds—the "Old" one and the "New." I kept my voice quiet when I said, *Amen.* I was a little embarrassed about imposing a quest born of grief onto the other tourists, but still I felt the syllables echo downward to the water, all that aggregate salinity and rainfall and melt, all of that mass willingness to be hypnotized by the moon, down to the deeply impacted and ancient seabed—all that sand, rock, coral, mud, dust, bone, ash, rubber, plastic, evidence of long-extinct organisms we will never know once existed.

The essayist Charles D'Ambrosio writes, "Hell is crowded not because sinners are commonplace, but because incompletion is the norm . . . Because [Orpheus in the underworld] looks back, losing his bride, his work remains unfinished, forever . . ." I wonder if, on their journeys, our babies looked back at us. I wonder if Louisa is home now, in the backyard, rocking in a plastic chair, wrapped in blankets, amid the nosy fireflies. I wonder if, in questing, I'm just another kind of Juba, trying to revise and therefore repeat some sin of history. If expressions of sympathy are eventually a drain, who can blame us for our search for anything holier, quieter?

Maybe I'm only dreaming now in the Atlantis, but I don't think so. Twisted into the bedsheet, I'm convinced that dusty spider has eaten that moth, and that dustier gecko has eaten that spider. I decide in the middle of the night that it's time for me to go home.

On Fuerteventura, we have a land once named for worms everlasting. We have giant rats and giant lizards, and people with dog heads. We have the caves and the goatskin shoes and the "traces of buildings" and shards of pottery and broken tools and ancient crypts that belie King Juba's claims of initial discovery, that belie the stories of the Castilian conquest, that the Portuguese were the first to set foot on these isles and to establish communities here. Still, these are the dominant narratives, though archaeologists are busy undoing them. Still, as may be a condition of living in the present, we have no idea how to revise what we've already accepted as "the past."

According to AnneMarie Luijendijk, of Princeton University's Department of Religion, in her article "Sacred Scriptures as Trash," "entire Christian literary manuscripts were discarded deliberately as trash by Christians themselves." And, indeed, rabbinical teachings tell us that the act of disposal is a holy act, and the thing disposed of should be disposed of properly and reverently, as it too may perhaps be the holiest thing in sight, a testament, in fact, to our time on earth. We must carefully choose, honor, and dispose of the stuff we wish to abandon to the passage of time, the detritus on which future civilizations will attempt to rebuild our stories. In the face of all loss, mortality, and a sense of filling an incompleteness, we must reverently heap up the evidence of our lives, that we were—like the ancient island civilizations once enslaved by Juba—indeed here.

"The priest shall dress in linen raiment, with linen breeches next to his body," says Leviticus 6:3–4, "and he shall take up the ashes to which the fire has reduced the burnt offering on the altar and place them beside the altar. He shall then take off his vestments and put on other vestments, and carry the ashes outside the camp to a pure place." Trash, in so many of our doctrines, must be disposed of in a graceful manner and in a holy vessel. (The Dalai Lama even reportedly made a gesture of blessing before a mound of trash he surprisingly encountered upon exiting the White House via a back door on February 18, 2010.)

And, while, according to Rabbi Jack Paskoff, in his sermon titled "The Holiness of *Shmutz*," our greeting of garbage with reverent ritual may always remain a "vexing mystery," and "while it might have been easy for the priests to forget that as they woke each morning to perform their duties as God's garbage men, herein lies the lesson we were meant to learn. Spending Sabbath dinner with family and friends gathered around you—candles glowing, sweet wine upon your lips, the smell of challah in the air—there is holiness in such moments to be sure. But there will be dirty dishes to be washed after the candles have burned low, and the lesson we can learn from the ash upon the altar is that there is holiness in those dishes just as well." "I await the opportunity to take out the garbage with joy: it is a sacred act, an expression of love, representative of the holiness of marriage," continues Rabbi Dovid Bendory.

"There is no reason therefore to blame the god," Plutarch says, "if he allowed his prophesies to run to waste like water, or to echo like the rocks with the voices of shepherds and flocks in waste places."

And, say archaeologists Michael Shanks, David Platt, and William L. Rathje in their article "The Perfume of Garbage: Modernity and the Archaeological," "[Ninety-nine] percent or more of what most archaeologists dig up, record, and analyze in obsessive detail is what past peoples threw away as worthless—broken ceramics, broken or dulled stone tools, tool-making debitage, food-making debris, food waste, broken glass, rusted metal, on and on. These are society's material dregs that even those most clever at salvage couldn't figure a way to use or sell. But ask archaeologists what archaeology focuses on and they will mention 'the past' and 'artifacts' and 'behavior' and 'attitudes and beliefs,' but you will rarely, if ever, hear the words 'garbage' or 'refuse' or 'trash' or 'junk.'"

Maybe a thing only brightens after it has been thrown away, turned away from, the ways in which the stars muddy themselves when we stare directly at them, but brighten as soon as we look away. Maybe some things want to be engaged only peripherally, and that's where they will flourish, and when our love for them will be most strong. Gods, goddesses, the histories of our islands, the children we will never have . . . Or maybe, this is just another wishful story we tell ourselves about ourselves.

Again and again, across doctrine and history, we are driven by self-interest to misapply the term *holy*. When our "holinesses" are allowed to accrue (the holiness of discarding, and the holiness of that which we discard), destruction is often the result, and so the stories we tell ourselves are not only wishful, but also atrocious.

And the vortex does what it does, spins so colorfully, a noxious galaxy off the shore of Fuerteventura, briefly waving as it sweeps by on its rounds, as if the second hand, minute hand, hour hand, gears and wheels and rotors of some clock, agitating our refuse, our stories, our sadnesses until they become something worthy of the gods, and all that which we've lost or thrown away will be renamed, *artifacts*, *essays*, *Mynah*, *Arlo* and *Aldo* and *Geronimo* and *Giuseppe*, and *Agnes* and *Aponi*. And they, like the gods once did, will vacation here, in the guise of some tiny plastic dragon, on some beach that future scholars—should any still exist—will only confuse for pure, for paradisiacal, for fortunate.

Two Stories
Brian Evenson

THE EXTRICATION

IN THE EARLY DAYS OF THIS WORLD, life-forms were not as distinct as they are today. There were no separate species but only a single fecund mire of creatures indiscriminately breeding, changing, and striating with each new generation. With every blind coupling, new forms of creature came into existence.

Mere speculation, you might say, were you free to speak. Yes, speculation. Perhaps the truth, perhaps not. And yet the idea struck me as offering a compelling map for the future.

Which is why you are here.

How are you? Are you comfortable? Can I get you anything? A cup of water perhaps? A crust of bread?

No, I shouldn't needle you. We both know your needs are being provided for, being dripped slowly into your body by way of a central venous catheter. To allow you to feed yourself I would have to undo the straps that keep you immobilized. I am not sure that is such a good idea. Not until I have convinced you of the necessity of what we are trying to accomplish.

But don't worry. I am a patient man. I will not give up on you. I will convince you.

As the world sickens further, as the air grows poisonous, as the oceans die, so too must we shift and change if we care to survive. We must extricate ourselves from humanity and become something other than ourselves. Something that can adapt to the harshness of this new world. We must loosen the strands that differentiate us from other creatures, unravel our coding—loosen it just enough that our bodies are free to become more than what they are.

By us, I mean of course you.

*

You see these suspended bags? If you tip back your head and crane your neck and look behind you, there they are. These ones to the left, the ones bloated with clear fluid, need not concern us: they are simply meant to keep you nourished and hydrated, to keep you alive. They contain, as well, a painkiller. Nothing too addictive. Or, rather, yes, quite addictive, but the treatment plan I have developed for you allows me to taper you off slowly. Withdrawal will not be pleasant, but you will survive it. I have learned from past mistakes.

It is this other bag that matters, the one to the right, the one filled with an absinthe-colored fluid. This will enter your body much more slowly. In the time it takes for the entire bag to enter your system, we will go through a dozen bags of clear fluid. But this, my friend, is the bag that matters.

I claimed these bags of clear fluid need not concern us, but of course they do. Think of them as a sort of clock. By the time the first bag is empty, you will sense something beginning to happen to you. By the time you reach the fourth, your skin will feel as if it is on fire, despite the painkillers. By the sixth you will begin to transform.

How you will change exactly, I cannot predict. It is different for everyone, and depends on what sort of choices your body makes. Some—most if I am being honest—dissolve into a kind of muck. They writhe and fold inward and expire sometime in the course of the seventh bag. I hose what remains of them off the table. A few, a very select few, have made it all the way to the final bag, the twelfth. By that time, they have become something else. Something at least theoretically more suited to live in this new world. They are more resistant to cold or heat; their skin becomes scaled or slimy or photosensitive; they lose or gain a limb or two or three.

I have chosen you very carefully. I have faith that you will be one of those select few.

Perhaps if I removed your gag you would have questions for me. Perhaps, instead, you would just shriek and scream. Those who came before you have done sometimes one, sometimes the other. There have even been those who, gag removed, remain stubbornly silent. I

105

am, I admit, tempted to remove your gag, if only to see if my guess about what you in particular would do is correct.

But the screams in the past have been too shrill to be anything but a distraction, and the questions asked are always the wrong ones. The silence I find even worse. Whatever you choose to do, it will only make me think less of you.

No, it is a waste of time. Better never to loosen the gag.

Have I been clear enough? The world is dying, is in fact already well on its way to being dead. Were it not, you would never have wandered in here. You never would have had occasion to think *What is this? An unoccupied bunker in which I can shelter myself? What luck!* and then have fallen into my trap. You would, instead, have a job in a small town as an accountant, say, or a data-entry specialist. But there are no real towns anymore, small or otherwise. And that I am alive here, in this bunker, is due only to the foresight I had. I could see the collapse coming and I said to myself I needed to prepare. The world was changing. We had ruined it. Things had gone too far to change them back. And so, I told myself, it is *we* who must change to meet the world.

Or you, rather. By we, I meant and still mean you.

Don't worry, friend. We're in this together. I want humanity to survive. I have done my best to calibrate the formula exactly right this time. I will stay beside you. I will observe the change.

True enough, I couldn't save the others, but that is no reason to think I won't be able to save you. The one just before you made it through all twelve bags and still lived, gasping, for thirty-eight minutes after that. His skin had begun to extrude a slick mucosal layer and I suspect he no longer belonged in air but in water. I learned so much from him, and I will use all I learned to save you.

Even if I do not succeed, perhaps we will learn enough so that the individual who comes after you will survive. Or perhaps the individual after him. And, once the procedure has been perfected, it will be ready for me.

When will we begin? your eyes seem to be asking.

But can't you see we have already begun? Look at how much less

106

clear fluid there is in the first bag than in the bags that will succeed it. Yes, we have already begun.

I will do what I can for you. I am rooting for you. Whether you survive the change or perish, I will be here with you, I swear, until the bitter end.

CURATOR

There were clear indications the cloud was moving again, headed their way. Where it passed it stripped the remaining leaves from the already crippled trees, left soil and water poisoned, stripped the flesh off any creature, living or dead, and then whittled away at the bones. It was no ordinary cloud, having been made by humans, and it did not disperse. There were some who believed the cloud had become sentient, but if this were really the case, so the archivist speculated, wouldn't it have come for them sooner? It had finished off the rest of humanity long ago: why stop before it was done with the last few?

"No chance it will shift direction?" the archivist asked.

"There's always a chance," said Gradus. "But no, I don't believe so. We'll wait as long as we dare."

"And then retreat?" she asked.

"There's nowhere left to retreat to here," said Gradus. "The cloud has destroyed everything else. No, we'll have to depart for good."

"*You'll* have to."

He bowed slightly, acknowledging this. "We'll leave, archivist," he said, "but you'll stay."

As Gradus and the others prepared for departure, the archivist set about her own tasks, sorting and sifting through all she was charged with. Gradus and the others would go in search of a viable alternative to this world, a new place to live, just as those ships that had departed before were now doing. The archivist would stay behind to watch the last bit of still untouched ground be touched and die and to make sure the hatch was well sealed, the archive arranged. In a few weeks, a few months at most, she would be dead too. She was as good as dead already.

As for Gradus, there was very little chance he would find what he was looking for. But what else was he to do? He and his crew, like the archivist, were as good as dead. The only difference was they would take a little longer to go about dying.

Once the preparations had been made, Gradus sought the archivist out. He took her by the shoulders, kissed both her cheeks. His lips were warm and soft.

"Nearly here," he said.

"Yes," she said.

"Yours is a holy calling," he told her.

"Or a useless one."

"Perhaps," he said, ever the optimist. "Perhaps." Then he embraced her again and departed. It was, the archivist suddenly realized, the last human contact she was likely to ever have.

A few minutes later the archivist was safely embunkered below ground. A dull rumbling began. A great gust of smoke and fire filled the screens of the monitors and the vessel rose. And then she was alone, with just her holy or perhaps useless calling to keep her company.

Once the ground had had time to cool, the archivist donned the black hazard suit and went above. The cloud was close enough now that she could make it out with her naked eye, a great roiling mass gathered on every horizon, converging on her.

She went back below and into the shelter. She would have to finish quickly.

Her task was to preserve a record of humanity in the face of its imminent extinction, so that whoever or whatever discovered the records might, through careful study, come to understand what humanity had been. She was not the only one involved in this task: each ship that had departed had taken a sub-archivist and a similar set of records with it. Each ship had multiple highly abbreviated sets of data etched microscopically on nickel discs and encased in thick sheets of resin. At careful intervals, a satellite or probe carrying one of them was released into space where it would float until it was either found or destroyed.

108

But she had remained on earth, the place humanity had originated, which made hers the most important task: each set of data to be released into space, whatever else it included, gave coordinates for where this planet was, and where on the planet her archive was to be found.

But earth was, so the archivist increasingly felt, the place where humans had done their best to destroy themselves. And then, once they had succeeded in nearly destroying themselves and had completely devastated the earth, they had, simply, fled to the stars, hoping to find new worlds to destroy.

Here is how monstrous humans are, she felt the record should say. *Humans are what they did to this world, their home. Here is why, once humans are extinct, they should never be brought back to life.*

Part of the record was more than a record: millions of preserved strands of DNA with instructions for how they could be reconstituted, inserted into artificial cells (the composition for several varieties of which were provided in the data), wound together into double helixes, and used—once this world was safe to inhabit again, once the cloud had done its worst and finally dissipated, its poisons neutralized, the earth slowly grown green again—to bring the human race back from extinction. Her archive contained pictorial instructions that could, in theory, be universally understood, so that whoever or whatever rediscovered the archive in a few thousand or a few million or a few hundred million years would be able to regrow humanity in a vat.

Would it be humans, returned from the stars? If so, there was no need for them to grow more of themselves, unless they needed to occupy the earth fully. Perhaps, if other things had managed to come back to life as microorganisms and then evolved into threats there might be an advantage in this. Or perhaps because of the small groups aboard each ship they would now need to diversify their genetic pool. Or perhaps the humans who returned, so long among the stars, would have evolved, becoming something else entirely, and would believe they were discovering not their own but another species.

Or perhaps it would be another sort of creature entirely, something with no relation to human beings at all, with a vastly different perceptual matrix. The pictographs had been designed for creatures with eyes, though the scientists had taken into account the different visions of humans and animals, even the fragmenting and multiplying vision

109

of insects. But suppose that whatever came did not have eyes?

Even if they did have eyes, who was to say that they would have limbs? Perhaps they would be sluglike or radially oriented or cephalopodic, and they would not interpret the two-legged, two-armed stick figures as meant to represent sentient beings. *What sort of tree is that?* they might think, if they knew what a tree was, if they were able, in the way we understand it, to think.

No, she thought. Even if anyone or anything found the archive it was hopeless.

Or at least *almost* hopeless. There was the barest, most minute chance that everything would go just right, that there was other life in the universe, that that life would discover a probe, that the probe would contain a still functional nickel disc microscopically engraved with data, that they (whoever "they" were) would figure out how to interpret the data, that they would take the trip to earth and, once there, would manage to take the steps necessary to resurrect humanity. There was a chance.

Which was why she set about meticulously destroying all the millions of strands of DNA and defacing the pictograms. Millions of other species dead, all because of humans—plants, animals, bacteria. Some killed unknowingly, others willfully hunted down, a whole world ruined. No, the best thing, no matter who or what arrived here, no matter what life arose in millions of years from the sea, was to make sure it was impossible for humans to come back.

When she had incinerated the preserved DNA, she put on her hazard suit again and climbed back to the surface. The cloud was much closer now; she could hear it howling. But it had not arrived yet.

How shall I spend my remaining hours? she wondered, and went back down below.

She went rapidly through the photographic images etched into metal that were part of the archive, carefully removing and feeding to the incinerator any benign images, any smiling images or images of peace, leaving behind only images of war: mutilated Civil War dead fallen on the field of battle, a mushroom cloud, the firebombing of Dresden. Smoke billowing from factory chimneys. A huge pile of dead passenger pigeons, tens of thousands of them, a man standing atop the heap. A man standing before the trunk of a huge redwood, and then the same man standing on the stump of the same tree, smiling. The dark face of a boy ravaged by hunger, a dying gaunt polar bear on a rapidly melting chunk of ice, children in cages, a wall of skulls, a white man grinning with another darker man swinging from a rope behind him, emaciated victims in camps on every inhabited continent, the slaughtered carcasses of animals presided over by their smiling killers. An island mostly underwater, abandoned houses still visible beneath the waves. Miles of devastated ex-forest, miles of sick and dying land. Death, famine, war, and conquest: the four horsemen of the apocalypse.

She was no longer an archivist, she realized, but rather a curator, making careful decisions about what would or would not be put on display and exiling everything else. She was far from done sorting through the images, had barely reached the twenty-first century, when she began to reconsider. Was it enough? What, if anything, would be enough?

For a long time she stayed there, absently holding the image etched into metal in her hand, as if hypnotized, and then she put it down. No, she had to destroy everything. She had to do her best to make sure that if anyone were to come, they would find nothing at all.

And so she began to carry the archive, every bit and piece of it that had been amassed over the years and meticulously reduced and put into a format that would have a chance of surviving for an unimaginable length of time, to the incinerator. And did not rest until it was all gone.

Once she was done, she stretched. She sat on the floor of the now empty room and considered. The probes in space she could do nothing about. She had done all she could. Here, there was little data left, nothing significant waiting beyond the room itself and whatever would be left of her own body.

But from the traces of her body they could, potentially, extract DNA. Who knew what procedures they would have developed in the intervening millennia?

She put her hazard suit on again, climbed the ladder, and opened the hatch. Leaving it deliberately ajar, she climbed back down.

The toxic cloud poured through the hatch slowly, and began filling the space. It would scour the shelter. For a time the suit would protect her against it, but only for a time.

When the cloud was billowing as high as her waist and pouring more quickly now down through the hatch, she stood and climbed up the ladder again.

Outside, everything was covered by the cloud. She could see nothing but a gray indifferent light. If she held her hand a few inches from her faceplate, she could see it; if she moved it any farther, it became a vague shape. A few inches more and it was lost.

She began to walk. After a while, the hazard suit began to feel stuffy, and she realized that her air circulator was no longer working. She banged on it and it started to whir again momentarily, then stopped for good.

Maybe, she thought, *I will die of lack of oxygen before the cloud consumes me.* She brought her hand near her face and saw how the rubberized fabric had already begun to pit and crack, and then thought, *Maybe not.*

She imagined her desiccated corpse being found in the suit, stretched shadowy forms standing over it and cautiously prodding it, thinking the suit a carapace, a hardened parcel of skin. Would even that misunderstanding tell them too much?

But, she knew, this was impossible: after the cloud was done with her, there would be almost nothing left of the suit, and very little of her.

She walked on, hoping to get as far away as she could from the shelter, far enough so that her remains would never be found. A warning began to sound in her suit, the words *Breach Imminent* flashing on her faceplate. And then, perhaps a hundred steps later, the first crack opened in the hazard suit's fabric near her knee, and she began to experience an itching sensation that spread slowly up her leg, gradually transforming into a searing pain that soon had her screaming, and then left her dead, and all the earth along with her.

Five Poems
Sabine Schiffner

—Translated from German by Helena Van Brande

WITH GREAT DELIGHT

My mother teaches me
to speak
she says imagine your language
as an infinite amount of seeds
and she teaches me the flora's names
the aquilegia
that blooms in the forest shade
she shows me the Kaiser's crown
I loved that one once
and she searches her alphabet
for my name because it resembles
the hollyhock that grows
close to the house and
the buddleia
butterfly bush
and the sunflowers
often hanging up at home in paintings
she even talks about the rarest flowers
like the sundew
not just you but every person
that we pull out from the wetland
is that unique
a rare plant that sprouts
out of rough soil
my mother is a speech teacher
in the realm of dirt and flowers
and she sings with great delight
the rose the lily the pigeon
the sun

Sabine Schiffner

TORDO

The birds coming
from Chernobyl
are broken winged
say the islanders
says a famous Ukrainian author
who's written over eighty books since her exile

fear reigns in Mallorca
this summer as well as last summer
even the scorching heat
doesn't drive away the fear
as if uranium might fall from their wings

chant mon petit oiseau
sings my eighty-year-old grandmother
who has lived through two world wars
Chernobyl and the deaths of all her generation's relatives
her bemused bespeckled face
those waterfront-blue eyes and her golden heart
and every day she sprinkles fresh sand in the cages

chant pour moi
if I could fly to distant Mallorca
as I'd love to do on the wings of song
light as the redwing
beloved throughout the Mediterranean

and she thinks about the light breakable bones
of the fieldfare that her father brought back
from the hunt at the turn of the century
he pulled the feathered things from his saddlebags
that tasted like sweat grain and leather
we made them into a tasty lunch she says
fieldfare with dumplings

no one wants to catch redwings anymore
their flesh went rancid years ago
they huddle in large dark swarms again in Palma's parks
men bring dynamite to drive them away

114

but every year they come back more numerous than before

she should be caught and eaten
as in simpler times
when there was tordo in all the restaurants around Palma's parks
but today the redwing only tastes fearful
and nuclear

THE ANCHORITE

Around the logging
a whirl of orange-tipped butterfly wings
the saw buzzes through the valley air
a long stare from the oak pillars
to the beech pillars
his view confined meanwhile
by the camera's frame
that links it with the logging field
and transforms it all
into still life
a human weave disappearing
the distant grin of cuckooflowers
the bright orange of the butterflies is
the color of the wood's scars
the oozing
with every strike the man plants a carnal prayer
into the tree
and the butterfly flees the blows
in its head the sound
wood makes
when it breaks
a sound like a split bone
that speaks
the logging field sits next to the graveyard
this is my son
says the man and
readies his ax

Sabine Schiffner

SILVER FIRS

You can pass through
silver fir forests free of
evil spirits without fear
even on your own says mother

it's quiet deathly quiet the farther I go
through the forest the smaller and darker
the path with nothing growing over it except
the silver firs' taproots toward the earth's center always deeper

silver fir forests says mother
used to be where over and over
we played little red riding hood and
the bad wolf until a dog bit me

she sends me off just go already
go bring berries and mushrooms and
don't come back home without them
from the silver fir forest that's been gone a long time

LINNÉ

And in their own way they call out
be quiet and come along and
they fly over the soccer stadium along
the plains and wind turbines cell-phone towers
of Cologne
quietly quietly
over the familiar smoke from the coal-power plants
toward the south
no one knows where the journey leads
maybe they will fall and drown in the
wet marshes and only in the springtime
will they appear again that's what the old people
say the young people say if
global warming continues like this
they will never even leave

Coyote

Wil Weitzel

I GOT AS FAR AS BOISE, Idaho, which is pretty far, when I knew I was going the wrong way. There was no official money to help departing staff back at the predator rescue center in Nebraska, but the two biologists insisted on giving me bus fare. If things had been different, I wouldn't have taken it. I like to believe that. But I did take it because I wanted to get west to the ocean.

In Boise, there's a cheap place for meals I knew about from when I was working for the municipals doing bridge repair south of Idaho Falls and moonlighting as a courier, mostly for the ski company, Sun Valley. I never got close to the resort—stuck in cities—but I met this woman who covered the morning shift at the café, starting at six thirty. For a long time, maybe a month and a half, I was her first customer.

"Here to help me open?" she used to joke when she'd find me out shuffling in the cold. I would haul up their blinds and bring the chairs down from tabletops. She'd serve me black coffee, first of the day, then before the old-timers came in she'd sit down at the table and cross her legs.

I never touched her. Even so, there was that tension, coming from the possibility I'd invite her out somewhere, or reach across and fold my hand over hers. Or ask if she liked floating rivers still coursing through their beds far to the north and could get a week off. I'm not sure she would have been altogether against any of that.

But I took it mainly as kindness on her part. Maybe loneliness. Still, you see her face. It blends in with the hot feel of the coffee. The smell of the place in the morning before anything's been spilled.

Now, when I got off the bus in Boise, well short of Oregon, which was where I thought I was headed, I made it over to this café. I figured I'd spend a night in town then get back on the road. It was three years since I'd been in Boise. But everything looked the same. Inside the place, there was no waitress because it was past the dinner rush. And I didn't expect to see her anyway. I think I was a little afraid to find her still working there after that amount of time. I believe if I'd spied her coming from the kitchen with that same hand-sized spiral notepad, it would have made me want to bus tables and walk around with a clean shirt taking orders and delivering tabs, so she could go out and look for something else.

Anyway, there was the same old, spindly cook I'd met a few times before. He didn't own the place but he used to come in around ten o'clock and we would exchange a few words on the rare occasions I was still hanging around at that hour. He'd start prepping for the lunch crowd and make a hell of a lot of noise back in his small kitchen. Walter, his name was. I remembered that.

"I've got something for you, Walt," I told him now, fresh off the bus. I knew he'd watched me in the old days with that waitress. The familiar looks, I guess, she and I would send back and forth. Though, despite the tired way she'd shrug and laugh, then kick softly at a chair leg when I said just about anything, the two of us knew next to nothing about one another.

The cook, Walter, looked a hundred years older. He stared at me now when I leaned over the counter.

"You got some time later on?" I asked.

I could tell he was surprised. I didn't look good. I got pretty battered the night they attacked that rescue center. My arm was in a sling. I had a long, deep gash running under my eye that still stung when I opened my mouth. But I was right about him. The idea to look him up came when my confusion hit its peak. Sitting on the bus, I thought of that serious-minded old cook before we'd even crossed out of Wyoming, when state signs for Moose and Hoback sent me memories of Grand Targhee and the deep snow in those mountains and their steep ravines and a whole era of my life. I'd expected him to be at the café. Though the waitress was sure to be long gone, settled in some neat house in another state, he wasn't the kind to change jobs. His sad, exhausted eyes set over cheeks caved just enough to leave questions about his teeth left a stark picture in my mind.

Now the tight features relaxed, started to separate. The eyes took on that little bit of water. His tiny, raw-boned frame heaved out its bass voice, ballooning from the depths of him.

"All right then," he said. "When we close if there's something you need to talk out."

I gave Walter the full scoop. I hadn't opened up to anybody in years. And it's only a type of openness. But tell a stranger a thing you've never worked through, his face right there can let you know which parts are the ones that matter and where you're just circling around.

"I haven't been out in the woods since I was young," said Walter, feeling his way. "So I couldn't say. Myself. But if I had to—"

He stood up after an hour and a half because it had grown emotional between us. I laid it on him, everything that happened, my wandering, the seasons in the backcountry, for nearly twenty years. Then events at the predator rescue center. The night of the raid, which still haunted, left its cold print on me.

"I haven't heard this one before," said Walter. "Not exactly. So I can't truly advise you. But if I had to advise you—and I do see you're pushing me—" He looked over warily, as if I'd turned into his mortal enemy. He looked particularly at my shoulder pulled back so the clavicle would set, as if that's where my heart, or the thing he was talking to, was specifically located.

"No, I haven't been out there to those relict forests. Mostly been right here in Boise. Though I have spent time on the river back when it was flowing more regularly—" He cut himself off and shook his head like he was deeply disgusted at the mention of his own life circumstances.

"But I can *see* all the way out there to what's left of the wild spaces. I got line of sight—not on your rusted pine. Not those bottomland wastes of larch and alder—not snags and burnt timber. I mean the last fir belts still growing up sides of mountains. Black spruce that's stunted, sure, hurt by pestilence, our toxic winds, but still alive in high country. I *know* what those trees look like when it's first getting dark, even if I can't see them anymore. Their leeward bottoms grow that much thicker for starts—such is the feeling they'll give you."

I nodded fiercely to encourage him because I could sense Walter was getting close to it, whatever it was. He looked riled, taken by fever.

"And *that* stays with you, let me tell you. You don't need to travel out to those areas making their last stand. You'll know them by *in*stinct—now. That's your one word for it."

By this point, Walter was walking around the café like it was his house. I was sitting, huddled and small, trying to make myself smaller, more insignificant, at a center table he'd chosen. Meantime, he was on the move. Touching walls. Changing the hang of the old photographs of warehouses and cattle barns. Performing invisible adjustments on the napkins, each a quarter turned from the one below, piled up to make a neat, alternating star.

"In your *blood*, now, right? No other word. I don't have to go *out* there again in my life to still *know*."

119

I gave Walter every indication I was knowing too. I opened my eyes wide and closed them and brought my shoulders up and down, a little painfully, to emphasize my breathing.

"I can *hear* them go quiet—they're pockets of life. Where you've still got the denning animals. They're sheltered by something. Rocks maybe. Or trees. The cut-out banks of rivers. What's that going to mean," Walter asked, "when we lose those last refuges—and not just us?"

I was afraid to break the spell. I realized the café was a little like those forest places he was describing. A holdout. Maybe a sanctuary. Walter was winding down. He was skeletal, an old white guy who'd lived in Boise his whole life. I'd laid out my years drifting back and forth, sleeping where there were woods, or in somebody's guest room, a garage. Trekking through drifts sometimes far off from people. And he'd just spent himself savagely in those forests he knew only from imagining them.

"Never once heard someone explain it that true," I told him.

Walter sank back to the table and collapsed on his chair and we were two slumped figures. I could see us from a long way above. As though that café where the waitress used to work had no roof on it anymore. I was looking down on Walter, who was a gray-and-white speck, and this other broken form that must have been me, slung up in a collarbone harness.

"You say he put his back to you then?"

"That's right."

Walter's deep voice got real quiet, confidential, as he finally closed in on the center of his concerns. Like finally they were rising from the earth toward us both.

"And he hurt them, you say. Did some damage to those men."

"He did damage."

I went through it again, more slowly this time, with all the details I could remember. How I'd worked as a janitor, at first, hosing down pens at the predator rescue center in Nebraska. When there was political trouble surrounding the center, I took shifts as their security guard. First thing, a pair of local men with livestock interests came to threaten the two biologists, a young man and a woman, who were there for the winter on an internship. Meantime, the two lead scientists, married with a child, were on leave for those coldest months, and the caretaker of the facility was a retired grocer who didn't live on-site.

"We're going to shut this whole thing down," said one of the guys

120

who showed up. "Best thing now is just you head back right where you came from."

"Don't try to protect these killers," the other one chimed in, pointing over toward the feeding area. "Or make excuses. They kill. That's what they *do*." This second man, who was short and squat, made a grotesque expression, squinting and contorting his mouth. "Pre-da-tor," he said, sounding out the word on the sign outside the facility, for the benefit of the biologists. "But now see—" The man made a line in the dirt in front of him with the stiff heel of his boot, then deepened it. "That would just mean killer."

"These animals are innocent," I said, stepping up beside the biologists. They were fidgety men standing in front of us, and I was pretty sure they'd been put up to this. "We ate most of their range away, or it's dying back, piece by piece. So coming after your penned goats and chickens is what they've got left. Their world's going away."

"That's a sad story, mister. Now look, see, you've got the tears coming. Why don't you be sure to be here then—when we come back."

I looked over at the faces of the biologists. They were directed at me in anticipation. I'd never said much before. Just taken the job scrubbing tiles because I needed some way to feed myself. Quietly, they began backing toward their cramped office.

"You got a specific time?" I asked the men once the biologists had made it to their office. "Because I'm a planner."

One of the two laughed loudly, but the other, the short, thickset one, didn't laugh. He stared at me hard.

"Good to know, mister. Now see"—he wrinkled his nose like he'd caught the sudden scent of an animal hidden just behind or somewhere inside me—"I'm real glad you let that out."

I suggested the biologists, who'd alerted the police, stay nights at the Days Inn in town. The rescue center was past the outskirts, far in the northern section of the state. Surrounding tall grasslands were hit hard by desertification, but part of a prairie recovery project that, if funding came through, was to become a reserve. A local rye-whiskey manufacturer had put a wolf on its bottle to garner funds for the project, and the area was just large enough to serve as a trial reintroduction zone for displaced animals, including those from the refuge. It was still fenced, but big enough to allow the animals to hunt in the scablands, along a fossil river, and into degraded ash and yellow beech stands. But that hope brought bitter resentments and much debate in the local gazette. The animals, meanwhile—a juvenile cougar, pair of

121

female gray wolves, five bedraggled prairie coyote pups, and one large, restless, shaggy, and displaced eastern mountain coyote—looked like they were in slow-brewed shock, maybe unaware of what swirled around their heads, but surely conscious of captivity, of walls.

I explained to Walter in that café how by the night the men came back I'd had the dark shift for two weeks. How I carried no weapon because I'd assured the biologists the men would be armed and my own weapon was bound to bring fire. It would encourage them to shoot animals. The biologists had shaken their heads at this logic, but I'd insisted. Local police officers visited and swore to include the facility on patrol routes, but they couldn't dedicate a squad car. One thing for sure, when the moon rose over those struggling edge lands, the animals and I were out there all alone.

There were five of them, more than I'd figured. I told Walter how I came down on the first one who had a rifle from the flat roof of the coyote building where I'd stowed all the animals. How one man worked the door while the others laid into me. How, when one got me in the low shoulder with the crowbar, that side of my body went hard and cold. Without any power.

I explained how once we were inside the squat, bunker-like building they went for the coyote pen first. How the ceiling was low and they were wearing headlamps, so lights flared out in all directions and crashed under the dim, flickering fluorescents. How the prairie pups cowered together in a mass in the back of the pen. And how the big one, the mountain coyote, stayed in the rear and sheltered them with his body.

Then when I told him how one of them pulled his handgun and ducked into the pen, Walter stood up abruptly from the table and started pacing again.

"They'd hurt my left shoulder, but my right was still strong."

"Good," said Walter. "That's good." He looked toward his kitchen with great intensity. "Least we got that."

"One was down from my wrench outside the building, so there were just the four inside."

"All right, that's fine," Walter murmured. "Just four of them now."

The big mountain coyote growled but didn't move when the man raised his pistol and said something I don't remember. "Here's this" or "You're done." Something like that. But just then I took hold of his arm and there was somebody on my back in that same second, and we fell all scrambled into the large pen.

"I got up first," I told Walter.

"Course you did," whispered Walter, staring now, I could see, at his knives, which were hung neatly, according to size, on a long magnetic strip that ran above the low shelving. They looked too perfect to cut something. Too clean from my angle. Like they were museum pieces.

"I got over the gunman. Broke his wrist because I could hear it on the cement floor of the pen. But the other man cut me with a short knife I hadn't seen. He swung it in big motions rather than use it with knowledge, and once it came over across my face."

"Goddamn him," said Walter. "*Goddamn.* But that one now—" He straightened up his body at the thought, seeming to jump forward in the story, having heard it already. He started toward the open kitchen, moving purposefully. His hands came out from his hips. I could tell he was choosing his weapon after long years of knowing exactly what does what and how well.

"That man did get caught in the throat," I finished for Walter. "That was when the big mountain coyote lunged from the back of his pen."

Walter glided past his culinary knife row like those knives were bright phantoms, unusable. He bent down toward a low drawer I couldn't see, beneath the level of the counter. Then he rose up with a dark, single-barrel shotgun. It was heavy, I could tell. It weighed on his thin-set shoulders and rickety frame. The stock was of an old, fine wood, wire filigreed, and the action had been polished to shine under the lamps of the café.

"Those two men were both down then," I went on. "Not moving. I couldn't see their weapons straight off."

"So you stepped out of that pen," said Walter without looking at me.

"I'd been cut at my ribs but didn't know it yet. There was the wound on my face pouring in my mouth. Two of us, we came out, him behind me."

"You and the animal," Walter confirmed, sighting something now on the far wall. There was a painting there. Some cheap-framed hillscape draped with lush, green primary forest that dated from an earlier era, maybe Walter's era, and looked now dense and impossible.

"They spread out, those two men still up, at the perimeter of the room. He was snarling terribly at my back. Then both the men came in, both with something hard, maybe a pipe, crowbar."

"That's all right," pronounced Walter with great concentration. "We got ourselves even numbers now." He was sighting something in the old forest at the far end of the room. It must have been large by the look of him. Something, I presumed, he couldn't miss. His arm, the shoulder, were absolute, unwavering.

"Only one of them made it as far as me. And my wrench was lost back in the pen. I took a beating. But the fight behind me was real short. It probably wouldn't be called a fight."

I could see Walter was waiting patiently for me to go on and retell that last part. He was poised now for his shot. He didn't have a scope, but he was contorting his wrinkled face to squint down the long, thin, polished barrel.

"The man back behind me yelled hard. Then just small stuff, soft curses, barely talking."

Walter pulled the trigger. The chamber was empty but I could hear the bolt snap back, and the dry sound of the action stayed in the air afterward. He lowered his gun, a great weariness come over his face.

"When my guy stumbled out of the building," I went on, "the coyote stayed over the man down beneath him and sniffed his hair, one ear, then his neck, and wavered a few seconds. Then he limped back into the big pen and stood over the others. When nothing was coming, no more fight, he sank back to those prairie pups."

Walter was quiet for a long time, taking everything in. "That's good. Then that's fine," he said at last. "Now I'm real sorry to do this to you."

"You don't have cartridges, Walt."

"I don't need those."

"All right."

He had the gun pointed toward my heart.

"That girl you knew here—well, you know she's dead."

I realized I'd underestimated Walter badly. Turns out he had an elephant memory. Thinking too I was just one in the droves that came through.

"She's killed by a mugger. In these streets. Waiting for her boyfriend ten blocks from right here where you're sitting. In winter." Walter coughed up something that sounded bigger than he was. "January at that time. She was going home from work here."

"All right."

He walked toward me, as if his gun held shot pellets he could spray into my chest and then, for effect, over my side of the room.

"I'm sorry," I said.

"No, *I'm* sorry."

He brought the gun barrel up to my chest and printed the bead sight on me firmly, just below the slanting crosscut of my shoulder harness.

"Now I don't need cartridges for what I'm going to say."

Walter looked in that moment like he was barely alive. He was old and tired as could be. The pressure on my chest stayed steady though, important.

"You got my attention."

"Now he's calling out to you, that animal, over the miles you've gone away."

"Calling out."

"That's what I just said."

Walter brought the gun back from my chest and turned it around gradually, like the arm of a clock. When it was vertical, he pressed the whole thing the long way into my good arm.

"Take it," he said hoarsely. "Don't you leave him there like that unprotected. Our whole world's coming now for its last animals."

"They've got police, Walt."

Walter had come over to my good shoulder and was trying to hoist me out of my chair.

"I don't care who you think they've got. Police won't work. Not what he's up against. You're *connected* now." He spoke that word with terrific meaning and looked me straight in the eye to be sure it got through. He shook his arms violently toward the sky and flung his hands down at the ground so I thought they might just strip off him.

"All there is to it. You gotta turn yourself around."

When I walked into the rain in Boise it was after another hour and we'd made settled agreements about where I needed to go and it was deep night and Walter was there in the lit-up doorway of the café, nodding at me, shooing me away, and I was carrying an antique shotgun that belonged to an older West, too powerful, warmed by his hands, to be loaded to fire.

By the time I got back to the predator rescue center in Nebraska, the biologists were no longer there. They'd been making arrangements to move the animals before I left, and the pair of gray wolves and the young cougar were already gone. The caretaker was on site during business hours and there was a part-time intern and several local volunteers who came in and out. But the couple who had founded the refuge were still out of the country. For the three days I was gone, a policeman supposedly had been true to his word and parked his squad car outside the building that held the remaining animals—all coyotes—for the lengths of the nights.

When I walked into the squat bunker, I saw they had him all on his own, as we did before the men first came to threaten the facility. He was half sleeping, the way he always slept, lids open just enough to give a view straight ahead. I walked over to his pen and crouched down beside the wide grate. The eyes shifted under his lids so I could see them do it. Then he rose, stiff at the left hip, forepaw wounded on that side from where he'd been struck by the raiders, and shifted to the back of the pen. I wondered if they'd fractured his pelvic bone.

"Sure glad you're alive," I said.

He stayed standing in the rear, his body gone leaner, less muscular in those three days. I was filled with a rush of shame for leaving him, and sweaty relief at the same time.

"We must have hurt them worse than we thought."

That night, we moved him and the pups by truck into town, to the hospital precincts. They put him out, and veterinarians drove in and ministered to his hip. The founding couple who were in Rwanda, working with primates, arranged the whole thing. The biologists and I had spoken with them on the phone the morning after the raid, and the couple had hired lawyers. The police had interviewed me at length in my sad state. They'd asked for descriptions, had me sign forms. When I explained I'd hauled the three men who were left, one at a time, out to their truck with my good arm and shoulder, then stanched my rib wound with a sheet from the office cot, they'd looked at me hard. But I'd told them I didn't want those men, even in such bad shape, any nearer the animals than they had to be.

Now, since the biologists were gone, I stayed with him through almost all of it. He kept his eyes on my legs below the knees when I moved. After two days in a pod on the hospital grounds, a truck rolled in to transport him and the pups to another refuge outside Asheville, North Carolina, and I offered to ride in the cab with the driver. The couple in Rwanda thanked me on the phone. They were tearful, I could tell, from their voices. The most generous kind of people. They kept saying, "Normally we'd have somebody there. You don't need to do this. If you've got to get out west directly—"

"I want to do this," I told them. "After what we've been through."

I didn't go so far as to say I was pretty sure he'd saved my life. There's no telling what those men would have done if they'd gotten the chance to unleash. To beat on me without holds. I believe they meant to shoot up the animals, then truck me out, hurting, somewhere. But I was afraid if I told anyone besides Walter about what he'd done they could put him down, so I framed the story to the police, even to the couple, as his rising up to defend those pups.

"Well, if you weren't there—," the man stumbled on the phone from Rwanda. "We sure do hate to think."

"It was two of us," I said. "Really was together."

As we ate the miles from Nebraska down into Missouri, I started spending some of them lying back in the trailer near the crates. I'd say things to him like, "Just above Jefferson City now" or "Tell by the slowdown—that's St. Louis. Hang in there, though. We'll be through." He'd stare off toward the pups clumped up in another crate, their bodies crammed into a tight mass just visible between close slats.

In Evansville, Indiana, I bought a three-dollar beanbag at a thrift store and plunked it in the trailer and started singing to him, both of us coming in and out of sleep. I sang songs I'd heard from my mother—"Puff, the Magic Dragon" and "Mr. Bojangles"—and he brought his lids down almost to close. In Bowling Green, the driver and I got drunk in one of the smallest bars I've seen, with seats enough for seven people strung in a line together. I think the intimacy of the place, with the bartender leaning in so his thick whiskey breath swam over our ears, got us to drinking in earnest. Then, in London, Kentucky, I took the wheel for a while, which the driver explained was against all regulations. When I reassured him that I didn't have a license, so there were bigger problems that would prevent it from coming back to his job, somehow he took to that logic and we cranked the radio way up, and then, when that ran dry, moved to the proud stack of Grateful Dead bootlegs he kept under his seat.

The whole time, though, my mind was on something else. The driver, Mel, wore wide-frame, knockoff Ray-Ban sunglasses even at night, saying something about the contrast, and he was round as he was tall with a great head of hair flowing halfway down his back. He tilted that head back and guffawed at almost any story as if it were the most outlandish thing he'd heard. We traded the wheel back and forth beyond Knoxville, and I even convinced him to take a shift on the beanbag to keep the coyotes company. But mostly, as time wore on, Mel stayed up in the cab while I drove and shook his head at what seemed like the sadness of the world poured over by long, rising screeds of Jerry Garcia's guitar. "Damn shame," he said as the miles sank under us, and I could tell he'd gotten sentimental at the thought of our arriving at the predator shelter near Asheville and the prospect of the whole party ending.

We were in the mountains by then and I was starting to long to be away from the noise for a while. It was deep summer already, late

June, and the deciduous trees that had hung in there at mid-elevation bore the heartbreaking green of full season. I was thinking a lot about Walter. But the main thing through that whole trip locked onto my mind with a vise grip was the shaggy, brindled, wide-ruffed, tawny-eyed eastern mountain coyote in the back. He looked shrunken and shapeless stuck inside his crate, an animal in deep mental and physical retreat. That's why I couldn't concentrate fully on the music. What I was thinking of was something like what I believe Mel began dwelling on in the broken forests that rose into the Smokies. I was thinking, little as it had felt like it in St. Louis, the trip was going to close out. We were going to pull that rig over and turn off its engine and they were going to unload those crates out from the back of my life.

The facility outside Asheville was much larger than the one in Nebraska, with many more animals. The couple in Rwanda had sent an email and notified the management I was looking for a job. The man who ran the place was kind and understanding, but he didn't have funding for additional positions. He seemed to have an intuitive understanding of my state, however, and said he'd let me feed the coyotes we'd brought along for a few days. They were kept in a separate building that was like an intermediary zone, before they would be relocated to one of the large, semicovered outdoor pens. It was stuffy in there, close quarters, with more of that same yellowish ceiling light they'd had at the other refuge.

Mel had four days off after his run from Nebraska, and he spent the first two days in town so we could rifle through the bars in Asheville for local, mountain-brewed beer. But the magic between us had worn down now we weren't moving. And I didn't feel like getting drunk. So we said goodbye overformally, as though we were business colleagues who'd finalized the deal on a cargo shipment that was to come in far away, on another continent. I stood two blocks off the main drag in Asheville where he'd parked his rig and told him he shouldn't drive straight from the brewhouse.

"You of all people," he laughed, a little offended.

"Oh, I know."

I waved at his rearview, seeing him in there, hunched in that dark cab, for a few long seconds, before he hit second gear and started powering, loud and slow, out toward the interstate.

When I got back to the refuge, I found the small building with the coyotes locked up and retired to the bunk they'd set up in a side office apparently little used. That next morning, I asked if I could spend some time with the animals before I shoved off. I figured I could have invented some use for myself there. I could have gone back to fence repair and security shifts. I'd volunteered to catch on at a job before. But it was too sad. The place was businesslike. Well staffed. Everything was organized, properly funded, and in its place.

The manager, Ralph, had taken a liking to me. We had some sort of kinship based, I believe, on my wrecked beanbag, which he'd seen in the trailer bed beside the coyote crates and I'd moved into the hold-over building. He slowed down when he talked to me and his eyes traveled out over my slung-up shoulder to show he was reflecting.

"I can't let you stay with them too long. You may already have done that," he said. "Because our focus here's still reintroduction." His boots were fidgeting a little on the asphalt and making a grating noise. "Less he sees one person, a human, gets comfortable, starts to trust, the better. Especially with his species." He looked up at the sky as if the fault were above us. "They're not so popular."

"We knew that out in Nebraska," I said. "Makes sense. But what he's been through. I don't think he's partial, if you've seen his paw, that hip, to humans."

Ralph laughed.

"Go on in there," he said. "Take your time."

But I wasn't long. We were already habituated. So it wasn't that. It was just I could sense the preview of the bad feeling I was getting, and half of me was hoping one of us would start hurting physically enough that I couldn't leave. Like maybe his hip would flare up in a way we'd have to deal with immediately. Or maybe my rib wound, which had been sutured, would start seeping dangerously.

"You'll be fine," I told him. "They'll let you out of here."

He looked over at the pups like he did whenever I spoke to him. In fact, whenever I walked into a building where he was penned he'd wait to recognize me then immediately glance away. The only times I saw him stare at me in Nebraska were when I was coming or going, and then it was at my legs. Sometimes, when I turned back for something I wanted to check on, walking out from the bunker there, he already would have shifted his wide head and be deep-watching my movements under those weak, flickering lights.

"Ralph's a good man," I went on, but I was running dry. My ribs, my face wound were hurting. Stinging at the look of him. Just being there, inside another facility, without those tall wheels of Mel's rig to ride up on, brought back the hard touch of metal and knives.

"You take care," I told him. And then, though it hadn't been exactly in my mouth to say, "I won't be far off."

I said goodbye and Ralph played gruff but I thought he was going to break down right there. I realized Mel must have worked on him after the unloading when I was inside the building with the animals. Mel, adjusting and readjusting his fake shades, could talk a blue streak. He must have told him about my hours on the trailer bed back with the coyotes. The five months I'd spent with those animals in Nebraska. Since Mel was the sensitive type, he probably relayed how I'd get quiet about the coyotes. Avoid questions about a bond or felt connection.

"You got a name for that coyote of yours?" Ralph asked me.

"No. Nothing like that."

"Big fella, though. Powerful through the haunch."

When Ralph was getting nowhere he bid me farewell.

"You gonna haul that beanbag with you?" he asked after he'd given me a bear hug. Ralph was tall with a round potbelly and thin, knobby arms but he could deliver a hearty embrace. He looked at the contoured straps of the beat-up, high-volume backpack I'd angled over my good shoulder. He couldn't see the bandage I wore over my ribs or the heavy wrap I'd wound about my torso, but he could see my cut face and the grungy clavicle harness.

"You gonna be all right there?"

"High summer," I said. "Be just fine."

"Come to think of it—you know—we'll be moving them next couple days. Soon as tomorrow maybe. Sure you don't want to stick around least for that?" Ralph pointed over toward the hold-over building. "Fore you just rush off?"

I could tell he was offering me a job, and as I walked away I thought I was making a big mistake, but I couldn't stop. How long can you scrub floors or mix ground meat and cornmeal or watch over quiet nights at a place while the world closes in on everything wild? I figured they'd get him to a larger enclosure where he could rely on predation, then reestablish him next door in the Smokies, if not way up in Algonquin. But now it wouldn't be until after another winter, into late spring when prey was more active and less concentrated. I knew from Nebraska wherever forest and prairie lands were drying out and fragmented, with habitats losing ground, intraspecies violence could kill released animals straight out of the gate.

I started walking down the asphalt drive. Then, when I thought I was clear of view around a bend, I jumped a wood fence and headed out into a grove of pitch pine. It was warm and bright and ten o'clock in the morning. Everything, in that slow breeze, was lit up and trembling. I needed to check in at the clinic to get my stitches removed, and so I took a shortcut through fallow sorghum fields and wound up in town two hours later on a direct route.

They fixed me up at the expense of the couple in Rwanda, who, working through Ralph, had given me the name of the clinic. At that point, I figured I'd follow the track Mel had cut toward the interstate. But my steps went instead from the clinic to the bar, and now I did get drunk on something they called Burial Beer. I wished to hell Mel hadn't deserted me and that I wasn't carrying Walter's old shotgun wrapped in a quarter blanket and toed down in my backcountry pack so I had to leave a bivvy sac draped loosely over the whole thing to disguise the front bead sticking out.

Then I wandered back the two hours to the woods outside the refuge and made camp. I ate a bag of pine nuts Mel had bought in central Missouri and opened a can of cannellini beans Walter had slid into a stash pocket of my pack. My ribs were sore as hell. I laid on my back watching the few stars revolve and was awake the whole night, so far as I could tell, looking at the same ragged patch of darkness between two twisted pitch pine limbs, resprouted from fire and making a wild second tree out of the ruins of the first, its thick, plated bark holding just the slightest light.

In the morning, I tried to pull myself together and was ashamed when what I wanted was to go back to the hold-over building and loiter around the place and see what I could do to be of service. I made the sorry deal with myself I would check to see if they'd moved him already. I was thinking it might give me a picture, before I headed off, to see him just once in their more spacious semioutdoor pen. Tracing the perimeter fence, I figured. Scoping his boundary.

But Ralph caught sight of me from a long way off. It was just the luck of things, I guess, but I came up the road and was planning to stand inside the tree line and scan the large pens. I stared at him as he came out from the office, thinking it was early to be at work. He stopped in his tracks on the second step and stared right back like I was a ghost. I waved a little too long and when there was no response brought my hand down.

We stood there, the two of us, and I looked out over the pens and saw three slim subadult red wolves, gathered together far in the distance inside the outermost enclosure. But there were no other animals. I didn't have the heart to look any more at Ralph. I turned away from him and stooped low to hitch my pack a little higher and started away from the refuge down the asphalt road. I climbed back over the fence and checked my camp to make sure I'd left nothing. I evened out the ground where it had been damp under my weight, as I always did. It was the oldest instinct.

Then I set off through that same overgrown sorghum field and got an hour out, little more, when there was a dark, animal shape off my bow, right at the woods line, coming even with me, and my heart skipped a beat. I knew old Ralph had done it. It was so early, I guess he was the only one around. He'd opened the gate and made a test of it. And when that shape stayed even, I caught him now and then in my peripherals, not daring to look full-on, thinking, once I'd given it half an hour and we were dangerously near town, Walter was somewhere far out there at twelve o'clock, clattering his pans. And at the thought of him, still believing in the world, I turned my forty-five degrees and the coyote and I shaded together into the mountains, toward what forests were left.

Memorydrive
Kristine Ong Muslim

KINTSUGI, AN ANCIENT JAPANESE ART FORM, entails repairing cracked pottery by reattaching the shards with gold lacquer powder mixed with the adhesive. This is done so that a warm glow appears to radiate from the jagged tracery made by the fractures between the glued parts, emphasizing the "scars" that define a critical moment in the history of the pottery piece. I thought at that time the idea of glorifying brokenness as part of taking something to its healed state is particularly cruel. It also bodes malign magic. Using gold lacquer powder to illuminate scars, telltale marks of physical injury, is like making a gilded shrine to appease by fetishizing whatever sadistic, schadenfreude-eating deity may lurk out there. It is only later that I realize the intentional erasure of scars is so much worse.

I don't know where I am going with this. Jay is still dying, and there is nothing I can do about it. There is no way to keep him alive.

I have to give Jay his pain meds in two hours. I remember how he once told me, "I know the pain is there. I just could not feel it because of the drugs." My reply to him is something along the lines of how deadening the body's faculties for feeling pain is like doing a reverse kintsugi. I remember him smiling, and that is everything to me.

The world is part desolation, part hoping that one doesn't end up in any of the desolate spaces. Sometimes this desolation sits on the surface of things much like a patina does, unsightly yet tolerable. Sometimes, desolation seeps right to the bone, burning flesh on its way down. This is what happened to Kolmannskuppe, a ghost town in southern Namibia.

On December 18, 1980, Kolmannskuppe was made, as all ghost towns are made and not born the way a community is born. People afflicted with diamond fever, a malady that lasts for forty years, flocked into the town named after a man who had to abandon his ox wagon during a sandstorm. If you really think about it—which is what I've been doing all this time—that naming convention sort of sealed the fate of Kolmannskuppe. Naming a village after someone known for his singular act of abandonment can damn a village into a ghost town.

I saw the two-story house of Kolmannskuppe's mine manager a long time ago. That was before I met Jay. The house was beautifully decked with brick and smooth stone. It was easy to mythologize that house. Built atop a layer of hand-tooled stones, it used to be a fortress against the sunny blue of the cloudless sky and the muted gray of sand and pebbles. The house had a terrace—now long buried in sand—that offered a view of the windblown Namib Desert. There's nothing out there to see from the terrace, no lush palm groves or serene oases. But it must have been human nature to continuously seek out a platform for viewing what lies ahead, what lies outside an otherwise artificial sanctuary—even if there is nothing out there left to see.

Some nights I imagine, and for a short time forget about Jay dying in the other bed, that somewhere in the wastelands of Namib Desert, the red sand dunes are stirring to swallow whole the usurpers of the arid landscape.

When Jay shifts position in his sleep, his bedsprings no longer creak. He has lost a lot of weight.

There is something I have to tell you. The next time you see someone's face appear a little blurry, like no matter how much you focus on seeing the face you still can't quite make out the features, you must act quickly. You can save that person's life. Warn that person that something bad is going to happen to him. I don't know what separates those who have been saved by this intervention from those beyond saving.

For about a week now, Jay's facial features have been appearing a bit ill-defined, fuzzy. It is as if they were obscured by smoke. It is not my eyesight. I know that his death is, indeed, inevitable.

Also, if you catch a glimpse of someone appearing headless—even if you only see the disturbing sight momentarily and even if you are sure it is just a trick of light (and I tell you it isn't)—do not waste your time mentally debating whether or not interfering with that person's fate is going to make you look crazy. It *is* going to make you look crazy. Just approach the person close enough so you can ruffle his hair. You can also touch the head. Make up an excuse, a joke, something clever, anything, just anything to account for the gesture that is definitely going to be misconstrued as rude—or, yes, crazy.

Then walk away. It is pointless to say anything to explain your weird behavior. That person will likely live, until maybe the next time he gets called. Called by whom or what—I don't know. I don't really want to think about it. It is the one part that scares me a lot. What if there is nothing out there, and what if there is no afterlife. Then I'll never see Jay again.

Here's a trite idea, yet one that still holds, because there is nothing to disprove it: the natural environment records impressions of past trauma. Specific material conditions enable a replay of recorded impressions, just like any recording.

In 2013, a mysterious epidemic resulted in a mass die-off of starfishes on the West Coast of North America. The grisly death spiral of the starfishes involved having their legs wither away before detachment from their bodies. Devoid of appendages, the lesion-stricken sea stars turned into sticky gel-like masses. The wasting disease is caused by a type of densovirus with no history of virulence; climate change has transformed it into a pathogen. These days, you can sometimes see small blobs in clear shallow waters, if you spend time walking along the North American West Coast. If you approach the blobs, which resemble sea stars in the late stages of the wasting disease, they disappear.

"Recorded impressions of past trauma," I tell Jay. He has no energy to make counterarguments to turn the whole thing into playful banter, something we enjoy—used to enjoy—doing.

I hear the neighbor's television, as there is no shutting the windows in this infernal dry heat. It is that televangelist doing his weekdays-at-three-in-the-afternoon routine again, that televangelist preaching what I am hoping will turn out to be the methods of his eventual destruction.

One of the things I love about the dark is that I don't get to see and be reminded of the visible representations of the irretrievably lost and those that have slipped from my grasp, because it is possible I do not deserve them. Mental images, I can block them. One can always reach for memory repression in the same way one resorts to a tourniquet for a gushing wound. As long as it is only short-term stifling. A tourniquet left for too long to do its constriction can result in a gangrened part, necrotic, that must be severed from the body.

135

Today's heat wave has killed sixteen people; all have been either children or the elderly. Bird attacks are becoming more prevalent too, as another person passing by Avenida's forest park has suffered terrible damage on one eye and can no longer see through it. Still, more and more people spend time in the vicinity of the forest park, a breezy place of refuge from the suffocating heat of paved surfaces. Toward the end of the news report on the forest-park incident, the TV presenter says something like, "One doesn't just read history to understand the present and predict the future. One also reads history because it behooves us to change the future."

It is the word "behooves" that has gotten to me. It sounds pretty archaic, rankling and charming at the same time. I like how it has guilt-tripping to encase its imperative. *Behooves.*

Behooves. Even at this too late a point.

In the dark, I hear Jay in the other bed shift from his sleeping position. He is breathing evenly, a good sign. It means he is comfortable.

A man on my doorstep talks about relocation. But I am too worried about Jay to pay attention to him. Apparently, a network of underground caves has been detected, and parts of it are underneath four of the modular row houses here, excluding ours but right next to ours. He is offering a 30 percent bonus on top of the present value of the properties within and along the vicinity of the dig. The relocation expenses are covered too. He gives me a list of available units where we can transfer, as well as their locations.

The "30 percent bonus on top of the present value" is all I need to hear; we can really use the money.

"I take it you know what's underneath," I tell him.

He smirks, says nothing. He doesn't need to. He has a badge with the familiar blue logo of a corporate outfit whose name I can't quite place in my mind. He smells faintly of mothballs and guava jelly. Has the whiff of self-importance, the hungry look of a careerist. He also sounds exactly like the type to paraphrase a quip from "The Tragedy of the Commons" to justify placing in private hands the sole ownership and control of natural resources. I say yes, because we need the money, plus moving to another unit is not going to be that much of a hassle. Also, I want to get rid of the little lackey fast.

Jay welcomes the news, as expected. "I hope whatever it is they find," he says, "if it doesn't serve the world for the better, I hope it is unusable."

I love our new place. It overlooks the tree-lined edge of the forest park.

The morning TV reporter calls the find from the underground cave network "the biggest archaeological discovery of the decade." She goes on, "They are intact pieces of pottery made by an early Neolithic tribe unknown in prehistory." The rest I have not been able to hear as I am scrambling to get Jay his portable oxygen. He is having trouble breathing again. This potentially deadly combination of temperature inversion and smog. Then add to this noxious soup the failing body of the terminally ill.

"I am sorry for the trouble," he says between gasps.

"No, please don't say sorry. Just hold on for a bit longer."

"That's what I've been doing."

Sometime midday comes the news of how the rarest of rare pottery has crumbled—literally crumbled—in the temperature-controlled room of the museum where artifacts are restored. I know it hurts Jay to laugh, so it comes out as a low chuckle. I join in on the laughter.

It *behooves* all ruins, born of another time and place and context, to resist restoration, that soft, seductive brushstroke of empire and global commerce.

The last paragraph of the latest news article about the crumbled pottery from the dig contains this sentence: *A museum technician said he saw the jars on the table where they had crumbled days ago.*

"Recorded impressions of past trauma," Jay says with the lilt in his voice, a lure for ensuing banter. He is trying to cheer me up.

"Or hallucination. Maybe the technician's just tired."

I want Jay to nap. He is growing pale. And his facial features—hazy. It is not my eyesight.

"My time's running out, you know that," he says. "I wish I could stay longer."

"I'll see you in the next life then."

"I thought you didn't believe in that crap."

"These are desperate times."

Jay is still alive. For now, he is still alive. But he won't be for long.

I still don't know where I am going with this. Jay is still dying, and

137

there is nothing I can do about it. There is no way to keep him alive.

The next two days have been particularly eventful. News of polar lights and ice fog in several places along the equatorial region. News of a bleach-resistant, ash-colored mold that grows and spreads fast on glass, concrete, and metal surfaces as soon as the surrounding air temperature exceeds 28.4 degrees Celsius. In a rapidly warming planet, most places, even in the shade, have air temperatures beyond 28.4 degrees Celsius. News of rising columns of black basalt on the coast of Thailand, with the bizarre projections forming an artificial island a few miles from Chaweng Beach. News of turtles suddenly materializing to lay eggs on beaches whose waters have long grown acidic, and then disappearing right after only to reappear, growing in number and frequency with each sighting, an inescapable haunting of a world destroyed.

Valley of Glass
Karla Kelsey

I begin my lecture on the Philosopher's major works saying before the
 eighteenth century discovered violet, violets were blue and the purple
 snail was red
I say Delphic priestesses had been referred to as bees and in Egypt bees
 flew up from Ra's tears
I say a drop of honey to lure the bee and what is love but the name of each
 insect, animal, leaf, mineral, sea, and philosophy cannot ignore this

*

Lecture interrupted: across the screens of our devices the Tyrant announces
 plans for what he's named New City to be built over environments
 now lost
New City, he explains, is to be built frugally and fitted out with virtual-reality
 skins
Behind him shimmers an amalgamation of cityscapes: Singapore, Tokyo,
 Dubai, New York, Rome
Crime-free, he promises, disease-free
Meanwhile across the remaining old cities carbaryl, acutely toxic, will
 continue to be sprayed ridding all gardens of aphids, fire ants, fleas,
 ticks, spiders
The announcement ends with the Tyrant taking as had Napoleon Bonaparte
 the bee *volant en arrière* as his insignia

Not until much later, the Philosopher says when I visit the elder home, will
 we understand what it means to have seen the last of the deer

*

Prior to philosophy I went looking for the sea's blind gash but found the
 horizon to be a brown haze, marine layer refusing dissipation
I found roses dusted with sulfur as bees are woven into wall hangings,
 carpets, upholstery fabrics

Karla Kelsey

"I," then, not pointing to a specific physical or spiritual object, but to
    frameworks within which our experience might be described
And then waking to find my abdomen slightly furred

*

While nobody seems to remember the invention of virtual-reality skins
    we are certain they had been at first a mere fad for changing
    the view
An instance of *if only*, satellite dishes and clotheslines exchanged for the sea
    but the announcement of New City reveals the fact that "I," when
    searched for, has yet to be found

We continue to admire the flowers, quietly bury the birds by the shed
Failing bee colonies, we learn, have been reinvigorated by nano drones
    fitted out with strips of fuzz made from horsehair paintbrushes

A nano drone taken into the body will allow the Tyrant to map his subjects
    from the inside out

*

What is artifice if not a beckoning device the Philosopher proposes,
    turning his back on the activity room's screen and so persuasive
    with his aquiline nose, shock-white hair
Mapping provided by nano drones now connects the body with virtual reality
    by hijacking not only the reptile brain and prefrontal cortex, but
    the entire bodily system

Love capable of taking the bee into the mouth
Love a struggle for power and pleasure within a globalized grid
Love regardless of theory you become it and it becomes you

For an entire season the public gardens hold nothing but deadheaded roses,
    android deer sighted in the courtyard of the elder home
I-am-I we know with certainty but what does it mean to believe this

*

Carbaryl disrupts the insect's nervous system until it fails this is certain
Cicadas in the grass tremoring this is certain

140

The Philosopher writing what the Philosopher is given to write but
  heightened by the elder home
This is certain, a softened overripe pear
Bringing to the Philosopher instead of the supermarket's bouquet of multi-
  colored carnations a small box of foil-wrapped chocolates although
  the Philosopher had always disdained sweets
Collecting bee specimen from deep in the forest after heavy rain does not
  ensure a natural sample
Teaching my students his earliest texts

There were no, I say to him, real flowers left

*

The Philosopher writing his last text, his death text, his American text on
  certainty we had not been surprised
The Philosopher quoting history's largest industrial accident, thirty tons
  of poisonous gas produced in the manufacture of carbaryl leaks
  from Union Carbide's pesticide plant to its surrounding shantytown
  in Bhopal, India 1984
The Philosopher extending aesthetics in recognition of the immediate death
  of 2,259 followed by thousands more

Hollyhocks programmed into the wallpaper slightly breathe flaunting, we
  might go so far as to say, our uselessness
The West Coast overtaken by drought and then fire then flood
The Tyrant inviting us to imagine the architectural wonders of New York,
  Dubai, Beijing, Shanghai, Tokyo projected over simple steel and
  concrete constructions
We know objectively the assertion "I am here" might at any moment end

What we had so recently asserted burnt clear by the fires of doubt

*

Let us meditate on the precarity of I-am-I
After all, one simply is or is not
The bees taken from the freezer and dried have of course already expired
For example, the Philosopher says, let us revisit our favorite scenario:
  likely your father had held the back of the bike steady as you learned
  to ride

This now, if it exists, exists as a little home movie of the mind, California
    light cast over the drive, a specimen captive behind glass what is there
    to say of this
Carbaryl had been discovered and developed in the 1950s by Union Carbide,
    a chemical and polymers company whose products become paints
    and coatings, packaging, wire and cable, household products,
    personal care products, products for the pharmaceutical, automotive,
    textile, agriculture, oil, and gas industries
Pliable branches secured to the ground by nylon ratchet straps

Let us appreciate how very far we have come, the Tyrant says, from the vision
    of virtual reality administering only the dense flight or fight of porn
    and gaming
Separating out the natural from the artificial and then adding the natural
    specimens to the wasps and winged ants pinned to agar

*

And then the Philosopher struggling out of his heavy beekeeping jacket
    says into my recording device: the phrase "I know" falls short when
    confronted by this landscape's limestone masses because approached
    from the east they become the bodies of semiabstracted sculpture,
    abandoned kouroi lounging in a meadow just beginning to flower
Union Carbide producing not only common household products but also
    the Bhopal disaster, Hawks Nest Tunnel disaster, Calidria chrysotile
    asbestos lodged in the lungs
I tap play and he says *the phrase "I know" falls short when confronted by*
    and I tap stop and drag the recording back and I tap play and he says
    the phrase "I know" and I tap stop and drag the recording back and
    I tap play

*

You have a choice, the Tyrant says across the screens of our devices, to see
    the world as everyone else now sees, augmented by virtual-reality skins,
    or to persist in seeing the world alone, as only you see it, dry and brown
    with infrequent patches of blue and green
The question of creation amplified by the fact that we cannot say for certain
    vulnerability had been intended
The Philosopher's kouroi in actuality perhaps mere boulders, perhaps
    mastodon bones, perhaps concrete blocks

I promise, the Tyrant says, you will never choose a return to the quotidian

The West Coast by drought and then fire and then flood and then drought
    rendered uninhabitable and so designated by the Tyrant as a field
    for nuclear testing

A return to the quotidian, the Tyrant suggests with a wry smile, might
    become an alternative form of prison
If collecting bees directly off flowers beware the defense line of the sting,
    throat and abdomen unprotected by bone

*

New City, the Tyrant's officials have announced, is to be built in the
    country's former heartland
We no longer say out loud the word *California*
Greek kouroi sculpture, the Philosopher had revealed in one of his earliest
    texts, arises out of Egyptian sculpture shifting from two dimensions
    to three, from surface to volume, from symmetry to studied anatomy,
    stasis to movement
Poppies much larger than your hand are no longer mere physical objects
    but have become a symbol for the absence of balance
The Tyrant owning location, contractors, building materials
Oregon also unspoken
For certainty is, as it were, a matter of tone
Greek artists worked stone into fragile detail, for example the circa 510 BCE
    Aristodikos kouros has a refined hairstyle, star-patterned pubic hair,
    modeled torso, freestanding arms
In the absence of roses to both hate and love who you become in the rose-
    print dress

Found in over 160 insecticide products carbaryl is commonly sprayed on
    commercial crops such as corn, soybean, cotton, citrus, pear and
    is also applied in suburban yard and garden settings because
    particularly useful in raising and maintaining ornamental and shade
    trees
Washington also lost
The Tyrant owning virtual-reality technology

The sky injected with intoxicating shades of American Beauty, Coral Dawn,
    Blush China

Karla Kelsey

*

The Tyrant's investigation into spring cabbage infested by an angular cascade
    of beetles leads to an increase of mandated insecticide
New City intended to gloss over the heartland's loss not only of agriculture,
    but also of natural resource extraction and manufacturing industry
From the Philosopher's window in the elder home: a garden fitted out with
    a weeping willow and a little wrought-iron table and chair
A promise that New City will be not only disease-free but free, the Tyrant
    says, of all undesirables
Or the projected image of a garden fitted out with a weeping willow, table and
    chair, sweating pitcher of iced tea, and the remembered certainty of once
    training heather over a portico
Recent studies show that carbaryl's synthetic chemicals interact with human
    melatonin receptors, disrupting circadian rhythms and thus raising
    the risk of diabetes and other metabolic diseases

With the slight twist of the head developed in the celebrated contrapposto of
    Polyclitus the direct frontal gaze the Egyptian figure had previously
    exchanged with its viewer had been broken
As if in panic plants grow so fast now, overtaking the greenhouse in over-
    abundance
Hewn, hewn from earth

What can be thought while sitting next to the Philosopher as he stares for
    what feels like hours into the garden of the elder home
My hands are my hands, my breath my breath, and the dusky scent of violets

Tap play and silence and tap stop

*

A silver gelatin print of the Pacific, the Philosopher says, depicts nothing
    but water, light, and air, yet its metallic weight references the eight
    million tons of plastics dumped into the ocean each year
References the coastline flooded, fields droughted out
We speak about experience as it manifests through the body and try but
    cannot succeed in translating ourselves into abstract systems
The spine, for example, akin to a cairn of stones, relies on the sacrum to
    establish balance

144

Karla Kelsey

Loose sand and agricultural toxins cycloning over the basin
By "lost" we mean "completely uninhabitable"

First one university will be closed, the Tyrant promises, and then another
    and another
Catastrophic shifts framed with familiarity illegible to the remaining birds
    who plummet into the windows of skyscrapers, planes
Projected on the activity-room wall: fireworks illuminating the Bay of Naples,
    Vesuvius quiet in the background as the Philosopher confesses he
    now rarely sleeps

The sea has birthed a desert, the desert has birthed a valley, a valley of glass

You become it and it becomes you
So little organic flora remains, so little organic fauna
What is the self, the Philosopher says, but another body soon lost

Think of It
Quincy Troupe

think of frogs boiling in brown water when
watching people sweat in hot spaces
while walking through blow torch streets
in concrete cities all over the globe
because head in the sand climate denial exists,

you might wonder what it is all about
burning to death while sleeping, or swimming
in lakes, or oceans where there are no fish,
or making love with windows thrown open
& hear no singing birds when climaxes come

causing men & women to scream with joy,
or caught singing somewhere out in a meadow,
trembling, removed from sizzling asphalt & bricks,
people dozing here in quiet, saccharine moods,
trees fluttering green heads above, kissing sweet,

wind tongues licking honeyed flesh, lathering
scorched cheeks—this can be rare because many
only think of stashing blood money away
because life is beating hearts—not gizzards—
it means loving trees, flowers, animals trapped

in forest fires, tribal people, birds, saving fish
baking in deep hot lakes, polluted cauldrons
filled with skulls, teeth, bones, fingers, arms & legs
littered over these unreal lunar moonscapes—
graveyard sea bottoms—holding unforgiving

memories in pits of our human depravity revealed,
signals no remorse here in empty holes of eye sockets
looking up into space through clouds of dust
after volcanic eruptions shook worlds
when skies clouded over with cinders of ash,

falling stones splashing into lakes race toward
boats fleeing whirlpooling waves full of screaming
survivors, all of this carries unanswered questions—
is this the reckoning we all must face now,
when thinking of how our bones will reveal

themselves in the future, inside texts of history,
books, where metaphors are created from bullet holes,
armies marching to war because of religious faith,
when the choices are whether to write sentences
evoking poetry filled with music, love,

dreaded voices of sacred spirits, voodoo priests,
musicians creating holy rhythms we dance to—
what are the questions we must raise now, are they
washed in genius colors from brushstrokes of painters,
portraits of what our bones will reveal in the future?

think of them now, those bone-chilling questions,
when you look out across the world, bend your vision
& look around mountains curving through space,
with your lens wide open, holding no malice, then
pray for clarity, dream, hope you see beauty there

Once Out of Nature
Troy Jollimore

> Judging from the past, we may safely infer that
> not one living species will transmit its unaltered
> likeness to a distant futurity. And of the species
> now living very few will transmit progeny of any
> kind to a far distant futurity; for the manner in
> which all organic beings are grouped, shows that
> the greater number of species of each genus, and
> all the species of many genera, have left no de-
> scendants, but have become utterly extinct.
>
> —Charles Darwin, On the Origin of Species

> But I will not weary the reader with useless en-
> thusiasms for obliterated pictures or smashed
> churches or shattered towers and palaces or
> rubble-choked streets. If they are gone, they are
> gone; and there is no use in making people un-
> happy by saying that they have forever lost beau-
> tiful things.
>
> —Richard Aldington, A Wreath for
> San Gemignano

ATMOSPHERE OF GEMS

JOHN JAMES AUDUBON'S ILLUSTRATION of the Carolina parakeet
depicts seven of the birds. One for each day of the week or, if you
prefer, one for each of the seven wonders of the ancient world, the
seven deadly sins, or for each color of the rainbow. One, whose head
is green more or less all over, is a juvenile. The rest, the adults, have
green bodies and yellow heads. (The Seminole people referred to the
Carolina parakeet as "puzzi la née," or "head of yellow.") On each
little yellow head there is a masklike patch of red covering most of
the face. One can't help but be struck both by the bright, toylike
colors—the birds look as if they have been painted in a factory for
children to play with—and by the mischievous expressions on the
feathered faces. They look as if they are smiling. This is not gratu-
itous anthropomorphization on the artist's part; they look this way
in photographs too. They are also said to be social and quite lively,

148

even raucous—again, all of this comes across in the illustration. The parakeet on the bottom of Audubon's picture is staring directly at us. A challenge? An invitation?

How many people in the United States are aware that there used to be a parrot species native to their country, and that until the late nineteenth century large flocks of these colorful birds could be found in swamps and bottomlands of the southeastern and midwestern United States, from Florida to parts of Texas and Colorado, and as far north as Pennsylvania in the East and Nebraska in the West, with occasional sightings in Michigan, New York State, and elsewhere? They were particularly numerous in Florida, where the more colorful subspecies *Conuropsis carolinensis carolinensis* was centered, though the bird's range extended along the coast in both directions. The slightly less vividly colored subspecies, *Conuropsis carolinensis ludovicianus*, was found farther to the north and west. Both the *carolinensis* and the *ludovicanus* disappeared completely some decades ago. The last captive Carolina parakeet died in the Cincinnati Zoo in 1918, in the same cage where Martha, the last captive passenger pigeon, had expired four years before. The last wild Carolina parakeet passed away some time after that. It is not known precisely where or when.

The parakeet's beauty had been remarked on for centuries by explorers and settlers. William Strachey's *The Historie of Travell into Virginia Britania*, published in 1612, which gathers observations from many early settlers of the mid-Atlantic Coast, includes the following passage: "Parakitoes I haie seen many in the Winter and knowne divers killed, yet be they a Fowle most swift of wing, their winges and Breasts are of a greenish colour with forked Tayles, their heades some Crmysen, some yellow, some orange-tawny, very beautyfull."

"The parakeet is a beautiful bird," Henry R. Schoolcraft wrote in an 1819 publication, *A View of the Lead Mines of Missouri*. "It is a kind of parrot; its colours are green, yellow, and red, all bright colours, and it is a pleasing sight to see a flock of them suddenly wheel in the atmosphere, and light upon a tree; their gaudy colours are reflected in the sun with a brilliance of the rainbow."

"We have seen no bird of the size, with plumage so brilliant," wrote the minister Timothy Flint a few years later, "and they impart a singular magnificence to the forest prospect, as they are seen darting through the foliage, and among the white branches of the sycamore." Around the same time, the soldier and adventurer Alphonso Wetmore wrote, "The paroquet found in Missouri deserves notice, as peculiar in character and attractive in its plumage. This is a bird strongly resembling the green parrot in colour and form; and it is reported of them, that at night they repose within the cavity of a hollow tree, hanging by their curved Roman nose-beaks."

Longer than a Man's Lifetime in Missouri, an 1877 autobiography by Gert Goebel, a German settler in eastern Missouri, contains the following evocative description:

> These flocks of paroquets were a real ornament to the trees stripped of their foliage in the winter. The sight was particularly attractive, when such a flock of several hundred had settled on a big sycamore, when the bright green color of the birds was in such marked contrast with the white bark of the trees, and when the sun shone brightly upon these inhabited tree tops, the many yellow heads looked like so many candles.
>
> This sight always reminded me vividly of a kind of Christmas tree, which was used [in Germany] by the poorer families . . . A few weeks before Christmas a young birch tree was set in a pail of water. In the warm room it soon began to produce delicate leaves. When on Christmas eve such a tree was decorated with gilded and silvered nuts and with apples and candies, it did not look unlike one of these bird-covered tree tops, only these enormous Christmas trees of the forest looked vastly more imposing than the little birch in the warm room.

Large numbers of these living ornaments had also been encountered by Warren Angus Ferris, a trapper, cartographer, and diarist, near Franklin, Missouri, in February 1830. "Near the village," Ferris recorded, "we met with innumerable flocks of paroquets—the first I had seen in a wild state—whose beautiful plumage of green and gold flashed above us like an atmosphere of gems."

FOR LIGHT, FOR STARS, FOR RAINBOWS

> *Dear girl. They will not—it's we who do—end.*
> —David Baker, *Never-Ending Birds*

Thou wast not born for death, immortal Bird, Keats sang to his nightingale. The temptation, for poets, is so often to make birds symbols of immortality. Surely a creature that can defy gravity can also defy death. (In his program notes for *Quartet for the End of Time,*

Olivier Messiaen writes: "The abyss is time, with its weariness and gloom. The birds are the opposite of Time; they represent our longing for light, for stars, for rainbows, and for jubilant song!") So we grow up thinking of birds as analogies for the soul; for the soul too is pictured as the part of the person that defies gravity, that is immaterial and weightless. The part that flies.

There is also this: among the living things of the earth, birds are among the most beautiful. So if, like Keats, you are inclined to think that *A thing of beauty is a joy for ever*, then you are all the more likely to see the birds as permanent fixtures, an unchanging part of the natural landscape. Vibrant, animated artworks that, like the Grecian urn to which another of his odes is addressed—and, for that matter, like the ode itself—*shalt remain, in midst of other woe / Than ours.*

If the nightingale seemed immortal to Keats, it is largely because he identified it with its song, for it is the same song that is sung by one generation of nightingales after another, and heard by one generation of poets after another, who feel nearly identical emotions, perhaps, at the sound, and who find themselves moved just as their predecessors were. Contemporary biologists often speak of DNA along similar lines, as the immortal material that persists while the organic beings that carry it are born and perish. Which makes sense, really, because DNA, like a song, can be thought of primarily as information. Consider how many people these days store their music libraries "in the cloud," and how many fantasies of "de-extinction"— of reviving lost species, à la *Jurassic Park*—have been fed by this metaphorical resonance. The same resonance that convinces people we will soon be able to escape death by uploading our personalities, our memories, our very identities, into some form of data storage. We like to believe, these days, that so long as you possess the information, you can reconstitute, reanimate, the thing. Poets too die while leaving their songs behind, songs that entice us to believe they are not really dead. Keats is long gone, almost two centuries now, but we still, some of us, recite "Ode to a Nightingale" and "Ode on a Grecian Urn."

They might have been different birds, but Keats, like most of us, couldn't tell one individual nightingale from another, so it seemed to him not only that the woods were always full of birdsong, but that it was the very same birds that were singing:

151

> Thou wast not born for death, immortal Bird!
> No hungry generations tread thee down;
> The voice I hear this passing night was heard
> In ancient days by emperor and clown:
> Perhaps the self-same song that found a path
> Through the sad heart of Ruth, when, sick for home,
> She stood in tears amid the alien corn;
> The same that oft-times hath
> Charm'd magic casements, opening on the foam
> Of perilous seas, in faery lands forlorn.

You can't step into the same river twice, said Heraclitus, but for the most part the river *looks* the same, and the noise of the running water sounds the same. Until recently the default stance was to regard the natural world as a permanent and largely unchanging edifice into which human beings come to be and pass away, an enduring background against which we conduct our ephemeral, ever-changing affairs. And so Keats was persuaded, or persuaded himself, to see a kind of eternal life in "those dying generations"—to borrow a phrase from a poem by Yeats, written a little more than a century after Keats's great odes. "Sailing to Byzantium," which clearly has those odes on its mind, finds its speaker averring that, should he be offered the choice, he would never again, having suffered this mortal life, choose to occupy an organic body. Let him instead be a mechanism, something crafted and made, something that will not rot; let him be a mechanical, artificial bird, *Of hammered gold and gold enamelling / To keep a drowsy Emperor awake; / Or set upon a golden bough to sing . . .*

THE GUN IS KEPT AT WORK

"Animals first entered the imagination as messengers and promises," writes John Berger in *Ways of Seeing*. We are told that when, in the winter of 1780, a flock of Carolina parakeets landed on a house in Schoharie, New York, the local residents took it as a sign that the apocalypse was imminent. "The more ignorant Dutch settlers were exceedingly alarmed," wrote botanist and physician Benjamin Smith Barton. "They imagined, in dreadful consternation, that it portended nothing less calamitous than the destruction of the world." The incident took place, of course, during the Revolutionary War, and indeed, a year later, the building was burned to the ground by British troops.

Audubon wrote in his *Ornithological Biography* that these

Troy Jollimore

parakeets were "fond of sand in a surprising degree, and on that account are frequently seen to alight in flocks along the gravelly banks about the creeks and rivers, or in the ravines of old fields in the plantations, when they scratch with bill and claws, flutter and roll themselves in the sand, and pick up and swallow a certain quantity of it. For the same purpose, they also enter the holes dug by our Kingfisher. They are fond of saline earth, for which they visit the different Licks interspersed in our woods."

Those who described them noted their sociability and curiosity. Like other parrots, they were sometimes kept as pets—though, unlike many other parrots, the Carolina parakeet could not, or would not, learn to imitate human speech, and some, including Audubon himself, found their vocalizations irritating. They traveled in large groups and seemed to display a kind of loyalty that worked against self-preservation: many observers described how, when one was shot, others would fill the area, as if to stand with their dying comrade. Here is Audubon again:

> [T]he Parakeets are destroyed in great numbers, for whilst busily engaged in plucking off the fruits or tearing the grain from the stacks, the husbandman approaches them with perfect ease, and commits great slaughter among them. All the survivors rise, shriek, fly round about for a few minutes, and again alight on the very place of most imminent danger. The gun is kept at work; eight or ten, or even twenty, are killed at every discharge. The living birds, as if conscious of the death of their companions, sweep over their bodies, screaming as loud as ever, but still return to the stack to be shot at, until so few remain alive, that the farmer does not consider it worth his while to spend more of his ammunition. [. . .] Should a person shoot at them, as they go, and wound an individual, its cries are sufficient to bring back the whole flock, when the sportsman may kill as many as he pleases.

The explorer John K. Townsend provides a similar account from 1834, writing that the Carolina parakeets he had encountered

> seemed entirely unsuspicious of danger, and after being fired at only huddled closer together, as if to obtain protection from each other, and as their companions are falling around them, they curve down their necks and look at them fluttering upon the ground, as though perfectly at a loss to account for so unusual an occurrence. It is a most inglorious sort of shooting, downright, cold-blooded murder. . . . And so, a few men bearing arms could easily eliminate entire flocks at a time.

153

WE, ONLY, CAN SEE DEATH

. . . And, little town, thy streets for evermore / Will silent be; and not a soul to tell / Why thou art desolate, can e'er return. We find ourselves imagining different orders of being, and then asking, as if it were up to us, which we would like to belong to. As if, the poems ask us to imagine, we had the chance to choose our own fundamental natures. Reading "Sailing to Byzantium" or "Ode on a Grecian Urn," we pose to ourselves the question: to be a living thing, or a work of art? To inhabit a world of eternal silence and immateriality, or to live in the organic realm of birth, action, and death? Or perhaps it is not ourselves we are asking, but the universe. It is not *quite* as foundational as "to be or not to be," perhaps. But it is not too far off the mark.

The longing to be a work of art, and to become, in this way, immortal, runs alongside other longings, and the connections between them are always complex. Closely related is the somewhat more attainable desire—Keats, at any rate, managed to attain it—to achieve a kind of artistic immortality, through fame. *I think I shall be among the English poets after my death,* he predicted in a letter to his brother. But Keats also knew that fame would not constitute genuine immortality. And so, throughout his poems and letters, we find Keats longing to defeat mortality in a different way: to know nothing of fame and the desire for fame, to know nothing of death and the fear of death, to know nothing of mortality and the desperate human need to somehow overcome it.

"O for a Life of Sensations rather than of Thoughts!" Keats exclaimed in a letter from November 1817. Nearly two years later he writes, to his fiancée Fanny Brawne, "I almost wish we were butterflies, and liv'd but three summer days—three such days with you I could fill with more delight than fifty common years could ever contain." There is a profound contrast between this sentiment and that seemingly expressed in so many passages of "Ode on a Grecian Urn." Consider again the consoling words to the "bold lover," who is invited to accept without regret the impossibility of kissing his beloved as the inevitable cost of their eternal existence—or, for that matter, the sensibility expressed in those final lines of "Sailing to Byzantium." To be a mechanical bird rather than an organic one, as a way of sidestepping mortality and decay—the sensibility that would accept three days of butterfly delight over fifty years of human life is the opposite

154

of this, the other side of the existential coin. It attempts to solve the problem of time—which is to say, the problem of death—not by detaching from life and holding oneself in an invulnerable and immaculate space, but by plunging into life so profoundly and unreservedly that there is no detachment, no separation, no crack into which fear or knowledge or human self-consciousness might seep.

To know nothing of time, decay, or death. To know nothing of mortality, and hence nothing of immortality, either the immortality of fame or the immortality of Plato's eternal forms; this, for the Romantic poets—and for those who followed them, like Rilke—is a way of being immortal, of escaping death. In the eighth of his *Duino Elegies*, Rilke writes,

> We know what is really out there only from
> the animal's gaze; for we take the very young
> child and force it around, so that it sees
> objects—not the Open, which is so
> deep in animals' faces. Free from death.
> We, only, can see death; the free animal
> has its decline in back of it, forever,
> and God in front, and when it moves, it moves
> already in eternity, like a fountain.

It is as if humans, by virtue of their poisonous self-awareness, live in an entirely different world from the animals. As if, unlike them, we were required to wage a never-ending struggle against our own natures in order to inhabit the world at all.

IN THE CLOUD

The very idea of extinction, as fundamental as it is to the world we live in, is a relatively recent conceptual innovation. The tendency for most of Western history has been to regard the world as permanent and unchanging. In particular, the tendency in Western Christian thought to see the world as being governed by a benevolent deity posed a profound impediment to the idea, argued by Georges Cuvier and a bit later on by Darwin, that *kinds* of beings might go out of existence, just as individual organic beings do. Why would God create beautiful creatures only to allow them to pass out of the world? In "An Essay on Man," Alexander Pope had written:

155

All are but parts of one stupendous whole,
Whose body Nature is, and God the soul;

To see nature as a body is to see it as a unity, something created at one moment whose habit is to stay together, remain constant, and preserve a fundamental integrity; not as something that changes form, that loses parts and grows new ones—as something, that is, that evolves. A central element of the intellectual revolution achieved by Darwin was to replace the body metaphor with a different one, the metaphor of nature as family. "When I view all beings not as special creations, but as the lineal descendants of some few beings which lived long before the first bed of the Cambrian system was deposited," he wrote, "they seem to me to become ennobled." Families, after all, are constantly losing members and replacing them with new ones. Moreover, there would have been a natural link in the Victorian mind between the word "extinction" and the idea of the family: until Cuvier came along, the English term "extinction" had mostly been used in connection with royal or noble lineages that had died out or were in danger of doing so. Still, the idea that biological lineages—species—could also die out was bound to upset the Victorian view of the universe as an orderly, well-run machine. Darwin, while admitting that "Neither single species nor groups of species reappear when the chain of ordinary generation has once been broken," softened the impact of this intellectual blow by placing a positive spin on the idea of extinction, viewing it as a kind of hygienic process, a way of making space for what he liked to refer to, in a phrase redolent of mid-twentieth-century advertising lingo, as "new and improved" versions of life: "The extinction of species and of whole groups of species, which has played so conspicuous a part in the history of the organic world, almost inevitably follows on the principle of natural selection; for old forms will be supplanted by new and improved forms." He quite famously—and wrongly—went on to write, "As natural selection works solely by and for the good of each being, all corporeal and mental endowments will tend to progress towards perfection." A comforting thought.

The Carolina parakeet, though, does not seem to have been done away with in order to be replaced by a "new and improved" version, and it is difficult to see its disappearance as part of a process whose general tendency is toward any form of perfection. These beautiful birds were shot in large numbers for many reasons or for no reason at all. Some farmers regarded them as pests that laid waste to fields of grain. Others killed them for sport, or for their feathers, which adorned fashionable ladies' hats. Scientists shot them, or had them shot, to be preserved and serve as specimens. It is likely, though, that the shooting, as widespread and unnecessary as it seems to have been, had less of an impact than the loss of habitat caused by human activity—a common narrative in many extinctions. Other factors too played a role. The honeybee, for instance, often builds its nests in hollow trees, the same nesting sites preferred by the Carolina parakeet. (Then again, we humans are implicated here too, since honeybees first came to North America on ships departing from Europe.) Although they persisted into the twentieth century, their numbers began precipitously to decline by the middle of the nineteenth century, early enough that Audubon himself, along with many others, commented on the rapidity of their diminishment.

NOW MORE THAN EVER SEEMS IT RICH TO DIE

From a certain austere ontological perspective, preferred by some who consider themselves scientifically minded (and who understand science itself in a certain austere way), there are no collectives, only individuals. But individuals are parts of collectives, and are shaped by collectives, and the nature of individual memory can make it meaningful, at least in the case of human beings, to speak of collective memory. Such memory is forged and passed on through culture: we write things down, we pass knowledge, concepts, and stories along to those who come after. We tell our children what they will need to know in order to live well, and we tell them too about what the world was like for us. Few of us, though, have been told about the Carolina parakeet. We have not heard much, in fact, about the dimensions of the world that have been lost through the years, the treasures our ancestors gave up, sacrificed, inadvertently destroyed, or merely allowed to slip away. Were there more birds in our parents' skies, more birdsong in the trees of our grandparents' childhoods, than in our own? (I seem to remember there being more birdsong in the trees of *my* childhood—but memory, of course, can be misleading.) How often have we been told that our parents, or their parents, occupied a country in which there was "an atmosphere of gems"? When it comes to loss, we seem to display not collective memory but collective amnesia.

157

In other ways, though, collective knowledge and memory make an awareness of loss available to us. We know, for instance, that we are going to die, and that before we die we will likely suffer. And this is something we would not necessarily figure out on our own; if a human being is the creature who knows that he will die, it is very often because he has learned this from other human beings. It is through language that most of us learn that we are mortal. But if not for language we would have no way to manifest our longings and laments.

Keats's desire for fame—which he saw as, in its own way, a means of achieving a kind of immortality, and hence a way of solving the problem of death—was nothing other than a desire to become an enduring part of human culture, to be passed on the way lasting memories are passed on. Not knowing about death would be a way of not caring about fame. It would mean not having to worry about whether one's work is likely to endure, not having to worry about whether one's life is "meaningful." From such a vantage point it is natural to conceive of animal consciousness—the kind of consciousness it is natural, from this vantage point, to aspire to—as a state in which one would possess no standards of meaning, in which one would not, and would not want to, know the meaning of anything.

It often seems that for these poets to not know the meaning of anything would be, in the deepest sense, to know the meaning of everything. As Rilke writes in the seventh Duino elegy:

> O to be dead at last and know them eternally,
> all the stars: for how, how, how to forget them!

That is to say, it is a short step from longing for a kind of animal consciousness in which one is entirely unaware of death to longing for death itself. As if death were pure and life impure, and thus—this is a thought we find lurking at a very deep level in both Platonic philosophy and Christianity—death could be seen as the ideal culmination, the true fruition, of everything life aspired to be. A theme that emerges clearly in "Ode to a Nightingale," whose speaker identifies thought with pain (*Where but to think is to be full of sorrow / And leaden-eyed despairs*), idealizes animal awareness as a mode of being that is free from such pain (*Fade far away, dissolve, and quite forget / What thou among the leaves hast never known, / The weariness, the fever, and the fret . . .*), and—perhaps despairing of the possibility that we might ever become like the animals in this way—ends up, inevitably, desiring death:

Now more than ever seems it rich to die,
To cease upon the midnight with no pain,
While thou art pouring forth thy soul abroad
In such an ecstasy!

FAMOUS LAST BIRDS

"Civilization does not agree with these birds," ornithologist and groundbreaking oologist Charles Bendire commented in 1895. We probably should not be surprised that this is so, given what we know about how our civilization has turned out, about what it appears to value. Beauty, it seems, is not high on its list of priorities. Consider the strip mall: such a fabulously, radically ugly thing, it is somewhat hard to believe that its existence is even tolerated, let alone that people deliberately construct them, and pour considerable resources into doing so. But to complain about the ugliness of the strip mall is not merely to reveal yourself as an anachronistic romantic, it is to identify yourself as an enemy of progress, and perhaps of democracy itself. To acknowledge, perhaps even to admire, the utilitarian genius and inarguable convenience of the strip mall is part of the ideological imperative of our times. Whereas it is permissible, indeed encouraged, to have no deep or abiding interest in beauty at all.

"How could we have lost, and then forgotten, so beautiful a bird?" asks Christopher Cokinos, author of *Hope Is the Thing with Feathers: A Personal Chronicle of Vanished Birds*. But it makes a difference who the *we* is—whether we are talking about the memory of individuals or rather have in mind that necessary but mysterious concept, *collective* memory. The collective *we*—we Americans, we inhabitants of this country—have indeed displaced, hence lost, and then forgotten, the Carolina parakeet. Having driven it out of existence, we have not preserved a niche, in the shared space of our memory, that it might inhabit. As for individual humans, most of those who exist now did not have the chance to forget the Carolina parakeet. They—we—never got to see them. A few of us have viewed pictures of them, or encountered preserved specimens, little stuffed exemplars stored in drawers and cataloged like books; almost no living humans have enjoyed the sight of them in the trees, in the skies, or on fields of wheat, which, as Audubon wrote in his *Ornithological Biography*, they "frequently cover . . . so entirely, that they present

159

to the eye the same effect as if a brilliantly coloured carpet had been thrown over them."

One way to go on, at this point, would be to list the species that we, if we are lucky, have gotten to observe for ourselves, but which our descendants will not have the chance to see, and therefore will not have the chance to forget. I could list the magical, majestic species that are, even as I write, even as you read, heading toward oblivion. But what point is there in making people unhappy by telling them that they have lost, and are losing, beautiful things?

Perhaps, then, I should instead follow Lewis Hyde's lead in his recent book, *A Primer for Forgetting*, where he suggests that

> if forgetting is a fall into birth and time, then a pure, triumphant memory will mean an end to emerging life and a fixing of time, everything stuck just where it is (stuck, we might say, in those eternal, unchanging forms). . . . True, when time flows, we are in the world of sickness, old age, and death, but we are also in the world of fertility, new life, and fresh action, and it is these that call for an allowed forgetting.

Memory, here, is linked with the stasis of the designs on Keats's urn, frozen figures incapable of "fertility, new life, and fresh action." Bury the urn—or break it—and we free ourselves from the past. But of course it matters in what order we arrange the ideas. Hyde's sentence would have had an entirely different impact if he had written: "True, when time flows, we are in the world of fertility, new life, and fresh action; but we are also in the world of sickness, old age, and death."

At any rate I do not wish to allow myself, or any of us, to forget the Carolina parakeet. So let us remind ourselves once again that the last captive Carolina parakeets, a pair named Incas and Lady Jane, lived in the Cincinnati Zoo, in the same space in which the last captive passenger pigeon, Martha, had recently lived, and died. Lady Jane perished first, in 1917; Incas endured for a few months longer. According to Anita Albus in *On Rare Birds*, Incas's body was supposed to be shipped to Washington, DC, to be autopsied and stuffed by staff at the Smithsonian, as had been done with Martha and Lady Jane. But the body, preserved in a block of ice, disappeared at some point on the journey and was never found. Is it possible that the disappearance of Incas is at least partly responsible for the fact that Martha, and the species she represented, have endured in our collective memory in a way that the last Carolina parakeets—who were, after all, considerably more beautiful than the rather drab passenger pigeon—have not?

All of the dates are questionable. In his 2004 book, *The Carolina Parakeet: Glimpses of a Vanished Bird*, Noel Snyder describes how he spent years interviewing elderly residents of Florida, many of whom remembered seeing Carolina parakeets. It is clear, from these interviews, that Incas was far from the last of the breed; the Carolina parakeet survived at least into the 1930s in Florida, and possibly into the 1940s. There is at least some small chance that tiny populations of the bird might have survived for years after that, like squads of resistance fighters hiding out in the hills. For Snyder, the Carolina parakeet functions as a symbol of a multitude of losses, including the loss of a certain vision of our country, and of ways of life that few now remember. In his elegiac introduction to *The Carolina Parakeet*—a book that presents, alongside the stories of a vanished bird, stories of the kinds of people who have vanished just as decisively from the American landscape: swamp guides, moonshiners, plume hunters, alligator trappers, egg collectors—he writes:

> The era when residents freely roamed an unfenced Kissimmee Prairie in search of abundant wild game has long passed, and an era of no-trespassing signs, housing developments, fast-food diners, and parking lots has taken its place. No vote was ever taken for launching these changes, and perhaps there are many who would have opposed them if given the chance. Others, who regret what has been lost, know as well that there is no way to return.

REMARKS ON COLOR

> *Until in the bird everything becomes a little more apprehensive and more cautious. His nest is already a little maternal womb made secure for him by Nature, which he only covers instead of wholly containing it. And suddenly, as if it were no longer safe enough outside, the wonderful maturing flees wholly into the darkness of the creature and emerges only at a later turn into the world, taking it only as a second world and never again to become quite weaned from the conditions of the earlier, more fervent one.*
>
> —Rilke, from a letter to Lou Andreas-Salomé, February 20, 1918

The fragment quoted above was written by Rilke the day before the last Carolina parakeet in captivity passed away, an event widely—

albeit incorrectly—viewed as the end of the species. Rilke would of course not have known what was about to happen thousands of miles away in the Cincinnati Zoo, and I have no clear idea what "the bird" referred to in this fragment meant to him or is supposed to represent. Nor do I really know what he means in referring to "a second world." Somehow, though, his use of the phrase makes me think of something the philosopher Alexander Nehamas once wrote, that beauty "is part of the everyday world of purpose and desire, history and contingency, subjectivity and incompleteness. That is the only world there is, and nothing, not even the highest of the high arts, can move beyond it."

And this, in turn, makes me think of the passage in an essay by poet Robert Hass on Wallace Stevens—in a discussion of Stevens's "Domination of Black," a poem of three stanzas whose first and third stanzas end with the line "And I remembered the cry of the peacocks"—in which Hass notes that as a child, first discovering the poem, he somehow failed to connect the central auditory image of the peacock's cry to the actual peacock cries he had heard. "Art hardly ever does seem to come to us at first as something connected to our own world," Hass writes. "It always seems, in fact, to announce the existence of another, different one, which is what it shares with gnostic insight. That is why, I suppose, the next thing that artists have to learn is that this world is the other world."

That this world is the other world. One single world, but a world thought of in two ways, a world seen from two points of view. One single world that can look to us, for all the world, like two. As Zhuangzi says, "If you were to hide the world in the world, so that nothing could get away, this would be the final reality of the constancy of things."

So that nothing could get away. Whereas what we seem to be surrounded with, instead, is countless, relentless proofs of the inconstancy of things. Which we, collectively, decide to ignore, even forget, in order that we may continue to live and enjoy the fact that we exist in the world.

If this world *is* the other world, then there is only this world, and no other. But each species, each creature, perceives the world differently, so that there are many worlds within the one, each with its own colors, noises, tastes. Tastes we humans cannot taste; colors we humans cannot see. Tastes, noises, and colors we can only imagine, or perhaps cannot imagine. The lines quoted from Rilke's eighth Duino elegy encapsulate a strong version of this: "We know what is

162

really out there only from / the animal's gaze." As if animals could see reality while humans cannot. We could, if we were not willing to go quite this far, assert a modified version of the idea: animals see a world we cannot see. And it follows from this that when an animal goes extinct, a world is lost. *Esse is percipi,* said the philosopher George Berkeley. To be is to be perceived. So when the Carolina parakeet went extinct, the world lost two sets of colors: those displayed on its feathers, and those the world displayed to its eyes.

"A color 'shines' in its surroundings," proposed Wittgenstein in *Remarks on Colour.* "(Just as eyes only smile in a face.)"

"The spirit has no voice," wrote Leonardo da Vinci, "because where there is voice there is body."

Suppose that Incas had indeed been the last of his kind. He would not have known that this was so. Unlike his human tenders and observers he presumably would not even have been able to form the thought, or wonder whether he was in fact the last, or to believe, or lament, that he was. It is highly doubtful that parakeets have a concept of "our kind" that is anything like the human concept so familiar to us. Nor would they have a concept of extinction. Extinction, like death, is a human concept.

What the parakeets had, in place of the concept of extinction, was a cry that was sufficient to bring back the whole flock, back to the place where the guns were being kept at work. Do we, in our catalog of laments, possess anything comparable?

"Every scheme for the analysis of nature has to face these two facts, *change* and *endurance,*" writes Alfred North Whitehead in *Science and the Modern World*:

> There is yet a third fact to be placed by it, *eternality*, I will call it. The mountain endures. But when after ages it has been worn away, it has gone. If a replica arises, it is yet a new mountain. A color is eternal. It haunts time like a spirit. It comes and it goes. But where it comes, it is the same color. It neither survives nor does it live. It appears when it is wanted.

Another comforting thought. But "wanted" is too optimistic: no matter how much we might want to see again the colors of the Carolina parakeet, they will not come. They continue to exist, perhaps, in some immaterial realm, the realm that contains eternal things, the things that haunt time like spirits. This is how they remain the same, by existing outside of space and time, neither surviving nor living, so that, "where it comes, it is the same color." But

Troy Jollimore

this realm is only the realm of the imagination. Even Keats's Grecian urn is a material thing that exists in time and will someday end, like DNA, like preserved specimens of birds, like photographs. Like the memories that are encoded in our very organic, very material brains, that we may struggle to preserve or endeavor to forget. Like a mountain, an urn may strike us as monumental, as permanent, but it too has its life, its narrative, its death. Just as we are learning to see the ocean, the atmosphere, the planet itself as temporal and finite, entities with their own lives, their narratives, their deaths. It is the realm that the urn depicts, not the urn itself, that is eternal. But that depicted realm does not exist. It only fools us, by allowing us to depict it, into believing that it does.

Who, if I cried out, would hear me, among the parakeet orders? What cries now would be sufficient to bring back those flocks? To repopulate our sycamores with living ornaments, their little yellow heads flaring "like so many candles"? For this world—*Where but to think is to be full of sorrow*—is the other world. A creature extinct in this world is extinct in every world. Once out of nature, it shall never again take any form, assume any body, whatsoever.

Thou wast not born for death, immortal Bird! But the atmosphere of this world is no atmosphere of gems.

In the Mist of Everything
Hilary Leichter

SHIRA THOUGHT SHE WOULD BUY furniture for the bedroom first.
Kevin made attempts at saving his garden. Doreen pushed the dough
down with the heel of her hand. Gabriel tried a new yoga pose.
Cynthia and Steve went for a drive. Toby said, The weather is just
great. Marybeth wore the same dress two days in a row. Adelaide
thought, I've ruined my weave. Polly had no one to take her home.
Boris wanted the job terribly much. Cynthia and Steve went for a
drive, even though the weather was no longer in their favor.

Shira bought a vanity for the alcove by her window. Kevin tried
something called Weed Nevermore. Doreen could smell the contents
of the oven from the couch. Something slipped in Gabriel's neck.
Cynthia and Steve made a wrong turn. Toby said, What do I look like,
a meteorologist? Marybeth said, Oh, what the hell, and wore the dress
for a third day. Adelaide pulled her hair over one shoulder in an exas-
perated swoop, leaving the other shoulder bare. Adelaide's girlfriend
thought Adelaide looked like a perfect mermaid just then. Polly's
phone was dead, and in this great new age, she did not remember
how to ask strangers for directions. Boris's interview lasted seven
minutes. Cynthia and Steve ended up somewhere unexpected. They
peered out the windows of their car and did not recognize the street.

Shira assembled the vanity herself, filling the drawers with pretty
little accoutrements, loose buttons and broken beads. Kevin accidentally sprayed his dog with the pesticide, then washed the dog with
a hose, drowning the edges of the garden. Why won't anything grow,
he cried, and his dog pawed at the barren flower bed. Doreen wrote a
note to go with the loaf of bread, and she used her favorite pen. She
wrote a rough draft on the back of some junk mail, and then wrote
the final letter in cursive. Gabriel called for help, but the Zumba
class could not hear him. Cynthia and Steve asked Polly if she knew
how to get back to the main road. Toby checked the weather again,
consulting several sources. No one could agree on the timing of certain events: rain, sun, wind. There had once been hourly predictions
for every earthly spray or shine. Marybeth tore the dress on a sharp

fang of railing. Adelaide's girlfriend squeezed behind her on the couch, wrapping a leg around her on either side. Polly thought Cynthia and Steve looked harmless enough, but they also seemed bewildered and sad. Their sadness made her feel scared. I can't help you, she shrugged. The secretary told Boris that he would hear back by the end of the day. Cynthia said, Get in, we can give you a ride. Polly looked like a version of Cynthia that wasn't Cynthia anymore.

Shira sat at the vanity and looked in the mirror, the lines on her face so apparent in the ruinous sun. She limped the vanity over to the far corner, by the closet. Kevin was flat on his back asleep in the grass, his dog perched on his chest. Doreen let the bread cool on the counter before wrapping it in cloth and tying the twine. Gabriel was flat on his back in the gym. He slid his way to the treadmills, wondering if he would be feeling better by evening. Cynthia and Steve received a message from Gabriel, canceling their evening plans. Toby's friends told him they would go to the beach, rain or no rain. Toby expressed concern, but the topic had already changed to swimsuits and coolers of cold drinks. Marybeth did not own another appropriate dress. This was the only one that fit her right now, in this moment. She fingered the huge rip in the front of the fabric. Adelaide said to Marybeth, Maybe we can lend you one? But Adelaide and her girlfriend were smooth and thin, as light as scarves tossed over a bannister. Marybeth collected the emergency cash from under her bed and went shopping alone. Adelaide and her girlfriend watched two movies in a row and read magazines while wearing fuzzy socks. The day had grown cold and wet, and their feet searched for other feet, heels comforting toes. Polly sat in the back seat while Cynthia and Steve drove around and looked for her house. Their phones had died too. In fact, everyone's phones were dead. Boris plugged his phone into the wall of the coffee shop, hoping to receive good news about the job. But his phone's battery was a glass that would not fill. Steve knew they shouldn't have gone for a drive, what with the news they had just received. Good that Gabriel had canceled their plans. But now this girl in their back seat, and with the weather getting worse.

Shira dismantled the vanity and put it back in the box, with a return label. What was she doing, pretending to be happy? She wondered if Boris was happy, if he had settled into his new life across the country. Did you get the job, she wanted to text him, but Shira restrained herself. And, anyway, her phone was dead, and her daughter Polly was running late. Kevin's dog ate the rotten garden, so that his Kevin could start over with a new garden in the morning. In his furry snout he smelled something worse than mulch, something worse than his Kevin's shoes. Something bad. He put his nose deep in the soil for evidence of what dogs already know. Kevins were always spoiling the unspoilable: earth, sky, treats, trails. Doreen brought the bread to Gabriel. Gabriel could not move from his chair, not yet, but she knew where he hid the keys. Next door, she petted Kevin's dog, and the dog ran from Kevin to Doreen, yelped at her ankles, a crazed look of warning in his eyes. Gabriel said, Doreen, and she had always loved the way her name sounded wearing his voice, the way he had no nickname for her. She put the bread on the table and cut him a slice. Toby stood on the beach, separate from his friends. There was something happening to the waves, their edges dissolving into the horizon, the same color as the sky. Marybeth found a dress that was more of a sack. She turned around twice and changed back into her weekend jeans. When she went to pay for the dress, the cloth felt damp in her hands. Adelaide and her girlfriend fucked on the couch, hoping Marybeth would not walk in. Everything on the couch was wet, but at that moment, it didn't seem strange. When Adelaide spooned her girlfriend afterward, she saw it: specks of water in the air, all around them. Look, she said! How beautiful! The specks of liquid collided in the light from the standing lamp, until they merged into something larger than specks. Polly banged her head when the street filled with water. The car started to float, then sink. Boris put his palm up to the sky and the fog hit him like a brick. When Cynthia received the diagnosis, she thought, Things can't get any worse. But things can always get worse, she now remembered, the car turning sideways and Steve beside her, struggling with the door.

Shira stood at the window and could not believe the outside finally matched her insides. Had she turned the world into a mirror? Kevin's dog choked on the new atmosphere, and Kevin tried to calm him. He was still flat on his back in the grass, terrified, looking up at a sky that had somehow descended. Doreen tried to carry Gabriel to the second floor, not even realizing that she was finally holding him. Gabriel kept saying it's OK, it's OK, it's OK. Cynthia and Steve lifted Polly to the roof of the car. Toby saw his friends for a final moment before the waves swallowed them whole. They were frozen that way in his mind, like a magazine advertisement, until he was swallowed a moment later. Marybeth tried to call Adelaide but her phone was dead. She felt her body start to, what, evaporate? She felt slight and slim, and ill. Adelaide and her girlfriend found a dry place in the kitchen. Polly gasped for air on the roof of the car, but there was very little air to be found. She would never see her mother's house again. Just a thick, sulfurous fog, getting thicker by the minute. Boris ran down the street wondering about Shira, if she would know what to do, if she was scared. Steve held his wife one last time before they became part of it. Cynthia's shoulders went foamy and wet. Her body became a part of it, and his did too. Now they were part of it. It didn't matter if they were healthy or if they were dying. They dissolved bit by bit into the street, into the trees. Into each other, into everything.

Third Étude Ending
"Soon Come" Rebegun

Nathaniel Mackey

—"mu" two hundred ninth part—

We were a search party the next time out. We
  scouted retribution and remunerative states
we would all pass thru, try though we might to
                                        rise
  above. Sprung similitude put us on parallel
tracks. Allegory might've been its name but
  it wasn't. To make it mean something was our
                                        aim.
    To make it mean was to make it more real,
      more than real, real abound itself... We came
  to a moonlit stretch, dry scrub underfoot, those
                                        known
    as the flown ones down for the night. They lay
dreaming about the bodies of the proper ones, a new
  notion come into their heads, a new recognition
                                        while
they slept, spawn of a tribe yet to come. We lay
    the same, we saw, parallel and spied upon, people
  of the pulse, the broken song's high cry, seeds, it
                                        ap-
      peared, eaten by sparrows... Blown away by
wind if not washed away by water, sprung recon-
naissance ran its course, new reconnoiter. We
  were back to where we camped in no time, psychic
                                        flight
  alone what carried us it occurred to us, a thought we
    took back, disproven by the bramble and the burrs
  on our socks... Threads of light came down, gowns
                                        of

169

light. The moon drew beauty from reticence, blood
   from its pale presentation. Another sonic sphere
  cried out. The wonder of thread was we were naked
                              un-
  derneath, Hofriyati, wonder yet to be gotten over...
  We feasted ahead of time on condolences, moot solace
                                   to
  come, soon
 come

        •

Words came from forty-some years before, words
  not given then given now. We camped on a slope,
the slightest incline ever, womanly amplitude an
                      image
  of the earth we fell asleep dreaming, a meadow
above a meadow above a lake. It lay inland from
Lone Coast we knew, north of Lone Coast, the
reach of the world as clean as ice or an edge of chill
                   as
  cold as crystal, edge to be taken off, drape or embrace... A gangly symmetry bound it together, the
it of it remanding the was of it, Lone Coast, Crater
             Lake,
  names not given now given. It all hung together
in an offhand way we were thinking, happy to've
come to see it so, happy to see anything at all we
          lay
so blinded. It was a state we had no name for, felic-
  ity's romp and ranging forth an astute glue, backs
given the contours of the ground we lay against... We
         were
  the flown ones, we'd have been plucked featherless,
  drape against undress the galactic war the proper ones
fought, our dreams of their bodies the planets. Comets.
        Mag-
 netic
 light

We had pitched our tents, not so much pitched as
popped. We thought ourselves blessed to be there
  feeling it, whatever the feeling might be, deliberate
                                                    ex-
    penditures of breath, long breathers between...
We were in a mood for study. We lived inside skin
  looking out pores wide as windows. Not since
                                                Ita-
    mar and Sophia studied each other had blood run
  so hot, not since we all first paired off, sat face to
face, legs open, erogenies abroad in the gap, yogic
                                                  stet...
    The moon drew blood thru induction, pear-squat
  inertia, whatever motor there was... We went farming
                                                    our
      heads all
  night

                            •

    Fabric vs. fold was the inequation we were now
  being taught. The night sky had a matte, muted look.
    Crater Lake lay so clear we saw to the bottom, no
                                                  water
      was in it. We were learning how the past bled
  into the present, the present bled into the past, team-
  taught by stars, bramble, brush. Deep study some
said. I was one of them. Breathing in to breathe back
                                                    out,
      landing elsewhere, the lip of a canyon water cut a-
    cross the world. Ours or another, abided with or
  abetted by, deep study breathing out to breathe back
                                                    in...
    Reentry we were called, we kept landing elsewhere.
      Nocturnal tillage, we the nightly farmers, heaven-
  ly rubes. We were kissing the world goodbye, a throwa-

way clime, high-crime climate, we the galactic eldren.
We
slept deep enough needing to pee was no problem, wet-
ting ourselves as we slept. Wet fold, wet fabric, the
turning to what was at hand, what lay dependent, that
of
which much had been said, whiling away eternity,
fingertipped eternity's end... Night's late whatsay, vale-
dictory we could see, lamenting what would be done
to the world. We were stumbling but still above ground,
the
Field of Reeds messed up. We were singing the death
of the earth, deep study, getting ready to be gone. We
were conflating the two, caroling dearth, some common
con-
ceit we broke
down to

———————————

Our campfire blown on by wind bore witness, the
wood of the world red, yellow, orange, lit up.
An iron grate we fell thru burning bore in as well,
we
the white ash we studied, woebegone but to know
what soul was... An Armenian wind blew thru my
femur, Eskenian on the box my head had become. I
stared
into the fire, my aunt looking down to see both her
legs gone. A lifted ember sparked, spoke, the wood
of the world ascending, all the shrill wind's insistence,
mere
sometimey
wind

~~We Held Hands~~
Lance Olsen

Tell me what you see vanishing and I
Will tell you who you are

—W. S. Merwin, "For Now"

───────────────────────────── CH. 01

This is not for you.

It's for me.

You need to understand that right away.

I don't know you.
You have nothing to do with me.
You could be somebody else.
You could be anybody else.

(Without you,
this story would just be
another story.)

───────────────────────────── CH. 02

It's the kind of cell-phone novel
you read absentmindedly
every day on your commute.

173

Except it isn't a novel.

That's the point.

You could call it
a trash journal.

An apology,
a kind of justification,
an excuse—
explanation residue.

Think of me
as remembering
out loud for a while
in the palm
of your hand.

(Or maybe
what I'm going to tell you
has everything to do with you.)

———————————————————— CH. 03

I'm not a writer.

You probably already guessed that.

I teach math at a middle school
in Tomioka, a small ugly
oceanside town.

Lance Olsen

I taught math at a middle school
in Tomioka, a small ugly
oceanside town
in Fukushima Prefecture.

For nearly fifteen years.

I grew up there.

(These tenses.)

(These continuous
misplacements in time.)

———————————————————————— CH. 04

I wonder if you can appreciate
when I tell you
I loved my students
but didn't especially like them.

They were a more distracted,
fidgety, self-conscious, exposed,
alarmed division of human being
than I could honestly say I liked.

In the end they believed
everything was about them.

They expected everything
would be about them forever.

Lance Olsen

They made their naivete
and self-importance
into a blunt weapon.

Look into their eyes,
and you could tell
people like me were just poor
stand-ins for their video games
with the ability to grade their work
and thereby ruin their futures.

(Once in a while they
may have liked me.)

(How can a teacher
ever really tell?)

Our continuous misplacements in time—
it's like trying to hold helium.

———————————————————— CH. 05

When I was a little girl,
my fisherman father
used to take me out
on his boat.

These are my happiest memories.

The amazing accomplishment
of his sun-rumpled face.

Lance Olsen

The way he had
of brushing his short thin hair
straight forward
to cover up
all he was rapidly losing.

He somehow reminded me
of a beautiful wrinkled
cotton shirt.

How he wanted his daughter
to see what he saw,
take pleasure
in what he took pleasure.

The briny spray,
the wave chop,
how we couldn't
stop beaming—
we briefly became
the same person.

"The child of a frog
is a frog,"
my father used to say,
and laugh.

——————————————— CH. 06

"It will always be dark
one inch ahead of you, Himari,"
my mother used to tell me,

177

Lance Olsen

propping me up
after I took a tumble as a child.
"Fall down seven times,
stand up eight."

She used to tell me:
"Himari, don't forget:
Not seeing is a flower."

——————————————————— CH. 07

That's where I was—
in my classroom, teaching.

It was a Friday afternoon,
as you know.

Almost three o'clock,
the day chilly and overcast.

My students restless,
ready to move on
to their extracurricular clubs
or enjoy the beginning
of whatever they thought of
when they thought of
their weekend.

I was ready to spend
another hour or two
helping the slow ones
who couldn't be helped

Lance Olsen

in bereft meetings,
then go home and listen
to Miles Davis,
or maybe Coltrane,
not-thinking
on my couch
in the living room,
pleasantly brain-dead,
over a beer and bowl of ramen.

I remember distinctly
standing at the front of the classroom,
chalk stick raised in my right hand,
pronouncing the words
linear functions

—and next—

—you already know
what happens next—

—well, you do and you don't—

(This story is creating us both, isn't it?)

—————————————————————— CH. 08

A painting is music you can see,
Miles once said,
and music is a painting you can hear.

What a lovely way to picture things.

179

Lance Olsen

Imagine being able
to encounter life
like Miles did.

All those endless amazements,
the competition of surprises.

——————————————————————— CH. 09

One night three years ago,
nearly ninety, frail,
increasingly diaphanous
(he called it the Age of Awe),
my father became disoriented
and fell on his way to the bathroom.

He hollered
for my mother
in the dark.

Trying to wrestle
him from the floor
is how she
had her stroke.

After that it was
difficult for her
to speak.

Though she knew
what she wanted to say,

she could no longer
unearth the right words
buried in her brain,
bring them to her lips.

It would take her
the longest time
to weave together
the shortest sentence.

My father, impatient,
ashamed of her,
angry too,
because part of her
had left him,
yet still deeply in love
with an almost imperceptibly
different woman,
would wait several seconds,
but no longer,
then step in to speak for her.

"No," she would say
in the sweetest voice
when he was done.

Smiling broadly,
her teeth
brownish blotches,
my slight, my fragile,
my tenacious mother.

"No, dear, that's not it."

In college I was
a serious student
in part because
I adored studying
and in part because
for some reason
I never learned how
to make friends.

Not real ones,
not the sort that
didn't just say
they cared about you,
but actually did
care about you
for decades
upon decades.

I majored in English
in addition to math.
I wanted to teach both
because for me they formed
two sides of the same activity—
exercises in advanced computation.

I still recall my tremendous joy
the day I learned
there were Japanese words
that carried no equivalent in English.

Lance Olsen

How can there be untranslatable
words in the world?

How can there be language-lacks?

The idea shocked me.

Komorebi: the sunlight
that filters through tree leaves.

The idea still does.

Mono no aware: the awareness
of the impermanence of all things,
a gentle sadness at their passing.

What do people say,
if they can't say
these things precisely,
if they have to say
something else more
roundabout instead?

——————————————————————— CH. 11

I am thinking just now
about Coltrane, Bill Evans,
and Jimmy Cobb
sitting around with Miles
in his recording studio,
doing no more than
clowning, having a bit
of a laugh with each other.

And then, without warning,
there was *Kind of Blue*.

-- CH. 12

I am thinking just now about
how it's one thing to play jazz,
improvise over a couple set chords,
and another thing altogether
to invent a new musical grammar
that possesses almost no syntax.

Don't play what's there,
Miles used to say.
Play what's not there.

--------------------------------- CH. 13

[["No, dear,
that's not it,"
my mother
would say
when she
couldn't say
anything else.]]

The politenesses,
the overt caring,
the good listening skills,
the expressions of empathy,
support, trust, genuine warmth—
all those traits that made
friendship into itself:
they all felt contrived, forced,
mechanical to me as
my awkward, angular
body does even now.

Shinrin-yoku: literally *forest bathing*:
walking deep into a woods
where everything is peaceful and silent,
to find a space of meditative replenishment.

What can you experience
if you can't experience that
in a single word?

Kintsukuroi: the art of
repairing pottery,
using gold or silver
to join the shards
in order to understand
how the piece is always
more beautiful
for having been broken.

———————————————————————————— CH. 15

That's where I was—
in my classroom, teaching—
students Friday-afternoon restless,
stick of chalk raised
in my right hand,
ready to emphasize
the same numerical point
for the umpteenth time.

I heard myself
pronouncing the words
linear functions

—and next—

—you don't really know
what happens next, do you?—

—you think you do,
but you don't—

—and next—

———————————————————————————— CH. 16

—and next this swarm
of dizziness skirred over me.

Lance Olsen

The classroom blurred out
before my eyes.

Surprised,
embarrassed,
I took a tiny step back
to steady myself.

I recall thinking:
And now it is 2:46.

I recall thinking:
*What an ordinary day
this has been so far.*

I recall thinking:
*This must be
what fainting
feels like.*

And then I
stopped thinking
for a while.

———————————————————— CH. 17

Does any of this make sense to you?

From one perspective,
of course,
I don't care.

Lance Olsen

From another,
of course,
I do.

Do you remember where you were
when the news coverage
scrambled into your experience?

Who you might have been talking with?

Or was it instead some work task
you were involved in completing,
intent, proficient, perfunctory?

None of this has happened yet,
although it will happen
in the next two or three seconds.

As you ticked through
your reflexive routine
somewhere else,
I stood with that chalk stick
raised in my right hand,
readying to make
my numerical point
about variables—

—and the classroom windows
began rattling.

I didn't make
much of it at first.

It seemed like a heavy truck
was rumbling by
down in the street below,
even though it also didn't
seem like that at all.

None of this
had happened yet.

And then that changed.

Everything started vibrating—
blackboard, pencils,
key chains, books,
water bottles, empty chairs,
even our internal organs.

The walls started making
crackling sounds.

My students exchanged
alert looks and—

———————————————————————————— CH. 18

—and this overwhelming din
blasted through the building.

It came from
everywhere at once—
bewildering, unhinging,
and I was a little girl again

189

back in my father's boat
riding huge ocean swells,
my land legs gone,
my bearings,
my sense of up and down.

—————————————————————— CH. 19

Acoustic tiles dropped
from the ceiling.

A computer monitor
shuddered off a table
and crashed to the floor.

A window splintered
as if shotgunned.

Then another.

I concentrated on
keeping my balance,
but my legs went out
from under me.

I was lying on my side,
the classroom canted
at an unbelievable angle,
the universe shuddering,
heaving.

——————————————————————— CH. 20

In music, Miles used to tell people,
Silence is always
more important than sound.

And the strange thing
was exactly that—

——————————————————————— CH. 21

The strange thing was
how nobody screamed.

Nobody said a word.

Nobody even moved.

The students had never
been taught how to behave
with each other
in such circumstances—
what expressions to wear,
how to interact,
what gestures to perform,
where to look,
which emotions to undergo.

Naturally we all knew
we were supposed to seek shelter
under a desk or in a doorway,

Lance Olsen

yet we all just stayed
exactly where we were,
waiting for the chaos to stop,
because, it occurs to me now,
we were convinced
it wasn't really happening.

———————————————————————————— CH. 22

That's what their eyes said.

Their eyes said:
Are we living inside
a video game now?
Is that where we are?

Their eyes said:
You're the teacher.
Do something.
Help us.

———————————————————— CH. 23

I kept trying
to edge up
onto my knees,
only for the floor
to roll out
from under me.

192

———————————————————————— CH. 24

It struck me I should shout
something comforting
to the students, encouraging,
tell them everything
would be OK, all they had to do
was hold on tight—
except when I
opened my mouth
my jaw snapped down
and I bit my tongue hard.

———————————————————————— CH. 25

The strange thing
was how it wouldn't stop.

I said to myself:
Twenty seconds.

A minute.

I said to myself:
Just ride it out
a bit longer
and we'll all
get to go home.

I closed my eyes
and marked time
until the tenses changed.

Only the problem
turned out to be
not that the world ended.

The problem
turned out to be
that the world kept ending
over and over again.

———————————————————————— CH. 26

And then,
all at once
the universe
became
voiceless.

————————————————— CH. 27

——————————————————————————— CH. 28

I lay there quietly
on the floor, breathing,
not-thinking,
returning to where
I had always been.

I sensed myself
slowly turning my head
to look up at the clock.

It was 2:52.

Six minutes had passed.

——————————————————————————— CH. 29

The students gently
began whimpering
among themselves.

There was a little blood,
but not as much
as you might expect.

There were several pairs
of glasses gone askew.

A handful of students
at some point

Lance Olsen
had joined me
on the linoleum tiles.

A few had finally
tried to crawl
beneath their desks,
only to have their desks
and books and supplies
tumble on top of them.

I know I should
have cared more.

I know I should
have taken charge,
tended them,
started acting as if
I fully grasped
the situation
and what to do
about it.

———————————————————— CH. 30

I know I should
regret not taking control,
not reassuring all those
frightened hearts.

I know I should feel guilty
for behaving so negligently.

But I don't.

I didn't.

I won't.

All I really felt, feel,
was how essential it was
for me to reach my car.

——————————————————————— CH. 31

And so I eased to my feet,
dusted myself off
as if I'd gotten some flour
on my black dress,
readjusted my clothes,
my psyche,
and hurried out the door,
down the corridor
lined with loud confused
chatter, down the stairs,
and through the main entrance.

——————————————————————— CH. 32

Alarms were cycling
in the parking lot.

I didn't hear them
until I stepped into the open.

197

Lance Olsen

Three crushed cars
lay under a partially
caved-in wall.

The air stank of gas
from a ruptured line.

Women in white masks
scurried around a pool
rapidly forming
where a water main had burst.

Others squatted in place,
unsure whether it was
safe yet to rise,
videoing their surroundings
and each other on
their cell phones,
snapping selfies,
making the moment
feel realer, attempting
to frame their panic.

———————————————————— CH. 33

It wasn't until
I was in my own car
that I realized
I had left my purse
with my keys
in the classroom.

It didn't cross my mind
to return for them.

I slid out from
behind the wheel
and began walk-jogging.

I hadn't covered three blocks
before the warning siren
sounded, sharp, monotonous,
gray as static.

———————————————————————————————— CH. 34

You could sense
the ground ripple
beneath you as the first
aftershocks arrived.

Many sidewalks
had buckled,
webbed with cracks,
pitched up twenty centimeters.

A chimney had collapsed
next to a modest house.

A small store
had shifted slightly
off its foundation.

I passed people
standing in the streets
in front of their houses,
taking in the information,
realizing how unnatural
fear and reality felt.

Everybody briefly
became curious and present.

Everybody briefly
became a believer.

The strange thing was
in those gaps
between siren blares
bird chitter filled
the cloudy afternoon.

——————————————————————— CH. 35

My parents' house
stood near the harbor.

Because of debris
and families everywhere,
it took me longer
than usual to reach it.

The front door was locked.

The side door too.

I banged on both,
calling out their names.
No one answered.
I found a rock
large enough to smash
a pane of glass, reached in,
and unlocked the catch.

———————————————————————— CH. 36

I discovered my parents
upstairs in their bedroom.

They had cached themselves
beneath the covers in their nightshirts,
waiting for the future to take place.

My mother smiled with her bad teeth
as I walked through the door.

My father squinted, confused by all this
newness going on around him.

I told them we had to leave.

They told me they had to get dressed first.

I told them we didn't have time.

I told them we had to hurry
as I eased them up and out.

Age had made
my father denser,
heavier, unwieldy,
my mother airier,
less cluttered,
as if most of her body
had already gone
on somewhere else.

They progressed
methodically, each
movement a difficult
quadratic equation.

Their advance was like parsing
a sentence by Henry James.

Shuffling them
toward the staircase,
I repeated how
we had to hurry.

I gripped my mother
by the elbow,
helped her down
to the ground floor,
then dashed back up
for my father.

———————————————————— CH. 38

We were in
the living room,
baby-stepping toward
the front door,
when the tsunami hit.

———————————————————— CH. 39

The door exploded
off its hinges.

A wall of seawater
rushed us.

I reached out
for my parents.

"Himari," my father
said, and the living room
was churning with chairs,
a couch, planks of wood,
pillows, newspapers, shingles,
a toaster oven, a bright-red gas tank.

We held hands
momentarily,
then the waves
tore us apart.

Lance Olsen

I heard my mother screaming
she couldn't breathe
as I scrabbled
onto the counter.

The water rose
to my neck in seconds,
splashed into my mouth.
I was forced
to tilt back my head
to catch a breath.

I recall thinking:
This is how I will die.
Of all the ludicrous possibilities,
this is how my death
will find me.

———————————————————————— CH. 40

The strange thing was
how I recall thinking:
Everything can only
get better
from here on out.

Nothing in my life
can ever again
be as horrible
as this minute.

Lance Olsen

Standing there on
the countertop,
bracing my palms
against the ceiling
to steady myself,
taking in little
gulps of air,
my goal was
to get through
the next five seconds,
then the next five,
then the next.

I am astounded now
by how I was utterly
unable to imagine
what I couldn't imagine.

—————————————————————————— CH. 41

I'm sure by that time,
no matter what you
had been doing, with whom
you had been speaking,
you were fixated
on the real-time coverage
rushing you, just like
the rest of the country,
unable to take your eyes
off the screen, somewhere
inside of which I was living.

Lance Olsen

From here on out
you know very well
what happens next, don't you—
the linked catastrophes
of those disabled
emergency generators
serving the reactors,
the hydrogen-air explosions,
the term *cesium 137*
suddenly everyday usage,
the term *exclusion zone*,
the photo of that starving dog
still chained on someone's deck,
of the perfectly intact
Coca-Cola vending machine
standing alone in tall grass
and shambles in front
of a garbaged gas station.

You don't need me for that.

It's just as well—
I'm sure you're near
the end of your commute,
reading more quickly
than you should be
to finish this before
the train pulls into your stop.

At this point
I could be somebody else.
I could be anybody else.

206

Lance Olsen

Now you are part of the story
without being part of the story.

Now you have lost your parents too,
even though they are perhaps still alive.

If they are still with you,
you will lose them some other day,
but there is no doubt
you will lose them.

This is how the present works:
we are all features of tales
we will never be features of.

At this point
the story is nobody's.

At this point
the story is everybody's.

——————————————————————————— CH. 42

Nowadays I teach
the same students
in a different drab building
in a different drab town
the same equations
I always teach.

Lance Olsen

After work on Fridays
I return to my new apartment
and listen to Miles Davis,
or sometimes Coltrane,
on my couch in the living room,
not-thinking, pleasantly brain-dead,
over a beer and bowl of ramen.

That's not the strange thing.

That's not part of this.

It's just how stories work.

Every story ends
in a spill of white space.

Every story ends in silence.

The strange thing is
how once upon a time
we believed deeply
Hiroshima could only
be visited upon us
from the outside
by dreadful intensities.

Or maybe how
I didn't really know,
not in any way that matters,
that meeting is always
the start of leaving.

Lance Olsen

The strange thing is
how once upon a time
I didn't even know
what a story was.

I thought I did,
but I was as wrong
as you are now.

I didn't know this:
I didn't know stories are
the events that happen
to other people.

When they happen to you,
they're simply called
the world.

Anthropocene/Burtynsky Ekphrastics
Jessica Reed

TECHNOFOSSILS, STILL RECOGNIZABLE FORMS

After Edward Burtynsky's photograph *Dandora Landfill #3
Plastics Recycling, Nairobi, Kenya, 2016*

The Green that will not be blended
is the filtered, bracketed, categorical green,
which emeralds on its own,

is like a mound of clear plastic bags
summing to a sheer gray. Two thousand
tons daily, the expression of blue blueness.

It's tempting to attribute this visual pattern
to some spontaneous process—the cosmic cataloging
of all things—for we've seen neurons and ants

self-assemble, we've learned to suspect some
invisible math necessitates it all, compels colors
to pattern and scheme, but look:
            residents are hand sorting scrap. Here they are,

one with a rip in his jeans at the knee, a knit hat,
            thick rubber boots to wade in. Another in a red
ball cap, pulling labels off bottles. A third man
has his head down, might even
            be smiling. It's tempting to think

NOTE. In conversation with Rainer Maria Rilke's Seventh and Eighth *Duino Elegies*.
Our growth, described as "more bacterial than primate": Edward O. Wilson.

Jessica Reed

that since our growth on this planet has been
      more bacterial than primate, that we are
blameless microbes, devouring,
         depleting, running out our own clock,
leaving microplastics in the rock, scouring
         the landscape we devastate this material—

I only know   that shit in nature
     just   keeps   _happening_:
         sediments slide   chemicals drift
coastlines erode   volcanoes erupt
and we are part of nature
      ((this should be uncontroversial; _Immer ist es Welt_))
so::
         plastics   aluminum   concrete
               accumulate
and there is this parade
               of consequences
         of contaminants
         of choking albatross
of people knee-deep
         in color-coded trash
because [nature]
is a never-ending
         show of shit unfolding
         in time and we, spread out
in this space-time fabric
         of _was_, _is_, and _will be_
               (all of it somehow _already_)
and it overwhelms us
and we order it
and it falls to pieces
         and we order it again
         and fall to pieces ourselves

211

Jessica Reed

RED AFTER THE TAKING

After Edward Burtynsky's photograph *Nickel Tailings #31,
Sudbury, Ontario*

what am I looking at
    an orange river   charred land
a fauvist scape

    there is also   a consciousness
    scanning nature for a similar—

an image makes demands
    an interior of a line filling space
a mind tries a narrative:

    say, a narrative in light:
        a mind can see a series
of tire piles in Westley, California, as Monet's many
entrances to the Rouen Cathedral, find *story*
in how the light lies, suggesting rust
at the peak of numerous black rubber rings
and that is a narrative?
                or maybe

    the light that lies is more Cézanne's
    Mont Sainte-Victoire, white-capped car tires
    crowding against shadows that *must* be painted
    can't be real   what I'm looking at
    (perspective   false
        promise of the linear—where
        must the light originate?)
              narrative threads

a mind—reaching—might see in uranium
tailings some perversion of Manet's *Boats
at Berck-sur-Mer*, leafless and branchless trees
as vessels adrift against a distorted horizon
    (a mind tries ((

a mind tries a narrative:
there was a separation
    of metals from the ore
and then [adverb of sequence, of story
    of the river line dissolving itself]:
        an oxidation (itself a natural process)

a mind tries a narrative:
    there is a someone whose job it is
    to work the pipes and spigot
    at the tailing facility, artfully waiting
    for the slurry to dry before adding
    another layer—a bit like oil painting,
        I imagine

I am looking at

    what is left behind
separating me   from it, nature,

    awareness dissolving itself
        It looks almost real:

    call it "red" instead—

to turn rivers of what's left red:

    some beast of color,
    some expression of *taking*
    of *took*, of *taken*

Jessica Reed

CULTIVATE/TOPOGRAPHICAL

After four photographs by Edward Burtynsky

Imperial Valley #4, California, USA, 2009

what you can't see

     is the Colorado River

     and from what height
epistemic vertigo

Salinas #5 Aquaculture, Cádiz, Spain, 2013

salt collection ponds
    no horizon

two rivers feed this network
    of polyculture fisheries
         (and just now an ant crawls
across the surface of the book,
         what awareness
of the two-dimensional rivers it traverses—
         (in the exhibit,
     the museum's rooms))

I was saying::
     rectangular ponds and channels
        built into naturally occurring
     salt marshes—

(these channels make more sense on the ground,
        where we cannot
take it all in)
     I am talking about perspective,
how this vast curved portion
        of earth
    flattens

214

a feeling that the river running off the top
   portion of the photo might
         reappear
and feed back into the side

Satellite Capture, Near Buraydah, Saudi Arabia, 2018

(no human)

      water, trapped in aquifers

    during the last Ice Age
       —fossil water—

pumped with diesel fuel
      to irrigate desert crops

runs dry in fifty years

Imperial Valley #4, California, USA, 2009

here you can make out roads

    landscape of uniform greens
winter salad greens   greens of medieval mosaics
      who claimed no individual authors

(no greens Leonardo would have painted
   he knew
      the eyes interpret depth
  with thousands of greens)

here, only
monocultures of mouths, open
        in insatiable hunger and appetite
    for what we have made

FLYSCH

After Edward Burtynsky's photograph *Basque Coast #2,*
UNESCO, Geopark, Zumaia, Spain, 2015

shoe prints in the wet sand
    deep treads on their small scale:
these profiles beside the jagged
    alternating sandstone and shale::

the hypotactic structure of sedimentary rock
    geological time made visible here
where coastal shores border mountain chains
    a view only possible in the flysch—

time's texture shown in these sheets
    sixty million years in eight kilometers
I am told (how to read
        Darwin's world history, "written
    in a changing dialect"?) the peculiar

epistemology of reading fossil, of tracing
    catastrophe in stone:
remnants of animals and air

        hot glyphs of carbon pulse, scripts
of industry and agriculture, our sentence
        taking its course: the stateliness
of the flysch, notation that does not

        (as boot prints) wash away—
delay of the predicate   of the meaning
        of declaratives none of us intend
but continue to write: hierarchy of sediments

speeding past the rest to settle
    on deep sea floors

The Magical Substratum
Heather Altfeld

—For Dr. Daniel Fisher

*If bones could freeze, then the brain could also be
dulled and the soul could freeze over. And the soul
shuddered and froze—perhaps to remain frozen
forever.*

—Varlam Shalamov, *Kolyma Tales*

*The rock art of the Old World, depicting various
elements of the megafauna, may have been Paleo-
lithic man's appeal to the Gods to save his prey
from extinction.*

—C. Vance Haynes, *Paleoecology of Beringia*

HOW CAN I BE SLEEPY *when the world is melting?* my daughter asked
at age nine the night Elizabeth Kolbert lectured at our local university, in response to my whispered *We should go, you have school
tomorrow, aren't you tired?* Kolbert was speaking about Shishmaref,
Alaska, and arctic glacial loss, her slender, petite frame backlit on
the stage so that she looked like a jeweled nightingale, her song
pitching higher and louder as the night went on, as though she were
trying to reach the ears of the moose and the alpenfolk, the penguin
and the reindeer, the execs at Exxon and the driver of the Tahoe
Expedition who cut me off in the parking lot that evening. *We are
running out of time,* I remember Kolbert saying, in response to an unintelligible, long-winded question from the audience, and of course,
as an apology to the glaciers, which she could clearly hear from here,
roiling in drips and drops, ions floating in a new sea.

*

"When, as a child, I heard the word 'Siberia' it meant but one thing
for me: dire peril to the bodies, sure torture for the souls of the
bravest, cleverest, and most independently minded of our people,"
wrote anthropologist Maria Czaplicka, who organized an expedition
of women to Siberia in 1914. This is the imagined Siberia, an endless

217

Heather Altfeld

frozen mass, riddled with ice and swamps, searing heat and unsurviv-
able cold, a land of prisons and labor camps, permafrost and exiles.
"To outsiders who know about Siberia only through hearsay," writes
historian Valentin Rasputin, "it is a huge, austere, and wealthy land
where everything seems to have cosmic proportions, including the
same frigidness and inhospitableness as outer space." The surface
area of Siberia would make it the largest country in the world, yet
its population is smaller than that of California. A nippy day hovers
around minus thirty degrees, the truly cold days closer to minus
fifty. Anna Reid, author of *The Shaman's Coat*, writes that winter
can be so cold that "Exhaled breath falls to the ground in a shower of
crystals, with a rustling sound called 'the whispering of the stars.'"
The name *Siberia* is of unknown origin, although it is thought to
originate from a Tatar word for "sleeping land," as though the land
itself had little to do with its own reputation, a slumbering giant
unaware of its own capacities for brutality, its own dimensions of
frozen beauty. Writer Ryszard Kapuściński tells us in his journal-
istic memoir of his childhood, "There is something in this January
Siberian landscape that overpowers, oppresses, stuns. Above all, it is
its enormity, its boundlessness, its oceanic limitlessness. The earth
has no end here; the world has no end. Man is not created for such
measurelessness."

This somnolent land has long served as the largest prison cell in the
world, one that held the likes of Mandelstam and Solzhenitsyn and
fourteen to eighteen million others for years, decades, whole life-
times, for infractions as small as the offhand remark recounted in
Svetlana Alexievich's *Secondhand Time: The Last of the Soviets:*
"Fathers were taken away at night; they'd vanish into thin air. That's
how my mother's brother disappeared . . . he was taken away for
something stupid, total nonsense . . . He was at a store with his wife,
and he said, 'The Soviet Regime has been around for twenty years, and
they still can't make a decent pair of pants.'"

*

Permafrost sounds a bit like a refrigeration system designed for house-
wives in the 1950s to replace the antiquated term "icebox," but it is
actually a scientific term for perennially cryotic ground. In order to
qualify as permafrost—as opposed to *taryn*, a Siberian description for
temporary icing that can survive the summer—the ground must be

218

frozen for at least two years. The permafrost of Siberia is one of the last frontiers. We have done our best to scope and map and violate the oceans, to enter and flee the atmosphere, to pasteurize the forests, but we have not been able to wholly violate the bowels of the earth with our physical bodies. The permafrost, of course, has been cored; we have sampled the interior of this delectable ancient Popsicle, but much of its contents remain mysterious. What lies buried deep within it is not only our past—flash-frozen in fragments of bone and lichen, bracelets in the tombs of princesses, the cryogenically preserved heel of a fox—but also our future. It is a silo of sorts, a granary of diamonds and ore and oil and bone, a bank shamelessly uninsured by the feds. "Earth's creator got so cold flying over this region that he dropped a wealth of treasures: gold, silver, diamonds, oil," Karl Gorokhov, a Yakut, told *National Geographic* in April 2013. Because the contents of this box are not completely known, they are more priceless, and because they are priceless, they are also worth robbing, strip-mining each of these exquisite layers of memory with the heat generated by our voracious appetites, releasing each secret from its dendritic vault long protected in the mortal substratum of ice.

Stored in this vast basement of strange frozen treasures are millions of years of memories left behind from the tundra's former inhabitants: species, eras, mothers, trappers, love. There are lost lice, ice-mice, tusks and teeth, *the bodies of steppe lions and lion cubs, all of their whiskers still there, the little pads on their feet, even their little tufted ears*, paleontologist Dr. Daniel Fisher at the University of Michigan told me, *tens of thousands of years old, and many even older than that.* Arctic hares and arctic wolves are surfacing as the permafrost melts, perfectly preserved, quite possibly purposefully buried by our human ancestors to protect them from predators; their bodies frozen midruminance, their limbs frozen midflight. There are seeds in the stomach linings of Ice Age squirrels, the kurgans (graves) and bronze treasures of lost Scythians and Pazyryks in the Altai Mountains, mummies complete with hair and tattoos, preserved in ice lenses, the eggs of forgotten species of frogs, iron horsemen, the remains of rhinoceroses and kings. Somewhere in the Valley of Death there are rumored to be seven metal cauldrons large enough to sleep seven explorers; a kingdom of alien life is rumored to still have a presence beneath them in the ice. There are cosmic clues to the 1908 Tunguska event, which flattened 830 square miles and eighty million trees, believed by the indigenous to be a visitation by a god, who had

Heather Altfeld

cursed the area. According to NASA, when an eyewitness finally spoke to Leonid Kulik, who curated the St. Petersburg meteorite collection, he said, "Suddenly in the north sky . . . the sky was split in two, and high above the forest the whole northern part of the sky appeared covered with fire . . . At that moment there was a bang in the sky and a mighty crash . . . The crash was followed by a noise like stones falling from the sky, or of guns firing." And of course, in the permafrost, there is carbon, and methane, mercury and smallpox, anthrax and Spanish flu, half sleeping in wait.

"In this frozen ground, corpses never rot. In these graves which rest on foundations of ice, life and death are separated by nothing more substantial than a breath of air. Bring back the breath, and the body is ready to live again, to come back and share in the slow, chilly existence of the wooden villages, rounding up stray horses, building snowplows, or leading pilgrimages to milder pastures," the narrator of Chris Marker's strangely beautiful 1957 documentary, *Letter from Siberia*, tells us. Three more degrees of warming, and ground that has been stable for eighteen thousand years will release even more of its perils and treasures. Just last year, a pair of forty-two-thousand-year-old cryogenically preserved female roundworms were uncovered from an ancient squirrel burrow, and came back to life in a petri dish. Liquid blood was discovered inside of a Lenskaya foal this year, marking the discovery of the oldest blood in the world, a discovery that quite likely will lead to a resurrection of this long-extinct species. As this world melts, perhaps even the bodies from these kurgans will be ready to live again, as though messianically being called forth into this world.

*

In addition to the population of exiles and ghosts, thirty distinct indigenous groups currently make up a tiny fraction of the Siberian populace, some of whom are Yakuts and Chukchi, Yukaghirs and Buryats and Koryaks, Dolgans and Tatars and Tofa, the Evenks and Khanty and Mansi, the Samoyedic peoples, Nenets and Enets and Nganasans and Selkups; all of these groups combined would make for an entire population just over the number of students currently enrolled at UCLA—the name *Samoyed* can be traced to the Russian word for "self-eater," reflecting the unfounded belief that these "small peoples of the north" were cannibals. The sparse numbers of the Samoyedic people were noted by Czaplicka, who wrote that they are "among the primitive races who are not benefitted by contact with European civilization, and who are therefore on the decline." Each of these thirty indigenous groups has unique languages and worldviews. Their cultures are as endangered as permafrost, so vulnerable that many are bordering on extinction (and many, already, are wholly gone), having been done in by most of what has killed off the indigenous everywhere—the twinned poxes of colonialism and disease, combined with the (often forced) move toward more urban centers to live more "modern" lives. Then there is suicide, with higher rates among indigenous peoples worldwide, particularly so in the Arctic region. The 2002 census of the Russian Federation reports that 123,423, or just 0.23 percent of the population, is composed of ethnic groups who "dominantly adhere to traditional beliefs." Given the relative demise of the central figure of many of these tribal groups—the shaman—this translates to something like 0.003 percent of a shaman per 1,000 kilometers.

Like the indigenous everywhere, native Siberians were observed and judged harshly by those from the West who encountered them. "All the inhabitants appeared in the street clad in the Ostiak costume," Maria Czaplicka writes in 1914, "which consists of a complete suit of reindeer skins, with the hair turned inside out. Finding myself on a sudden in the midst of such men, it was with difficulty I could persuade myself, at first sight, that these shaggy moving forms, encased in the coats of beasts, and wearing such a strange appearance, were human beings." Yuri Slezkine, author of *Arctic Mirrors: Russia and the Small Peoples of the North*, points out that the ways the indigenous were viewed reflected the values of the seers more than those being seen. "They have mouths between their shoulders and eyes in their chests," he quotes from a fifteenth-century tale, an era in which there were rumored to be dogheaded people in the East and mermaids in the sea. "They rove around, live of their own free will, and beat the Russian people," said a Cossack two centuries later, perhaps temporarily forgetting that the very word "Cossack" literally means "troublemaker." Other romantics of the nineteenth and early twentieth centuries idealized the native Siberians as "children of nature" and "guardians of ecological balance."

As the economic and political shifts of the twentieth century occurred, Slezkine tells us in *Arctic Mirrors* that the Bolsheviks offered

Heather Altfeld

mixed reviews of the indigenous, recognizing them as the "authentic proletarians," but admitting that they were "puzzled by the peoples from the late Neolithic period who, by virtue of their extreme backwardness, cannot keep up either economically or culturally with the furious speed of the emerging socialist society." Slezkine further notes that the Chukchi of far eastern Siberia "emerged as the most popular butt of jokes that parodied Soviet claims of rapid development and spectacular cultural advances by the formerly backward," confirming an assertion made by Anna Reid in *The Shaman's Coat* that "To Tsarist Russians, the indigenous tribes were an irrelevance, to the Communists, they were an embarrassment."

Many of these remarks echo those of North American settlers and policy makers with respect to the indigenous, who have been forced, time and again, to keep up, chin up, suck up, and emerge into civility with the rest of us already. The alternative, of course, is to disappear. When Farley Mowat traveled to Siberia in the 1970s, he went to a museum of artifacts in St. Petersburg with his mentor, archaeologist Chumer Taksami. Taksami told him as they looked at the remnants of the past, "These relics are now all that remain of the scores of tribes and nations that were obliterated by the European conquest of Siberia, even as so many of your Native American tribes were obliterated in the same period and of the same cause. When the Cossacks first came among us there were about one hundred discrete peoples living in Siberia. Now there are twenty-nine . . . the vanished races managed to exist with one another in a state of 'barbarism' for thousands of years but could not endure the benefits of European civilization."

While the spartan number of indigenous people currently living in Siberia may "dominantly adhere to traditional beliefs," this adherence is by a very thin glue, for the populace has, to a great degree, lost many of its native languages to Russian, its religious beliefs to Christianity, and its oil to us. The traditional beliefs referred to by the Russian Federation are animistic in nature. The Yukaghirs, for example, believe that reindeer have souls, or spirits, as do bears, and elk, wolverines, foxes, wolves, ravens, and trees. Insects, fish, birds, and plants lead "a mechanical and inconsidered existence," according to Rane Willerslev, an anthropologist who spent years with the Yukaghirs and wrote of them in *Soul Hunters: Hunting, Animism, and Personhood among the Siberian Yukaghirs*, an ethnography

222

Heather Altfeld

that illuminates the complex, nuanced relationship between a contemporary people and their conceptualization of the soul. Willerslev further explains the cosmology of the Yukaghirs as follows:

> Animals and other nonhumans are said to live lives analogous to those of humans. When they roam the forest or swim in the rivers they appear as fish, prey, and invisible spirits. However, when they enter their own lands, which are located somewhere in the forest or deep in the rivers and lakes, they are said to take on human shapes and live in households similar to those of humans. . . . People here are betwixt and between: their souls are both substance and nonsubstance; they are both their bodies and their souls, their selves and reincarnated others; hunters are both humans and the animals they hunt, both predators and prey.

Anthropologist Edward Burnett Tylor's 1871 book, *Primitive Culture*, offered the first concrete definition of culture as well as the first formal definition of animism. Both reflecting and reinforcing the cultural mores of the time, Tylor wrote, "The sense of an absolute psychical distinction between man and beast, so prevalent in the civilized world, is hardly to be found among the lower races. Men to whom the cries of beasts and birds seem like human language, and their actions guided as it were by human thought, logically enough allow the existence of souls to beasts, birds, and reptiles, as to men." Tylor was a strong proponent of cultural evolutionism, the idea that human societies had to pass through the stages of savagery and barbarism to finally emerge as civilized (or, depending on how you see it, as, at the very least, docile, complicit with those in power). Animistic thinking was considered part of the "savage" stage. "Savages talk quite seriously to beasts alive or dead as they would to men alive or dead, offer them homage, ask pardon when it is their painful duty to hunt and kill them," Tylor noted. "The Koryaks, if they have slain a bear or wolf, will flay him, dress one of their people in the skin, and dance round him, chanting excuses that they did not do it, and especially laying the blame on a Russian."

Animistic cosmologies are not unique to the indigenous of Siberia. Many Native American tribes have similar relationships to the natural world, as did indigenous tribes in other regions. And of course many religious traditions believe in the soul in one form or another. But the soul or spirit, as a primary agent, the engine of air, and breath, and growth, not attached to a primary god, not exclusive to humans—

223

these are disquieting, betwixt-and-between ideas and beliefs that do not fit well within our clean, linear Cartesian thinking. The Yukaghir, along with other native Siberian groups, believe that we have three souls. Active entities, such as animals, trees, and rivers, are considered "people like us," according to Rane Willerslev's book, because they are "'moving,' 'growing,' and 'breathing,'" but distinct from inanimate objects such as stones, skis, and food products, which are "'alive but immovable.'" The alive but immovable things have only one soul—a *shadow-ayibii*—but those that are like us have a shadow-soul, a heart soul, which makes them move and grow, and a head-soul, which makes them breathe. Russian ethnographer Waldemar Jochelson, himself exiled to Siberia in the 1930s, studied the lives and traditions of the Yukaghir, the Koryak, and the Yakut, and was told by the Yukaghir that only the ancient shamans actually completely understood these souls, and of course, these shamans were long gone—the flesh of their skin, as Jochelson is told, turned into amulets, their sacred bones used for divination, practices that have long since disappeared.

Hunting was once the primary means of sustenance for the Yukaghir, but is no longer viable as such, in part due to radical climactic changes that have in turn caused changes in the vegetation. When they do hunt, they seek an actual connection to their prey, believing that some elk will even prefer to be killed by a particular human. They "wear wooden skis and smooth skin from the leg of an elk, and waddle in his likeness . . . The animal will then come to perceive him not as an evil spirit or a predator, but as a harmless lover and a member of its own species," Willerslev says. Further, he tells us, "The Yukaghir do not take on the bodies of animals just so as to represent them. They do so in an effort to manipulate the world around them," becoming, "not the elk, and not-not-the elk." They know, in other words, that the elk is not exactly a person. But it has a soul, and thus, a *sort* of personhood, writes Willerslev, noting that "the Yukaghir do not necessarily see things as persons any more than we do, but instead live in a world of ordinary objects in which the distinction between human subjects and nonhuman objects is much more readily drawn."

Another Siberian group, the Evens, act and move on the tundra in such a way that they are conscious that animals and the tundra itself are reacting to them, according to David Anderson, who lived amongst

them. Further, in anthropologist Piers Vitebsky's *The Reindeer People,*
the Evens tell him that when a reindeer has been killed, cut up, and
cooked, it still reveals the character of the person who was its owner.
The Nenets, many of whom are still reindeer herders and depend on
the animals for food, transportation, and clothing, conceive of "deer
as life-giving people, the sun as heaven's eye, fire as *erkar,* and 'until
recently, treated water as a living being, which explains why they used
to have special melodies for lakes'" (from Alla Abramovich-Gomon's
The Nenets' Song).

The cosmological belief in a universe that mirrors the world of humans
necessarily allows for bears and reindeer and wolves and trees to be
seen not simply as prey or resources or beautiful machines worthy of
our consideration because of their utility in the ecosystem, but as
distinct souls with a complicated relationship to humans. Among
most of the Siberian indigenous, even entities that have died continue
to have souls. The environmental conditions in the Arctic have disturbed and disrupted not only temperature, hunting patterns, animal
migration, water levels, and ice; they have disrupted an entire world,
a world invisible to humans, and unacknowledged by those for
whom such philosophies appear to be primitive or useless.

The rituals and beliefs of the Siberian indigenous, like the rituals and
beliefs of the indigenous everywhere, have not survived the import
of Christianity unscathed (and in many cases, not survived at all).
The Russian Orthodox Church is and has been a powerful force in
the Siberian arctic, as have Protestant missionaries; Kate Marsden, a
British missionary turned saint turned author who set out in 1890 to
save the lepers who had been exiled to the outer reaches of Siberia
from the horror and desolation of their lives, carted around crates
and crates of Bibles and English tea to distribute to the "natives,"
recounting her mission in great detail in her volume, *On Sledge and
Horseback to Outcast Siberian Lepers.* And Czaplicka noted in *My
Siberian Year*:

> How far down their faith (Christian) goes is another matter,
> but they certainly keep up their old paganism side by side
> with it. It is always safest to have something to fall back on,
> in case the other should not work, and then there is the
> curious point about it, that the Christian god may be able to
> deal with men but he does not know much about reindeer,
> as, of course, he cannot have picked that up in Europe; for

the reindeer they must have the old gods who are used to
them.

Lynn White Jr., who wrote "The Historical Roots of Our Ecologic
Crisis" over fifty years ago, asserted that "Christianity is the most
anthropocentric religion the world has seen." He goes on to say that
Christianity had a direct role in the demise of animistic thinking,
noting that "a saint is entirely a man; he can be approached in human
terms . . . The spirits in natural objects, which formerly had protected
nature from man, evaporated. Man's effective monopoly on spirit in
this world was confirmed, and the old inhibitions to the exploitation
of nature crumbled."

What could the singular god of men know about restoring water to ice,
ice to taryn, taryn to permafrost, humans to their senses? The old
gods—the ones who first watched as we painted the shrinking world
of animals on the rocks and walls of our caves—must be shaking
their heads in profound exhaustion.

*

Primitive, barbarian, savage (subcategorized as both "noble" and
"ignoble"), and *uncivilized* were terms used to describe the indigenous the world over until the early twentieth century (*primitive* was
still used, even by anthropologists, into the 1990s). Politically, we
speak now of "ethnic minorities," a savvy, postcolonial term, neu-
tral, hygienic, bland, corporate, lacking nuance or collective interest
in the deep layers of unique language and tradition. The work of
anthropologists since the early days of Edward Burnett Tylor has undoubtedly helped to shift acceptances of cultural differences. Eighty
years after Tylor wrote about "the barbarism of the lower races,"
Lévi-Strauss wrote, "The barbarian is first and foremost the man who
believes in barbarism," reflecting and reinforcing leaps in tolerance.
But this shift isn't just the product of a more enlightened populace.
The global homogenization of cultures and belief systems makes
this wildly easier—we have less to accept and less to tolerate than
we did in a world of precontact cultures. And while consciously and
publicly we may no longer agree with Tylor that societies have to
pass from savagery to barbarism to the gates of civilization, beyond
the carefully metered language of academics, we're likely to hear
about the soul of reindeer or Siberian larches with one ear bent in

jest. (Google the Siberian larch, one of the primary tundric forest species, on fire this summer in epic proportions, and you will get a number of "decking" offers among your first hits.)

To many of us, the idea of animal souls, tree souls, water souls, souls that breathe, and shadow souls, *sounds* primitive; like permafrost, it is a terra incognita for Western thinking unless we have made ourselves students of such philosophies. The recent success of Peter Wohlleben's *The Hidden Life of Trees* indicates that people are *interested* in the idea that trees might communicate, that they may even feel; Wohlleben speaks of the maternal instinct in trees, and mutual nurturance in times of need. But these ideas are "new" to us empirically minded "civilized" ones, and further, they are more empirically verifiable than the curious notion that animals, and rivers, and trees are part of a spirit world, and that the actions of humans directly influence these relationships. Daniel Fisher told me of traveling by boat with some Yakuts down the Yana River into the Arctic Ocean—"from the kingdom of the river to the kingdom of the sea," as the Yakuts explained it to him—and said that everyone in the boat threw beads overboard as an offering to the sea spirit, so it would not be angry that they were traveling upon it. He also spoke of the significance of thresholds as sacred places to native Siberians—even at state-controlled border crossings indigenous travelers leave cigarettes or coins or colorful bits of twine tied to the nearest tree, thanking the spirits of the region they are departing, and the one that they are entering.

A common perception of these ideas is illuminated by the following anecdote: I had dinner with a colleague from our university last week, a professor in the College of Humanities, and was explaining the elements of this essay to him in the standard elevator speech of dinners. My colleague said something along the lines of *Well, of course, that's interesting, but it doesn't make sense. What is the point of believing in that kind of personification if it isn't actually true?* I felt defensive and momentarily embarrassed, caught in the act of considering something empirically indefensible; only children are allowed to imagine a world where everything is, quite literally, ensouled, a world in which creatures might live as we do. I was reminded of Tylor's assertion that "Barbaric philosophy retains as real what civilized language has reduced to simile." Fox houses, bird men, tidy elk, rivers and oceans that need appeasing are no less real than the magical ability of humans to melt versts and versts of ice simply by driving their cars.

We have translated the eco crisis in the Arctic into our own terms— terms that make sense to us, statistics of melt and temperature change, empiric projections—but these terms do not represent the animistic views of the native Siberians, Daniel Fisher explained to me. *Our scientific terms do not capture the actual problem, which the Siberians would say is one of great disruption to the land's spirit. The eco crisis we are experiencing involves many souls, because the land has a spirit, and if it is angry, and it can't be appeased, and they can't survive on it, then what are they supposed to do?* What is the point, then, between a cosmology that centers *around* the natural world, and one that centers around *our* importance in it?

It is this: if the personification of an animal or a tree gives us the sense that we are all in this together, then their suffering is our suffering, their deaths are our deaths, and their souls are inextricably bound up with our own.

*

I was found on the 13th of February, 1605, near Neubronn, in the district of Halle. Can you tell me, friend, what sort of thing I can be, with these huge bones and long joints? read an announcement in the Michaeliskirche in Swabia, where a large mammoth tusk still hung in 1926, the year Russian paleontologist and zoologist Eugen Wilhelm Pfizenmayer published *Siberian Man and Mammoth,* which chronicles the discovery of the Beresovka mammoth. Many native Siberians thought and think that the mammoth lived underground, in the underworld, that their origins were unknown and inexplicable, and that they were allergic, so to speak, to sunlight and air, so that whenever they surfaced to the upper world, they died. Pfizenmayer notes that Chinese stories of the mammoth referred to it as a "digging vole of the north, as large as an elephant," a "hidden mouse," the "mother of mice," and "the ice-rat."

"The flesh of this animal," one Chinese emperor says, "is ice-cold, and very efficacious in fevers . . . Their teeth are like those of elephants, and the people of the north make vessels, combs, knife-handles and other articles out of them. I have seen such teeth myself, and the things

made from them, and so I believe the accounts in our ancient books."
The Siberian Russians believed that the mammoths were elephants
displaced by the biblical deluge and that their drowned carcasses
floated out on the water and finally washed under the earth. Even
Thomas Jefferson believed that the mammoth lived elsewhere, somewhere in the plains in the middle of North America, unseen under
the earth.

It is still considered among many of the indigenous in the Arctic bad
luck to disturb the remnants of mammoths—their tusks or teeth,
when dug out or taken, can hasten one's death. Pfizenmayer writes
that the Tungusic "believe that the sight of a mammoth body brings
bad luck, and this superstitious fear is so strong that they actually
become ill if they come by chance on a body . . ." He had heard of a
Tungusian chieftain who had discovered the body of a mammoth
and was reproached by his fellow tribesmen for meddling with the
unlucky find, as it would doubtless bring sickness and misfortune to
the whole tribe and their reindeer herds. "The chieftain," Pfizenmayer
tells us, "later fell ill with serious nervous trouble."

The belief that the mammoth relics must remain undisturbed comes
into direct conflict with the sheer volume of animalia surfacing as
the permafrost melts, for the harvest of such relics is enormously
lucrative. Even in 1914, Czaplicka wrote that ". . . a man who finds a
mammoth tusk has to pay for it to the 'spirit' of the place by various
sacrifices. The search for such tusks is considered a poor pursuit for
a man, notwithstanding the high price which the ivory brings."
Mammoth tusks are not only highly valuable in the present day, but
given the turn of the Russian Federation toward capitalism, given
the price of bread, given the utter lack of other resources for sustenance, given the radical balding of the permafrost, a peeled earth
littered with specimens of bone and tusk, wolf heads and woolly
rhino skulls—it is worth the risk to one's spirit to disturb the
yedoma, where the mammoth graves lie. Once unearthed, the tusks
are frequently sold to the Chinese for prices that sustain a family,
even a small village, for a year, to be carved into intricate scenes of
villages and temples, pine trees and mountains, placid landscapes
honeycombed into the bone, and sold for upward of a half million
dollars. Hence a significant and growing number of indigenous people
of the region spend eight months a year hip-deep in mud and freezing lakes, hoping to extract a living—for there is nothing like the

threat of starvation to put a person in a pair of reindeer-skin boots so that they may go out and seek their fortune in the thermokarst.

Other groups—such as the Chukchi and the Nenets—continue to remain very cautious about disturbing ancient remains, which explains why when Lyuba, the nearly forty-two-thousand-year-old mammoth baby, was first discovered by Nenets hunter Yuri Khudi in 2007, he did not touch it, but, rather, went back to seek advice from an elder, knowing that it was a very important find. "Apart from its missing hair and toenails, it was perfectly intact," writes Tom Mueller for *National Geographic*. Though Khudi had never seen such an animal before, he knew it well from the stories his people sang on dark winter nights in their storytelling lodges—a baby *mamont*, the beast the Nenets say wanders the frozen blackness of the underworld, herded by infernal gods. When I spoke to Daniel Fisher, who was invited to Yakutsk to conduct the autopsy on her ancient body, we both choked up as he told me over Skype, *She was perfect—she still had her eyelashes! When we came to her heart, it was there in her pericardial sack, and I opened the sack. And I realized then that I was actually holding it, this ancient heart. Once it was a beating heart, and it beat until it didn't any longer.*

Lyuba—which means "love," in Nenet, chosen after Khudi's wife's name—died when she was less than two months old, trying to cross a partially frozen lake, too late in the springtime for doing so. It was probably, by best guess, the month of mare foaling, as the Yakut would call early spring, when she broke through the thin ice and inhaled a big snoutful of vivianite. When she tried to blow it out, it got stuck there, and she aspirated it. "Unable to dislodge the viscous mass, she suffocated," writes Fisher, in his moving account, *Adventures with a Baby Mammoth*. "Many have asked why Lyuba's mother—who was surely no less attentive than elephant mothers today—could have allowed this fate to befall her young calf. For better or worse, we have no satisfactory answer, except that accidents happen."

The treasures of mammoths and kings will continue to bobble up from the underworld, and those that do not bobble willingly are mined hydraulically, a practice that is perilous, illegal, and frequent. The Convention on International Trade in Endangered Species of Wild Fauna and Flora met August 26, 2019, to consider the idea of making the woolly mammoth an "endangered species" in order to ban the trade of mammoth ivory and other "parts," a proposal put forward in part with the intent of quelling the elephant ivory trade. The proposal failed, citing a lack of evidence. As for Khudi, whose beliefs about the spirit world have not yet been toppled, he made offerings of reindeer antlers and pieces of beautiful handmade sleds to the spirits after Lyuba was taken from the spot in which he found her.

Karl Gorokhov, the tusk hunter featured in the April 2013 issue of *National Geographic*, was said to be "running out of time" to bring in his tusk:

> Late summer blizzards are howling across Kotelnyy Island, 600 miles north of the Arctic Circle, and the deep freeze of another northern winter looms . . . It takes Gorokhov almost 24 hours of continuous digging to extract the tusk from the pebbly ice below. The specimen that emerges is thick as a tree trunk—150 pounds—and in near-pristine condition. Before hauling the tusk away, Gorokhov tosses a silver earring into the hole he has dug, as an offering to the local spirits. If he gets the ancient relic safely home, it could fetch more than $60,000.

"Open for Business," reads a header in the most recent issue (September 2019) of *National Geographic*, featuring the crisis in the Arctic. "Arctic Assets" reads another, a few pages later. "Nations—and their militaries—are scrambling to control long-frozen resources and new shipping routes," reads a third. Just last year, nine nations and the European Union signed an agreement to ban commercial fishing in the Arctic Ocean—a proactive law to pre-protect what is just under that rink of ice that will soon be melted and gone. *The Telegraph* reported in April 2019 that the Russian Federation had announced a new Arctic development strategy, including oil and gas infrastructure, ports and nuclear icebreakers on the northern sea route, and tax breaks to draw investors to the north. "This situation was 'sad for the bears,'" Mr. Putin admitted, but nonetheless the huge energy reserves in the Arctic needed to be extracted and "delivered in the service of humanity."

The melting of the permafrost looks, on the surface, to be just another story of environmental destruction. But for many, it is a frontier. An adventure. An opportunity.

*

Heather Altfeld

When we think of the differences between the "us" enculturated in Western thinking and those who have historically been conceived as archaic or primitive, exposure and familiarity with industrialized technologies, a relationship to democracy, or even soap, as Freud suggested, might be the most prominent distinguishing markers. But more significant, even in secular societies (with the exception of writing systems, the hallmark of cultural progress), is the overarching adherence to monotheism, or no theism at all. Animism—or any cosmology that resembles it—challenges the biblical charge represented in the most influential religious traditions of our time, as God gave dominion over the animals to Adam, who even names them for us, so that when we extinguish and bury the last of their kind, we have something to call them.

Paul Radin—the anthropologist whose chapter title, "The Magical Substratum," I've borrowed for the title of this essay—noted this, after his years of study and contemplation of animism:

> The belief in the general animation of nature has nothing to do with the supernatural . . . It is the prevalent view today that where animism or polytheism prevails monotheism is excluded, and where monotheism prevails animism and polytheism are in the main absent; that as we pass from animism to polytheism, from dualism to monotheism, we are proceeding from a belief in a multiplicity of spirits devoid of special attributes to a belief first in two deities and then to a belief in a single god—a god endowed with the highest ethical attributes . . . It is not astonishing, therefore, that even to many nonreligious individuals, pure monotheism should consequently connote the highest form of religious experience.

Humans evolve, in other words, from the collective to the individual, from the many gods to the solitary one. Radin believed, however, that this cultural evolutionism was incorrect—that the truest difference that cut through human society was not between animistic and monotheistic or between primitive and civilized, but rather between what he called "reflective and unreflective persons," the reflective group being the thinkers and seekers, and the others being "the overwhelming mass [who] belong to the indifferently religious group [and] are materialists, realists, to whom a god, be he supreme deity or not, is simply to be regarded as a source of power." It just happened, by historic accident, he argues, that monotheism won out.

It is this singular sort of vision, that of the improbable, solitary hero, that so often appears in the narratives and myths of Western thought and religion. This hero, cultivated and emboldened by its mass popularity in film and literature, is the one who can save us, redeem us, grant us salvation, lift us up into an afterlife beyond the fresh terrors of this one. It makes me wonder if part of the hardheaded delight in denying human-caused climate change is the force of this narrative at work—one scientist, one god, one phenomenal messiah, will "figure it out" at the last minute, just as we are about to self-destruct, rocketing through the ozone to deposit a triple ice freezer to freeze permafrost three times faster than any machine could even dream, just as the last of the glaciers is about to melt.

*

"Millions of years that went before me / are contained in that greeting of each grain of snow," wrote Abraham Sutzkever, a Jewish poet whose nearly forgotten book-length poem, *Siberia*, a tribute to the land and to the death of his father, was exquisitely illustrated by Marc Chagall. This is true, both figuratively and literally. In this magical substratum—which in places is up to seven hundred to eight hundred meters thick; the ice has been there, undisturbed, for *millions of years*—Daniel Fisher told me that some of the tusks he has studied in this region are hundreds of thousands and even millions of years old, far too old for carbon dating. Once melted, this ice cannot be recreated. Ever. Not even with the snow machines used at Tahoe in the dry years of skiing. Not only that, but in addition to the treasures of this underworld, carbon dioxide is trapped in there, referred to by some scientists as a "sleeping giant." The clinical signs of hypercapnia—too much CO_2—are as bad as any poison, scientists warn, and include flushed skin, a "bounding pulse," rapid breathing, muscle twitches, and hand flaps, otherwise known as asterixis, which Wikipedia notes is "sometimes said to resemble a bird flapping its wings."

Further, anthrax has already been released from various animal carcasses that have begun to rot as the permafrost melts—seventy-six of the Nenets people contracted anthrax in 2016, and over twenty-three hundred reindeer died. The following year, over eight hundred thousand reindeer were inoculated against the anthrax virus. Other alarming notes from the annals of alarming notes: "In what seems like a plot straight out of a low-budget science-fiction film, scientists have revived a giant virus that was buried in Siberian ice for thirty thousand years—and it is still infectious," reports Ed Yong in *Nature* magazine. Using permafrost samples, scientists have been able to "fish" for giant viruses by using amoebae as bait. The virus then replicates itself in what are described as "factories." Right now, these viruses are off in a laboratory somewhere, hard at work. Of the permafrost, scientist Jean-Michel Claverie, who works with these samples, says, "It is dark, it is cold, and it is also without oxygen. . . . There is no [ultraviolet] light . . . If you take a yogurt and put it in permafrost [that remains frozen], I'm sure in ten thousand years from now it still will be good to eat." Claverie told *Discover* magazine, "The permafrost is important because we can go deeper and find ancestors of those viruses . . . If it's an old known disease like smallpox, it will be sad for the poor people who get it, but it could be OK because it could be recognized quite easily, and you put the people in quarantine." He notes that he is "more concerned about unknown diseases deeper in the permafrost being brought suddenly to the surface by mining and industrial development in the Arctic—prehistoric pathogens, for which we have no defense." Speaking of the giant virus, Claverie tells *Nature* magazine that ". . . this guy is 150 times less compacted than any bacteriophage. We don't understand anything anymore!"

*

Like mining for tusks and oil and viruses, scientists have long worked to "locate" the soul within the human body. Aristotle dissected forty-nine species of animals looking for the soul. The Renaissance reinvigorated this discussion; some believed in a "cardiocentric soul" and others that the soul was seated in the brain. Da Vinci—after his many experiments, observations, and anatomical explorations—concluded that the soul was indeed in the brain. He asserted too that a mother shares a soul with her unborn child, writing that "One and the same soul governs these two bodies; and the desires, fears, and pains are common to this creature as to all other animated parts." Descartes thought that the pineal gland (the "worm of the brain") was its home, writing:

> Since it is the only solid part in the whole brain which is single, it must necessarily be the seat of the common sense, i.e., of thought, and consequently of the soul; for one cannot be separated from the other. The only alternative is to say that the soul is not joined immediately to any solid part of the

body, but only to the animal spirits which are in its concavi-
ties, and which enter it and leave it continually like the water
of river. That would certainly be thought too absurd.

Dr. Duncan MacDougall of the noteworthy 21 Grams experiment
studied the weight of the human body just before and just after the
last breaths were taken. He wrote, "The net result of the experiments
conducted on human beings is that a loss of substance occurs at
death not accounted for by known channels of loss. Is it the soul substance? It would seem to me to be so." But MacDougall's experiment
has never been successfully replicated.

So if the soul is *real*, where is it exactly? And why can't we locate it,
touch it, film it? Strangely, humans who are fully assimilated in the
technological era have little trouble accepting that machines have a
kind of anima, one that, viewed from the perspective of an outsider
unfamiliar with technological advances of late, would be completely
confounding. Siri is the embodiment of female sultriness and seduction as she tells us how to find the nearest Chevron. Corporations
have personhood that a Siberian larch can only dream of. The cloud
is our vault, our closet, our secret keeper, a safety-deposit box better
than any ice shelf in the permafrost. Our shampoos and soaps and
perfumes and potions are imbued with magical powers; they emanate
a pulse of sorts from our bodies as a living advertisement of sexual
desire.

The internet is our shaman, a priest who lives in a magical realm we
cannot see or hear aside from the vaporous hum that comes into the
room when a modem first awakens, a vacationless, selfless, model-
Protestant worker, advice giver, assuager of worries, purveyor of goods
and needs, seductress of things we did not yet know existed; it is our
witch, our matchmaker, our greengrocer, our stylist, our music teacher,
our neurotic mother, our veterinarian; we put our faith in it for everything from colon potions to stock options, parenting to preparations
for the end. Yet the handful of indigenous people who have long identified the soul as inhabiting many forms of life are just that, a minute
and disappearing fraction of the human population, an infinitesimally
small philosophical minority.

"[Some] may say of my argument that I have written soullessly of the
soul, and unspiritually of spiritual things. Be it so: I accept the phrase

not as needing an apology, but as expressing a plan. Scientific progress is at times most furthered by working along a distinct intellectual line, without being tempted to diverge from the main object to what lies beyond, in however intimate connexion," writes Edward Burnett Tylor in 1871, a sentence that could have been written yesterday.

*

Daniel Fisher told me that the Nenets are having a harder and harder time migrating their reindeer, due to the combination of melting permafrost, unpredictable and unprecedented rain in areas where there used to be snow and ice, changing vegetation in the tundra, and the oil industry—the Yamal Peninsula, where the Nenets live, is said to have the largest gas reserves in the world. "What happens to the land is very important to us," Nenets herder Sergei Hudi recently told Survival International. "We are afraid that with all these new industries, we will not be able to migrate anymore. And if we cannot migrate anymore, our people may just disappear altogether."

Among other solutions to the crisis of "impermafrost" is the idea that the resurrection of the woolly mammoth could actually mitigate the melting. Many geneticists are keen on doing so. And scientist Sergey Zimov—whose name has become synonymous with resurrection ecology—has worked to recreate the subarctic steppe grasslands where the mammoth once thrived, in a nature reserve called Pleistocene Park. By cultivating mammoth DNA and implanting it in female elephants, it will be possible to "curate" the return of the first mammoth or "Mammophant." The technology to do this is highly controversial, and still a few years away, but the argument for doing so is that the mammoth would reinvigorate the biome. "They keep the tundra from thawing by punching through snow and allowing cold air to come in," suggests Harvard professor George M. Church, part of the Revive & Restore project. "In the summer they knock down trees and help the grass grow." The Revive & Restore website notes, "The ultimate goal of Woolly Mammoth revival is to bring back this extinct species so that healthy herds may one day repopulate vast tracts of tundra and boreal forest in Eurasia and North America. The intent is not to make perfect copies of extinct Woolly Mammoths, but to focus on the mammoth adaptations needed for Asian elephants to thrive in the cold climate of the arctic."

The act of de-extinction, or resurrection, is essentially one of crea-tion; the birth and subsequent survival of a woolly mammoth would be one of the most significant triumphs of the scientific era, a crea-tion story of epic proportion. Creation stories figure prominently in the lives of most cosmologies; Rane Willerslev tells this one, from the Yukaghir:

> In ancient times there lived very small people and the climate was very hot. They did not have a name for themselves, but we call them "irkinyodutyuval mril nasy sarno," which means "so small that a squirrel fur can dress one person." They were naked, ate raw meat, and did not know how to make fire. It started to get cold and the small people killed squirrels and dressed in their fur, but they were terribly cold. Then Jesus came flying from the sky with a torch in his hand. He gave it to the small people, who thus came to have fire. The smoke from their fires made them grow bigger and bigger and they became humans.

Far fewer cultures have stories that act as premonitions of their demise. We have a story of our own ending right now, one that we have been writing for some time, but we are too civilized for stories. Besides, we have run out of time to listen. The Nenets and the Yukaghir and the Dolgan and the Chukchi and the twenty-five other remaining indigenous groups of the Siberian north—not to mention the indige-nous of other regions who have continued to carry their traditional beliefs despite all odds—have long noted and understood what we are just beginning to wrap our minds around: humanity is a rather sub-jective state and, quite possibly, a self-destructive one.

Fisher told me that in Batagaika about ten years ago, the locals began to dig for gravel to use as an aggregate for concrete. They dug and dug a deep quarry, but found nothing but *yedoma*, silt. Over time, the Arctic sun eradiated the hole, and the walls of the quarry began to melt. The meltwater flowed, creating subterranean channels and a river, eventually eroding the quarry over a hundred meters deep. "There is a terrible roaring from the torrents of meltwater, and when giant clumps of earth fall in, it sounds like cannon fire," he told me. The Yakut char-acterize this as a "very angry landscape." One of them asked Fisher, "Do you know Mordor? From the movie? This is Mordor!" Shamans come to the site to do chants and make sacrifices as apologies to the land, which the Yakut believe "opens into the dark heart of the earth."

Heather Altfeld

There is an unrelenting loss of lifestyles and communities and languages, irreplaceable losses, Fisher told me as the last of our lengthy Skype conversations came to an end. When we said goodbye, I was left with the strangest sensation that we were both characters in an episode of Rod Serling's old *Twilight Zone,* and that when our screens turned off, we would not be able to make contact with each other again, as though each of our ships had crash-landed on different planets, our equipment irreparable. The last quote I wrote in my notebook was when he said, *Soon all that will be left of the Nenets and all of these other groups in terms of their cultures are fragments of history and a handful of stories that only a few people will remember. And all of that is irreplaceable. Like the permafrost, once it is gone, it will be gone forever.*

> *I have been unable to stop the snowstorm, the sky is all broken.*
> —The Koryak, *Little-Bird-Man and Raven-Man*

Two Elemental Elegies
Andrew Mossin

MOVEMENTS FROM THE FIRE CYCLE

the motion of the ring is the motion of the animal
—John Taggart

I.

One day instead of a village you have
an empty field   the most basic features of

a field without color or contours   as if to
remember the sky when the fires

burned east to west   a rim of shadow
paralyzing sight   reflections of the sky

on wet panes   the nimbus of ash
forming along the red rectangle

square situated inside a tunnel   of white
ash separated from the sky   as if fire

had become the object of field   Field & fire
are objectives of understanding   as if to instrumentalize

vision the way a fire burns   a line of fire
burning at the periphery of sight   the hollow

limbs that are brought into view   radioactive
logs in a line   silver where the branches

point east to west   across the horizon the pointed
limbs in a field of gray metal   one line after

Andrew Mossin

another lit from within   white scar of light
red on the mud opening out.

II.

Where everything is moving   the children in a chorus

standing in the sun singing   children singing as a chorus

in the smoke where the village was   standing outside the zone of

contamination   their voices raised to form the inside of song

to carry their voices across   red earth on a brown background

their voices in a chorus of red   taste of feather grass & sorghum

as they rose to sing   their mouths that turned from each other

to sing apart from themselves   And they said it was God returning

them to their bodies   it was fire from the eastern

sky that was left to them   A chorus of swallows lifted one by

one from the trees in a field on fire   Inside a field thirsty for their

bodies to return   they sat down together in puddles of black rain

puddles that were red & green like someone had poured

paint on them   sat to recover their voices of lupine & mullein

in the yellow spring air   to recover words they sang in unison

standing in the sun singing in unison   under a red sky singing.

240

III.

To recover the species   rediscover its position
in the landscape   enter the space where it transforms

its transition from one state to another   Bird that forms
an image in mind   *Hirundo rustica*   barn swallow that

establishes relation to a before   this balance
one achieves between before & after   the barn swallow

and its history in a before   native to the
region so that it embodies its history   seasonal bird

re-presented in a structure of change   One counts
mutations of the germ line in percentages

2/10 to establish changes to the germ line   a record that is at once
observation of change and a document of

transformation   Swallow that flies into the morning sky
albinistic feathers on its head   throat and beak

tail feathers that are asymmetrical   bent tail feathers
that become signs of its mutation   a site of transformation

the body of the swallow   transformed
in the span of a decade   quietly coming into view

a mutation of blue and brown feathers   albinistic
markings of head and throat   acts of change

marking the territory of swallow   a dimension
of aftermath   in the singular form

blue-brown changes of color   scattered rain light
down the swallow's tail feathers.

IV.

Whatever comes in sleep enters   a slow trail of smoke
evolving a language all its own   elk and swallow are

images that populate the landscape   a slow and trailing line of ash
incommensurate in the time of writing   Witness

is a seraphim attached to a trail of graphite   smeared &
burning in the April night   heavenly as water on the

lips the angelic force moving across morning sky   White
trail of smoke in April   burden that burns one's genetic

makeup   Flowers at the gate   signs of ash on oak and elm
black rain from the April sky   Flowers at the gate no longer burning

A circle of forest   blue perimeter of swallows that defines
ash on white elms   swallows that rest inside a perimeter of white

ash in the forest   the purity of sight to select what is seen
in the forest   a single tree left at the edge   white elm edged

with ash   columnar structures at the edge of the visible
edged by forest that is no longer forest   grave site

where forest was   blossoms of the sumac in water
the skies of Pripyat   charcoal on blue foam board

rim of the visitation one makes   to ring the cycle
forest   swallow   tree   as if woven together

beneath skies offering no protection from ash & fire.

V.

Possible to trace   not possible to say   degradation

of light in the forest   Red forest in a low wind

Light that follows from inside the forest   moves outside

a circle of branches   gathered on wet ground

this turning of ash and wind   aligned in the red forest

To rename what it was   wild boar and elk

in a field without trees   to rename their passing

fox and deer returning to a landscape   the language

alienated from itself   this partition inscribed in red

wood scent of air that remains   burnt limbs of the poplar tree

One moves inside the zone to find them   to re-situate

chronology inside a disrupted limb   the markings of fox

and rabbit moving inside a circle   ring of red leaves

on a brown background   in the red forest

swallows resuming their call   black spots

of light on the brown floor   sky becomes an agent

of change   burning the river from both ends.

VI.

Lupine & flowering mullein where the road ends
spruce and hornbeam   lupine where the road disappears

in a circle of mullein and stevia   blue lid of sky
to transition from one world to another   not sky

where the road deepens   flowers that are a bridge
to the other side   stevia & sorghum at the forest's edge

How are we to say what was here?   First field of light
inside a perimeter   "zones of alienation"   lupine

& feather grass bordering an abandoned house   Blue
shutters on white stone   raised shelf of cowslip

Two are one   raised lupine & flowering mullein
form a chain of reflection   refractions of not-Eden

smooth face of white birch   dissolves in a slow
moving wind   shelter of mullein & feather grass

bald cypress low to the road   disappearing
under red skies   enfolded in flora from Lelyov

blue-green skin of birch blackened by ash.

VII.

What was left not Eden but its refraction   not Eden
but its reflection   on cellophane the wrapped limbs of

radioactive logs   gathered in a line & placed on the mud
red inside a seam of green   the logs laid over ants

spiders bugs that lined the surface   granular surface
of sky poured over burning logs   wet to the touch

earth where they were laid   like fences arranged
on a wet landscape   Not Eden but its

aftermath   a chorus of children in a ring
of wire & light   caught at the edge of the red forest

swallows where a field was   wild boar & fox
moving toward the perimeter   in the alienation zone

where they have come to rest   Not Eden
inside a ring of white logs   placed in the landscape

end to end   as far as the eye can see   end to
end   in a trail of ash & smoke

swallows & sparrows moving inside the empty shell
of sarcophagus.

VIII.

And in the deserted field there was
winter . . . cornstalks dead in a field of

crows. . . . And the chickens had black cockscombs
not red ones.

CITY EARTH

*. . . the sky so swift in the passage of the constel-
lations, in the play of their colors, that it is impossible to leave.*

—Charles Olson, *Mayan Letters*

*Let it be this way, think about it: this water should
be removed, emptied out for the formation of the
earth's own plate and platform, then comes the
sowing, the dawning of the sky-earth . . .*

*And then the earth arose because of them; it
was simply their word that brought it forth. For
the forming of the earth they said, "Earth."*

—*Popol Vuh* (translated by Dennis Tedlock)

To arrive at this place of numbers without sun
rotating on a limb of catalpa

freighted wind from the south
opening oneself to what is to come.

Here is visualization on the red
map a rope passed among strangers

who read the calendar of days
for signs of return.

Here is relic sign imparted to the last
departed on the Street of Death

where their names are written in sand.

*

The dead are waking beside us.

To be consumed by the rhythms of the desert is to be
uncovered on pallets of straw and magnesium

to be surrounded by hawk flares
in a sky constructed of magnesium.

Here in the beginning of a chapter titled "new beginnings"
the arousal of shame as the human objects are set

into the ground. . . . A depth of shadows
mechanically drawn. Here is our signature

etched in larkspur and bone.

*

The dead are waking inside a grid of poplar and granite.

Solitary practice inserts itself in this desert of larkspur.

One remembers solitude of rain's iridescence.

Red stone covered over in sand.

The murmur of skin underneath tented wind.

Animated by what is present / octagonal shape of star.

*

We are celebrating the birth of moon on a slow falling lake.

Let the surrender come to you in calligraphic bursts and spiral

jets of granite dust on red clay.

*

Anthracite flame from inside its canyon

Lizard & mule deer.

Cave city where no city is.

Dehiscence of land flow & flower beginning

on a surface of yellow flint.

Blue phacelia and desert willow. . . .

*

Coyote dawn.

Puma light from the west.

Each Silver Slipper . . .

Black mesquite's copper scorpion.

Heading toward its line planted in desert grass.

Dark where coyote strayed. . . .

Creosote on black   lines that form a creosote circle

looped by wild horned toads

a basin of red light . . . torn by floods

from Pangaea's mouth.

*

Herons & centipedes moving in unison

across deposits of molybdenum.

*

Noon's captive
toads flamingo vultures

huddled at an impasse
blind timber rattlers

Seven as a rite of passage

No locale
No closure

Frontier's cinder ruins across US 1
Smooth ellipsis of crow cry

Pine kill on petroglyph hill
Gnomic rasp of shifts

Draft shale mounds
of bleak iris

Heads of seagulls
atop basalt nuclear stockpile

Lifting a javelin's head from desert floor
built on a theorem of antelope.

*

To drop down knee level
on soft desert grass

A seeker built of skin & muscle . . .

*

Nimbus of pine & mule deer

Tracking the self out of hiding

On desert grass jaguar's lair

Encamped on horizon's elbow

Sagebrush where sea once was

Ornamental bromelias of forest

Anemone fires across blue cuts of sky.

*

Hinged city horizon
that rests inside the bank of cactus light.

Wave cavern
Bridge where light escapes

A pattern of after lifted out
High inside heron's ridge

Locale's circular scale
Planted over ridge lookout

Indention's crow flight
looping over city dirt slide

lift of its granite braille
hidden inside basalt's cut-through.

*

Raven wing

Meteorite show high in the western night

Isolated cusp of desert canyon

Pools and spills down the hills

Human bank of rock

This nether space of signs

Mortality's episodic drift

"My leg became the tool"

Drawn line cut into new earth

Lined earth drawn over

Dissolves of Snake & Crab.

*

In patterns form exists apart from the form

    Ossuary built city sky

Lock of grass

    Gnomic bone that has the meat inside

Lift of its bromeliad flowers

    Like skin dripped in fat

Ocean wood where it loses form

Skin's ambient cull

Signs of sky's house

Cut from skin's viscous meat.

*

Sun bark

Earth's declivity / A bend inside its arms

Torso's somber decal
stripped of ground to give up ground

Lake's traveler blind for evening

Javelin hunt where skin is tight
held together by rope's coil

And the circle is a graft on earth's skin.

*

Gave ground under the Seven Macaw

Drift's alembic core

Skull weather
writing itself out

snaking through wind's open harness

Blind peristalsis
Leg line on desert floor

Where yucca flower is part basin part
Orphic crown

Came under the spell of the Seven Macaw
Venus & Scorpius

rising in the east.

*

Junajpu's blowgun

black tint of its spill
blown into nance tree's hideaway

sky ink drawn to their lair
nance tree's scorpion rising

from sky's water released
loose wind heading east

rising above sky water's shell.

*

Foehn wind heading west
   arch of red desert dust   highway's barren
cellular mark   sundown's lure   caught
               fish at the sky's edge

*

Loft where loft isn't space anymore.
Position as one becomes it.

A form of writing across earth.
Cross where the lettering fell down.

"There is this route . . . this leg
that leads backward in possibility."

White splinter of sand circle
over circle in this exercise

of repetition finding
the crow line back through

cactus veins.

*

No utterance when
our dead rest apart from shelter.

Praying before dawn . . .

Drawn
backward into abyssal core

of red sun . . . Dart's morning shower
signaling blood

from the hyena's call
a ring of owl feathers

perishing beneath a ledge
of mountain ice.

NOTE.

"Movements from the Fire Cycle": Texts that informed this poem's writing include
Svetlana Alexievich's *Voices from Chernobyl: The Oral History of a Nuclear
Disaster* (translated by Keith Gessen), Robert Polidori's *Zones of Exclusion: Pripyat
and Chernobyl*, and Alla Yaroshinskaya's *Chernobyl: The Forbidden Truth* (translated by Michèle Kahn and Julia Sallabank).

"City Earth": This poem draws on a number of texts related to the work of the environmental artist Michael Heizer, including *Effigy Tumuli: The Reemergence of
Ancient Mound Building* and *Double Negative*.

Three Poems
Sandra Meek

BELLWETHER

Restless, fevered, we spreed west. We
were the hem. The mend. The shepherds.

The seeds. The belled sheep we led
rendered the green ever

elsewhere. Remember we'd weep
when we entered the pens? Nevertheless, need

be. We held the sweet necks. The reddened steel.
Weren't we the blessed? The trees

we pellet-peppered screeched, trembled, then went
serene. Remember the feces-flecked nests, rent,

egg-bereft? Deep September, he reversed
the legend: he'd be the serpent; *Eve*, he'd

tell me, the serpent's speech
served me. Eden, the hell we fled,

fenced, he'd tell me, fettered me free.
Senseless—me, kneeled, the meek he'd pet

between pecks. Hell-bent mess
we were, we weren't seekers, keepers. We

were knee-deep. Wed, we never fledged—
we hedged bets. Settled west. Me the sentence. He

the meter. The repetend. He, ledger; me,
ledge. He'd pretend, tell me the expected

sweetnesses: me, never. We were drenched
embers. The dew-eyed deer were few, then

fewer. The ferns receded, the beeches, the seed
bees. Remember the deer's shed velvet, the beetles'

bejeweled terre verte eyes? The evergreen shelters,
the steepled trees? The endless

ended. Then, the teeth-strewn glens. The wheel-wrecked
deserts. The shelled reefs, the depleted

breeze, the sleepless swelter. Remember
when they'd reel free, settle the trees, preen?

When they flew, they were the sleekest speed
we never held. When they fell—when we

felled them—they were the spell
ended. We were the nettle; we

the weed: we, the blessed.
We, the free.

STILL LIFE WITH CARIBBEAN REEF SQUID
(*Sepioteuthis sepioidea*)

What swam back from the doe-damp eye—
your own goggled face, unfinished
as the goby's you treaded sea against

the surf's surging to witness emerge
from its brain-coral cave, that fogged, head-
on perspective rendering it simple

beyond its being: a gas-masked gesture drawing
crosshatched to shadows. As against high-cotton
rag paper, stroke by stroke you remember

a man who sketched you as you slept, packing
on charcoal until it approximated
the darkness the face meant to rise

against. You saw it before you knew
its name, knowing only the creature
had seen you, knowing this only by its quick

disappearance. But the squid
do not startle. Fins rippling, sleek bodies gleaming
liquid as wax sprung from the head

cavity of a sperm whale sparked to specter
the flame it would wick to only when the knives
were docked, their arms extend, mimicking

sargassum weed: hovering, though you know
what's coming, still it surprises, how sudden
the unfurling, the arms flash-flowering to star

anemone, how fierce their drilling the dark
pockets for what harbored in the hope
refuge might lie in a bed

of hard corals. How you trailed this ravenous
unfolding, shadowing their trolling
the fringe reef—iridescent, crushed-pearl mounds

studded with fan corals lavender and lime, royal
purple, waved from stiff wrists of holdfasts
by leeward's muted, moon-driven surf. Dusky

anchovy. Hardhead silversides. Shrimp, dwarf
herring: all things soft, devoured. All things armored,
discarded: head-ribs-vertebral column a single

unsheathing. To walk on water is to miss
this world by half: this, immersion
taught you. No alarm's gold brightening, no brick

red of retreat. No diversion of ink clouding their swerve
into distance. Like sequins cast in organza
veils, a spray of sinkers woven to fishing nets'

translucence, they signed each to each
in shimmering chromatics you could read only
as radiance, diminishment

propelling you on. Whether hours or minutes,
you could not say. You followed. Then, led
to the coral's fossil-strewn shore, the shell

of you returned.

DEWEY

We were the tern-swept breeze, the steeples, the treed
keys. We, the shell-flecked, sheltered reef;
beet-red ferns in the swell, the treble-clefed eels, the secret
recesses. We were the greenest serpent
exed between the eyes. When they
descended—the vessels, the crew; the jeeps,
the jets, the free-felled shells—we fed
the fleet. They swelled the streets. The crème
de crème, the well-heeled perfect percent, weekended
elsewhere, where between refreshments they erected
secret decrees: Vex. Wedge. Tenth. Bleed. When the shells
fell, we fled—resettled, fled: these were the extremes
we knew. We were the neck
kneed. The resentment they engendered festered,
grew. When they blew the reef, we keened
the keeled perch, the sennets, the needles, the green depths'
peppered veneer. When they blew the reef they tempered
the steel we'd weld, they fermented fever they never knew
we few fleshed; clenched, we were relentless—we

Sandra Meek

wrested free. They were the sweltered cemetery breeze
between terns' embered nests. We were the rebel
steeple, the leveled keys. The trees regrew; nets mended, the reefs
teemed. Remember them wrecked, depleted. Remember
the rent fences, the shell-shredded sheep.
Remember when we were helter-skeltered, sleepless,
shelterless, bereft. We wrested
free, then. Remember, when the next
descend.

·

NOTE. Dewey is the official name of the town and harbor in Culebra, Puerto Rico. Culebra was occupied by the US military in 1901 and served as the primary gunnery and bombing practice site for the US Navy's entire Atlantic fleet from WWII to 1975. From 1970 to 1975, during "La Lucha," Culebra's 743 citizens resisted and ultimately were successful in removing the Navy from their island.

Ancient Inland Sea
Krista Eastman

I WILL BE THE TOUR GUIDE again, just as I was in college, except now the tour is forming on a long and limitless afternoon with my son, on time we have for dreaming. He has called out, "Let's pretend," has rummaged through his favorites—The Cave, The Diving Board, The Ice Rink—before selecting for us, finally, The Boat. Together we summon a new world from nothing, pulling its pieces from a battered old basket, pressing our earnestness to the task of assembling some details: the tannin-brown river water, the quick click and hum of flipping on the sound system to tap test the mic. At close of day, divvying the swag, one sticky stack of cash for the captain, one for the guide. I board a double-decker tour boat just as I used to, with the same white sneakers and navy shorts, the same close-fitting white chemise, and find that I still know every bit of this boat, that already I've tucked the shirt in tight and buttoned stripes onto my epaulets, that already I've started for work on the transfiguring musk of my "moonlight" perfume.

With the same old gusto and easy charm I say things like "Welcome aboard!" and "Watch your step!" and "Thank you for coming!" And the boat moves up the same five-mile stretch of the Wisconsin River, through the high banks of sandstone cliffs whose long, naked surfaces shift in color with the light all day and all summer. It's how I remember it—the jaws of my passengers crushing popcorn kernels, sucking brown pop up straws—but more than not it is different, like a dream where you're at home, but home is somehow someplace else. This time I won't make tuition money on the unthreatening nature of my hospitality, on tall tales of river rats and lumber jacks, or on the names of every passing "point of interest." This time there'll be no Twin Sisters or Devil's Elbow, no Coldwater Canyon, no Chimney Rock. This time I'm revisiting the notion of the ancient inland sea, and to do that I press passengers into their seats with my microphone, do what it is I need to do. Now we will all of us listen, I say, to the sound of water meeting water in the dark bilge below.

In the old days, when I performed on cue and the boat charged

259

Krista Eastman

upstream on schedule, I spoke of this "ancient inland sea" in an almost passing mention. "Scientists say this sandstone is what remains
of an ancient inland sea that covered most of North America five
hundred million years ago, making this some of the oldest exposed
bedrock in the world." Then three or maybe four of the lower deck's
faces would show signs of apprehension and wonder, turning to cast
humbled looks onto the passing sandstone. Still others had no use for
this information and with a tinge of hostile disinterest let the numbers pass, refusing to intervene as the significance of deep time blew
toward the boat's propellers. Then at the shore landings, at the end
of the canyon walk, one person might drop back to gain a private audience, to tell me about Jesus, about the world being only ten thousand
years old, or about some other low number I needed to know, such
as the 144,000 persons God would one day admit to paradise.

Today I'm both bodies in that quiet conference, the polite and passive guide with her remunerated willingness to listen, the passing
tourist whose ideas are rooted in the desire to influence, whose body
cradles the secret she believes to have been kept from too many for
too long. Here in the back of the canyon boardwalk, I too want to
save souls: The ancient inland sea that once covered most of North
America didn't have a name, a story, or a single worry for itself. It
lapped and swelled and swamped in shallowness for millions and
millions of years without once casting a long eye to its shores or the
future. And when it drained—which it did from time to time—the
hot, sandy floor never wondered at its being there, or imagined
another day forward, or stopped to wait with bated breath for the
arrival of the Brachiosaurus or for the roving eyes of bipeds signaling
to each other in eerie packs. No, the sea had not one special feeling
about its low, warm endlessness, or the time it had spent or was
about to spend on nothing. As for the trilobites living in the sea, the
record suggests they crawled out from time to time, their goal to
scamper about in the night on the shores of the sea's unexamined
existence.

Gathering themselves back on the boat, my passengers look pleased
with the narrow canyon walk crowded with ferns; the thick, wet
breath of real-life rock; the damp but functional toilets they found
waiting for them at walk's end. I stand at the helm, turning the mic
on and off as they half watch and wait. The list of things the ancient
inland sea could not anticipate seems to me then long and inconse-
quential. Would it mean anything to mention the cooking pot, the
patchwork quilt, the thimble? Boots, retinal scans, minivans, pet

260

grooming? Is it useful to mention that the warm, inert sea of our planet's ancient times could no more imagine dentistry than we can imagine the earth of our everyday lives as a vast sea swamping along not in silence but without us? The eighteenth-century Scottish geologist James Hutton was perhaps the first to apprehend the seemingly limitless age of the earth, to peer into the bottomless pool of deep time. Staring down the disappearing lines of the geologic record, he reached for a quill and with regal tremor wrote, "We find no vestige of a beginning, no prospect of an end."

I cannot help but notice the stern young man with a trim haircut and a tight baseball cap in the second-to-last row, and see right away that he will scoff at my nascent attempt to spout poetry on the speechless back of deep time. He is a man who breaks complex problems into units and fixes those units one by one. He has, he would say, "Zero patience" for multiple meanings brushed down over time. When eventually he does shoot me a warning look—his chin dropping to his chest, his eyes glowering up and out in such a way as to suggest he cares little for my love of this or any fumbling attempt— I think of the geology professor who told me it's impossible for us to really conceive of geologic time, that the only way to get there, the only way to seize it for a slip of one apprehending second, is via orders of magnitude, or analogy. Analogy, I remember, is metaphor is poetry is time wasting. I turn the mic back on.

When I talk to my son about something that happened before his birth, he always asks where he was when that thing happened. Once, on the walk home from the city pool I showed him an effigy mound, telling him that ancestors of the Ho-Chunk had built it thousands of years before. He seemed satisfied with this information and sure of himself in the way of any child on the imagined precipice of being a grown-up. But then he said to me, pride lengthening his spine, "Back when there was water in our basement!" In the beginning, that is, back before everything else, God drove ancient waters into the basement of our postwar home, the proof of this being a now faint water line. Together we left the record there, flip-flopping all the way back, me to make dinner as if in some future sketch of primitive woman, he to lie cool and naked on the big red couch.

How old is your son? a front-row passenger asks then, large working hands resting gently in his lap, a wide gold wedding band bridging the joints. *Three*, I say, and he smiles, his hooded eyes turning to some other day, to some boy of his who became a man. I realize then that the passengers have remained and will remain another thing altogether, that to summon them with too much detail will be to find new ways for them not to listen.

When I next look out the window, the ancient inland sea has receded. We list left, our bow buried deep into a low dune. I recall running as a child alongside the house I grew up in, a simple foursquare located in a rural dairy town, the house's butter-colored siding in perpetual need of painting. It's summertime, full afternoon, and I am borne alongside the house on great swells of joy and conviction, maybe piety, maybe passion. "Someday," I promise myself then, "I will write about this." And while in real life I kept running or walking, kept moving alongside the house, in some other story I stopped, took stones from my pocket, and began dropping them one by one, connecting them to whatever is or has ever been the present moment, installing for myself the long trail of the vaguest to-do. In the present, on this end of the trail, do not worry, I assure my passengers, who keep half rising in their seats to confirm that the water really is all gone, now we will all of us examine the promises we made a long time ago.

These days I suspect that what that girl meant to do, without realizing it, was to write about the specific beauty of a specific childhood, itself cradled by the warm luck of good times, and to do so urgently, to do it well before realizing that we were none of us important. And I think too that this is the thing I now wish she'd already done so that I might already be done with it. Someday, I will write about this, she said, and by this maybe she meant, yet again without realizing it, the sun filtering through a life not yet cognizant of its place in the world, or the task of chronicling, without self-consciousness, the beauty of being no one from nowhere. But probably she also meant to use her "way with words" to evoke the coming dusk: dad's milk truck in the driveway, air thick on lightning bugs, the stink of our kick-the-can sweat.

If I were to sit down now as that girl dreamed I would, with my quill and candle, my hair wild and uncombed, my breath visible in the barren attic room in which I always meant to live and work alone, I might begin by gesturing to the charm that can attend the child's effort to assign meaning to the world, to my own folksy tin pail of failed attempts. As a child, I believed my mom could hear my thoughts and I ran experiments to catch her. I thought that going to the drive-up in your pajamas was an event so rare and thrilling that doing so was based on a town-wide system of taking turns. And from

Krista Eastman

deep inside the mustiness of my church's weekly catechism, I once accepted that despair was the worst sin of all, that it was the final sin from which no one had been, or ever would be, forgiven. But I can't or won't do this for long. Here in the present, I am neither feeling wry about the container of my happy childhood nor moved to bring it out of the shadows of memory. I am haunted, instead, by questions not asked, by whole worlds left in place.

Now I drag a big green monster—an oversized stuffed plaything, its polyester fur dulled from decades of gathering dust—down the narrow aisle to the front of the boat and introduce him along the way. Say hello to Captain Ken! Captain Ken is a retired schoolteacher back here for his twenty-fifth season on the river! You are in safe hands with Captain Ken! I hoist him onto the too-small seat of the captain's chair where he teeters. I hold out my hand to support him and then, turning from the irritation I fear might be sweeping the boat in waves, use the mic to make the sounds of boat engines starting. We tour like this a very long time.

The ancient inland sea that covered most of North America did not emerge from nothing but from the long, intermittently legible arc of the preceding 4.5 billion years, from innumerable incidents of heaving, shifting, eroding, compressing, cleaving. Imagine the footage of this time passing, sped up by some unimaginable factor, the great netherworld grinding, a roiling fount of impressive eruptions. There is then, perhaps, the halting spread of new land, fingers choking off pits of life, and sometime much later the unmarked arrival of the Precambrian and Cambrian eras, several hundred million years of tropical weathering and erosion brushing the continent until it was nothing more than a low bowl of sand, for our purposes (if our purposes had lived here), the perfect sea bottom.

The ancient inland sea swamps in, no one there to consider it. And now there is nothing we can say or do but to hover godlike above, to suffer with our full bladders, with this dumb, discordant telling, piss before potties, earth before us. This hovering omniscience, though normally a position of great power, is in this instance both difficult and useless. If it's an origin story, if it's a human story, it's an ill-fitting one. Imagine the mythic lumberjack, the so-called pioneer, the American evangelist of bootstrapping, and then imagine him trying to fell and dig here, to sculpt a cabin from sand and muck, to start a fire in a swamp. Imagine him damp and seated on the low, wet shore, waiting

263

for the years to pass. Though he squats on present-day Wisconsin, what geologist Robert H. Dott called the "center of the stable heartland of the continent," the heartland has yet to make it all the way here, remaining in this long moment central to somewhere or something else. And so he wades in a tropical sea hotly lapping at the equator while the continent inches its way across the mantle, while his boots rot in place. Let us watch now as he endeavors to hold this spot and guard this vision—what will one day be *him*, what will one day be *his*—through the blank and muted roaring of five hundred million more years.

The Jehovah's Witness approaches smelling of spearmint gum and I warm to the notion of making our two hearts a conference once again. Maybe this *is* a human story, I whisper to her, eyeing the others with concern. *Maybe it's not*, she shoots back. She has signaled to Tight Baseball Cap, who begins winding up the cord of my mic with maniacal precision. *Just a short break from your lovely commentary*, an old woman says from the second row, clinking butterscotch candy on her teeth, *a chance to take in the scenery some*. She's a sympathetic invention and I know right away what she wants. The original tour, with its abundant views of river and rock, was a far more enjoyable experience. In those days, this boat sailed in leisure time, luxuriating in progress and destiny, in our special freedoms and superior intellect, in the beauty of being the center of the universe. In that tour, I'd point at the rocks, the plain simple fact of their "sliding into view on the right side of the boat, a rock formation resembling a buttery stack of pancakes," and together we would marvel at the triple force of wind, water, and frost erosion, at what had been wrought exquisitely and especially for us. On that tour, we did not dwell on the deep record of time, but made of it a souvenir, yet another something for the undisturbed heart.

Later, at day or season's end, we'd all disembark the boat, pressing ourselves with reinvigorated steps onto the land, our senses alive to the smell of hemlock, our hearts rinsed in the water's lapping, our stories brimming with innocence and benevolence, cash tendered and cash received. "Thank you for joining us, have a great stay in Wisconsin, and a safe trip home!" All summer I jumped the gap between boat and dock, tethering a straight line back to the shore, to the way we could not possibly remain, to the simple, stupid coming home of us all.

*

Next my son chooses The Cave and together we enter its narrow opening, he with minimal effort, me with limbs to spare. Once inside, our breath is close and we don't know what to do, or how to remain still for long. But we are attending to matters of great urgency— the point is to whisper and hide, for no creature or thing to find us— and so we make tiny adjustments to our silence, to our sitting. I imagine the intelligent creature who might find us here in hundreds or thousands of years and then parse us out, bit by bit, placing each bone in plastic, marking the whole lot of us for reasons I cannot know. *Diets rich, cavities present, causes of death unknown.* And though this creature might be weary of her lonely job labeling the dead, she will probably not hear in the rattling of my bones the many questions I keep for her. She will not marvel at how proficient I was in pretending any manner of things, how I could imagine myself good or bad or somewhere in between, how I could make stories anywhere, from nothing. But maybe she will muse on the excavated accounts of my irrational belief system, or wonder at the foolish way I scampered across the lost plateau of my existence.

My legs are stiff and I wonder how long we'll live in this cave, or if the pot on the stove is boiling over. I watch the boy who smiles at me with conspiratorial eyes, bringing his shoulders closer to his ears. I suspect him of feeling cozy in here, of forming a new womb against a world where mean things crouch in the periphery, things that are eager to nip him on the knee, to take off small strips of the innocence he's beginning to understand he can't keep, or which were never his in the first place, depending on your take. We are matched in our way, he afraid of the wild, fluxing perimeters of the right here and right now, me afraid of floating off into boundless or bottomless things, like outer space, deep time, death. I have no choice but to let him run on up ahead, to stop at the corner as I taught him to before crossing into the floods and the fire, into worlds coming undone. "I need to make dinner," I tell him before steam-burning my hand at the stove, my mom flanks bumping the diorama walls. Later, The Cave breaks, the blanket slipping from the couch's back, and my son is revealed at play, still wrapped in the cloak of his imagining. "Are you a nice monster?" he prompts two of his toys to ask the third. "Oh!" the toys rejoice then, without enough pause. "We are nice too!" For days and months, I repeat this one to myself, in a prayerlike way, at work, at the grocery, Are you a nice monster? Oh! We are nice too!

*

265

The ancient inland sea cannot wonder what we're doing here or how long we'll stay. But the passengers, with their brief lives and long disappointments, do not possess the sea's same languid grace. The reviews arrive whether I summon them or not. There's a bunch of binging sounds, plucky rounds of fire, then the words hover before me until I swipe left with my eyes. *The scenery gets three stars, the tour guide one. . . .Chick will not shut . . .* I close my eyes and turn on the mic. In the slightly static void of the sound system, I see the Catholic priest of my youth raise his robed arms up to his sides, his palms cupped to receive the heavens, his eyes closing because of his power and safety, because of that old yarn about the church's ancient rock.

Let us peer into the dark bilge below.

In the bilge, everything slops on a semiregular pattern, flopping up one steel side then the other. There is the small thumping din of oily water, plus the loosely ordered churning of the people and things that surface here inside—tiny pebbles of long ago land mass, trilobites and other Lazarus sea creatures, small children, unaware of time's passage, who follow the flow of plastic toys. What sort of progress, we might ask, can be made from this? What origin story, what ancient rock? The bilge has the look the living room gets when my son quits a world as quickly as he's summoned it, leaving everything to rupture all over the floor, when later that night I'm likely to appear again, Mother lumbering into the room's shadows in stained robe, with unkempt hair. I could pick these things up, exert some order, clean the line. But instead I lie on the old couch and look at the room of objects at large. Do not worry, I whisper to us and them, the water will come.

Mountains & The Wind
Eliot Weinberger

MOUNTAINS

1. Mexico

The mountain seems to be there, but the mountain is not what it seems, for the mountain is not solid, made of dirt and rock, but is a hollow shell filled with water. When you are asleep, your spirit leaves your body and goes wandering. Your dreams are the home movies of those travels.

When you are asleep, you can enter the mountain and talk to the water people. Human infants who die before baptism become water people, or humans who die struck by lightning or from the "rain diseases" of tainted water. The water people themselves have many children; there are more of them than humans. They are not gods or supernatural beings, but people, with names and ages and personalities. They speak the same language as we do, work and dress as we do, live as long or as short. But, like your spirit who visits them, they have no bodies. Their food is the same as our food, but what they eat is the smell of fresh fruit or roasting corn or the steam rising from simmering beans or the smoke from grilling meat. Evanescence is solid, aroma nourishing.

In the dream you can see their villages and cities, their apartment buildings and houses with patios. Awake, these are the rocks and boulders in the rushing streams that come down from inside the mountain, and on the banks and slopes. The streams are their highways; the irrigation canals that branch off are their streets. In the dream you'll see that the boulders have tiny doors.

2. China

1678: The path was arduous and the air made me dizzy. At the peak, my friend and I waited for the moon to rise. Overwhelmed by the view, we poured wine on the ground and pledged that if either of us ever forgot this sight, we would sink like the wine into nothing. A week later, he became delirious, babbling about the mountain, and died.

Someday I will come back, with a gourd for water and a bamboo hat, and I'll practice the breathing exercises. I may not attain immortality, but perhaps I will avoid an unexpected death.

3. Japan

In the old days, the Ones Who Sleep on the Mountain had, as their ultimate devotional practice, "Abandoning the Body": suicide. This was banned by the authorities and replaced by a rite called "Gazing into the Valley."

4. Germany

1826: My room in the tavern had a fine view of the mountain. Yet that night, something strange occurred. I was not asleep and dreaming; I was awake, staring idly from my bed at the moonlight that half lit the meager furnishings. As the bells from the two churches in the village tolled midnight, an old friend of mine, long dead, suddenly appeared standing before me. He was a doctor with whom I once had passionate debates: he arguing for the primacy of reason, and I for the imagination. He was wearing his old gray coat, leaning unsteadily on his Malacca cane. He told me not to be afraid, that he was not a ghost, that he was merely a trick of my imagination. He cited Part 2, Section 1, Chapter 3 of Kant's *Critique of Pure Reason* as proof that ghosts do not exist. He repeated again, as he often did, that "reason is the highest principle." Then he reached into the pocket of his vest to look at his gold watch, and pulled out a handful of worms.

5. Aotearoa

Some say they are human souls or ghosts, but most think they are a kind of people. They are pale and not tattooed, live on the mountain, dress only in white, and carry their babies in their arms instead of on their backs. They're rarely alone, only seen in groups, laughing, singing, playing flutes. When the mountain is deep in mist, the sounds carry and one can hear them. They are terrified of the color red. There was a man who claimed that he had once killed one when they were disturbing his crops and the body immediately turned into something like rotten wood. Another claimed he had married one; she would appear in darkness in his hut and leave before dawn. He had never seen her, so he tricked her into staying one day and found she was more beautiful than any human. Betrayed, she gathered feathers and plastered them to her body, climbed to the roof of his hut, sang an unforgettable song that the whole village heard, then flew off to the mountain and never came back.

6. Venezuela

1897: A flat plateau above sheer cliffs, the top of the mountain is rarely seen through the clouds. The people there have a drug that allows them to live for thousands of years, but most become bored and listless and, after a few centuries, stop taking it.

7. Iceland

He and one of his farmhands became lost in a snowstorm. Night was falling. They found a cave on the side of the mountain and took shelter at the entrance, reluctant to go further inside, and sat on two rocks. They heard something moving toward them from within the cave and then, in the darkness, they saw two enormous eyes and nothing else, shining like two moons or two shields. It was a giant, and it began to recite a strange poem of twelve stanzas in a terrifying voice. One stanza went:

> Dim cliffs break apart.
> Tongues of flame blaze even faster.
> Out of the ground
> A weird new clay begins to flow.
> The heavens split and crack open.
> The giants come to life.
> Twilight rushes from the torrents,
> till the world is extinguished,
> till the world is extinguished.

The giant repeated the entire poem two more times, then vanished back into the cave. It was dawn, the snow had stopped, the men hurried away.

On their way home a few days later, they looked for the cave but could not find it. He remembered the entire poem, but the farmhand could not recall a single word. One year later, to the day, his farmhand died. But he himself lived a long and prosperous life, and nothing else unusual ever happened to him.

8. India

According to the laws of rhetoric, a smile is white. Therefore, a snow-capped mountain is laughing at you.

THE WIND
[1671]

Seek for knowledge in the greater World!

Philosophers stammer at the wind.
It is one of the secret and hidden things.
It was born after the Creation. There was no wind in Eden.

Winds are vehement or mild, constant or mutable, general or precise.
Some are hot, some cold, some moistening and dissolving, some drying and
　　astringent.
They gather the clouds and disperse them.

They are vagabond and voluble. They are a broom that sweeps the earth.
They drive forward with a mad kind of violence.
They are fresh and merry gales. Windy years are the most healthful.

They come from every region of the sky.
There are countries where it never rains, or seldom.
But there are no countries where the wind never blows, and often.

Winds are made, or engendered a thousand ways.
The Sun is the chief begetter of winds.
The wind follows shooting stars.

Wind comes from great bodies of water, and the ice floating in the sea.
It comes from the burning of forests and dry meadows.
The melting of snow brings the wind.

On the peaks of great mountains, there is no wind.
The rainbow is dissolved by the wind.
The woods murmur before we feel the wind.

There are winds underground, vaporous and mercurial.
You feel them in the mines.
They are sulfurous, sent out in an earthquake, flaming from fiery mountains.

Caves are the prisons of winds, from which they are sometimes set free.
On the rocky cliffs of Aber Barry, near Severn in Wales, if you lay your ear, you
    can hear the sounds of winds underground.
There are wells in Dalmatia into which, if you cast a stone, winds will rise, as
    if the stone had broken some covering.

The North wind blows in the day. It scatters the clouds.
It makes the sea look blacker.
When it blows, men are more lively, healthful, and greedy for food.

But beware the North wind when sowing seed.
It makes sheep grow lame and bleary-eyed. It weakens their coupling.
Facing the North wind, they produce ewes and no rams.

The South wind blows in the night. It is wandering and free, soft and mild.
It gathers and nourishes the clouds, bringing rain.
Waves swell higher. The sea looks bluer and more bright.

It is agreeable to plants and fruits, killing their cankers and rust.
But men grow slow and dull and lose their appetites. Their breath turns rank.
Diseases reign. Timber and stones sweat.

The East wind is sharp and dry, vehement and large.
It draws the clouds to it, and they grow stronger, like fire in the wind.
It provokes long rains.

It is thought to be mischievous, neither good for man nor beast, as the proverb
    says.
It brings worms and caterpillars, hurtful to fruit. It is bad for grain.
In an East wind visible things appear larger.

271

Eliot Weinberger

The West wind is moist and nourishing.
It is vehement, and bends the trees.
But it is friendly to herbs and flowers and all manner of vegetables.

It is said that the West wind blew in the Golden Age.
It is the companion of a perpetual spring.
In a West wind audible things are heard further.

Winds are the merchants of vapors, which they carry from country to country.
They travel on long journeys, and sometimes arrive weary.
Columbus on the coast of Portugal knew that the West wind was blowing from
    some land.

Winds are prepared in the heavens.
They come hours before the eclipse of the moon.
They come at the rising of Orion, or when the smaller stars are not seen.

When the clouds look red at sunrise, wind is coming.
When the sun looks red at sunset, wind is coming for many days.
Mariners fear the fifth day of the Moon, for its winds make the harmless sea
    hurtful.

When the sea is smooth and calm, yet makes a murmuring sound, wind is
    coming.
When the echo of the sea on the shore is heard more clearly, wind is coming.
When the sea swells silently and rises higher than ordinary in the harbor, when
    the tide comes in sooner than it should, wind is coming.

When the hearth fire looks pale and makes a murmuring sound, a storm is
    coming.
When the coals shine bright and spark, wind is coming.
Leaves and straw and feathers start swirling on the ground before the wind
    comes.

A heron flying high over a low cloud means wind.
A heron standing alone in the sand, sad and melancholy, means wind.
Geese cry out for rain.

When seagulls flock from the sea to the shore and stay upon the dry land, wind is coming.

When crows fly to the rivers and lakes, chattering and bathing, a storm is coming, but crows walking up and down mean wind with no rain.

An owl hoots that the weather will change.

Spiders work harder when the wind is coming, knowing they cannot spin their webs in the wind.

When the sea is calm the wind will come from the way the dolphins come.

Pigs are terrified by the wind.

The Damage

Rae Armantrout

NOTICE

1.

The way a gesture
used to ward off trouble
became cheerful waving.

There was so much looming
and vanishing

to take note of
always;

we felt like play actors

before we knew
what we were about

and after.

2.

Turns out
the mummy's curse
is real.

You pump thick death
out of the ground
and burn it—

it kills you.

But in all the movies
curses are a cheap
plot trick.

The doofus
who can't read the hieroglyph
dies first

and no one misses him.

Them.

We *were* born yesterday.

We're sorry.

CIRCLES

1.

First they told me
the future would solve
the present.

Then they told me
the present
would solve the future.

The present is the world
minus intention.

I'm not allowed there.
They know this.

I begin a string
of letters, picketing
distance.

2.

The Cheerios
in the babies' cups
are full of Roundup.

"Circle,"
one girl chirps.

INNOVATIONS

The first idea
was to continue.

Hurtling?

But a thought
is a kind of stop.

*

To continue
is to start over.

*

The first innovation
was serial

survival.
Is that for real?

*

Is it clear that
a billion
spruce needles
are good

Rae Armantrout

while a billion green
detergent pods
are not?

*

"I'm so done! LOL,"
say the young,

correctly.

Scare quotes have morphed
into emojis.

RECENT THINKING

Some say the fact that the world is computable
is evidence we're living in a simulation.

And the fact that the simulations *we* create
are improving rapidly is further evidence of this.

It is reasonable to think that any simulation *might*
have been created by one more advanced than itself,

a potentially infinite regress in which
the word simulation becomes meaningless.

Experience suggests that simulations are games
with both player and nonplayer characters.

No character has explicitly stated
that we should destroy the biosphere
to test the limits of the game.

Rae Armantrout

THE END

Aspirational love
flickered between them
at the end.

The End.

Some might say
it was conventional
love, but
it was aspirational too.

It got in
all the newspapers.

Don't be a cynic.

                    *

Want to hear a different story?

All the insect helpers
were gone in an instant,

the worms
that made the beds,

the moths that worked on
Cinderella's dress.

"Where *are* you,"
intoned the baby girl,

holding both palms up
in the gesture we use

to make light of
our ignorance.

What an excellent mimic!

Wolf Tones
Sofia Samatar

—For Rosalind Palermo Stevenson

AND THEN THE SECOND TONE ENTERS, *high and fierce, the waves rising, a sudden spasm of hail scattering across the deck like a shower of pearls . . . a tone like a moan that vibrates through the ship, down through the cabins lined in red like satin jewelry boxes, those elegant little coffins, and down again through the vessel's bowels and down through the vast, imponderable weight of water, its icy knifelike blackness just on the edge of freezing . . . this is a tone that matches the trembling of the earth itself like a magical lover who knows the precise desired frequency of illumination . . . hair, black wind, the cello between her thighs, how are her hands not frozen, how is her face not frozen, that sliver of moon as the waves grow higher and white, their slopes a ghastly, fantastic white as she plays the howling insistent tone, she has found her stride, the ropes of her black hair flying and knotted about her neck . . . she is calling them . . . calling them . . . she is playing her lost summers . . . the mountains, the troops of monkeys on their way to the temple, the English church . . . and when autumn came it was time to leave the high mountains, to board the train, and she cried and cried, and they said, You cannot bear the winters here, you'll freeze . . . oh play . . . play the great winter storm and the avalanche . . . the wolves . . . she calls them over the waves, rough coats and flaming mouths . . . they are leaping down the slopes of the white waves, baying toward the ship, and she goes on playing, she goes on howling, she cannot stop. . . .*

The first time he saw her he felt as if he had been plunged into icy water. His breath froze and there was a struggle in his chest. You would think she had struck him, struck him in the sternum. She in her paisley shawl, incongruous. Five days out from shore.

*

"So you have gained your seal eggs."

"I beg your pardon?"

She gestures at his legs, her eyes smiling, crimped at the edges. "Your sea legs."

"Oh." He blushes. "Yes."

She holds out her hand. She has a soft accent, he can't place it—Indian, Persian? Her hair pinned up with a jeweled comb. Strands of hair are escaping all over her head, blowing about in the wind. "My name is Nesha."

"Wyland Alexander."

She repeats his name in her lilting voice. She tells him that, contrary to intuition, if one is ill, it is best to be on deck. When people are sick they want to go to bed, but this urge must be resisted. "Those cabins are death, death!" she says with a shudder.

"Have you been ill, Miss Nesha?"

"Oh, not for a long time."

He can believe it. She is statuesque, golden, nearly as tall as he. Of the two of them, she may be the heavier. This thought makes him blush again. He stammers something, he asks where is she going.

"North," she says.

She has no real destination. She is part of the ship's orchestra. If he comes to dinner, he can hear her play. And what does she play? She turns up a palm and shows him her fingertips, each topped with a callus like a bubble of hard, dead ice.

Now, on the cruise ship, heading north again after all these years, he remembers the gleaming dining hall, the chandeliers, and after dinner the couples dancing, dancing over the sea, and how he sat at his table and smoked and watched the orchestra. A student. Nineteen years old and bound for Paris on the *Agate*. It was a French ship, unsegregated. A new life was beginning. Some French boys gestured that he should join their table, but he refused. The orchestra played swelling, tremulous, popular tunes. *A rainy street*, they played. *A blue café*. Couples dancing cheek to cheek. A tense conductor with flyaway, graying hair. The light of the chandeliers flickered on his baton. Today, on the cruise ship, there is a singer who croons to a synthesizer. There is karaoke.

*

280

Sometimes at night he wakes in the drone of the ship and his body fools itself easily, deliciously, into thinking it is that other ship. What time is it? After midnight. He must have overslept. He's missed dinner. The last dancers will be trailing about the floor. At this time of night they move so languidly, slowly, as if underwater, or as if suspended from the ceiling on long chains. They are hanging from the chains of her long notes, the one she releases from the cello, sleekly, one after the other. In the orchestra, there is a dark-browed violinist with bowed shoulders who, during the day, sheathes her precious hands in a pair of black satin gloves, but Nesha is the heart of the group, you can see that at once, even a self-confessed musical idiot like Wyland can see it, the way she scatters light. When he sits at his favorite table on the far left, near the stage—a table the other guests soon form the habit of leaving open for him—he can sometimes catch the conductor's glance as it seeks Nesha out and finds her: a glance of confirmation, satisfaction, and cold fire.

Afterward, a patter of tired applause. She talks and laughs with the other musicians, putting her instrument away. He, at his table, is over-wound, crackling, beside himself with impatience. He fumbles with his lighter; at last he gives up and lights his cigarette with a candle.

"May I help you?"

"Thank you," she says.

He carries her cello, which is as awkward to handle as a human body. After she plays, she cannot sleep, no matter how late it is. She wants to run, to roam the deck in the cold air. She tells him that when she was at school, she never used to be able to sleep; she'd get up to all kinds of mischief in the dormitory. She hid the other girls' shoes, she tied their long hair to the bedposts. She was reprimanded and almost sent home. In the end she was only punished, deprived of the daily recess hour, locked up in the headmistress's office, but she didn't care because there was a radio there, she'd play it very softly, leaning her head against it to hear, she could feel the vibrations all through her cheek, her chest. She tells him that the cello is an instrument of vibration. He says he supposes this is true of all musical instruments. Yes, but the cello is special, the finest instrument for producing certain mysterious overtones called *wolf tones*.

"What do they sound like?"

281

Sofia Samatar

"Like wolves howling," she says, laughing. "Like the wild wolves of the North."

She's childish at night, giddy, her ankles flashing under her long skirt. And he, in his coat, holding her cello, is freezing, he can see his breath in the starlight, and he thinks his life is always going to be like this. A succession of wonders, one after the other, forever, until he dies. The world is so full. The sky is crammed to the edges with stars. She tells him about Sir Chandrasekhara Venkata Raman, who theorized wolf tones with his mechanical bowing machine.

She says: "I was meant to live where there is no night."

The Arctic Circle, he thinks with a shiver. But they are going to Marseilles. From there he will travel to Paris. He has a letter from his patron in his pocket. He has forty dollars sewn into the lining of his coat. He tells her he is going to be an artist. She doesn't laugh. "An artist, how marvelous!" He stammers as he attempts to explain, without boasting, how his patron, a great philanthropist, picked him out from among the boys at the technical school, first for drawing and painting lessons and then for Paris.

"Then you're one of us," she whispers, squeezing his arm. He can feel each finger through his coat.

She says kindred spirits are rare, and he nods, though deep in his heart he doesn't believe her; he still thinks he is going to find them wherever he goes. Wolf tones, she tells him, are only produced between E- and F-sharp. They occur when the frequency of the vibrating string matches the vibration of the instrument's body. A perfect match, she says, it's too much; it's overwhelming. The note has to split. It beats. It howls. Musicians say: *It wolfs.*

He wakes and thinks he is on that other ship. But as soon as he swings his legs out of bed, he remembers the truth. His body reminds him of the truth. He is old. He switches on the light. It's 4:00 a.m., not too early for an old man to rise. He grasps his cane.

He washes his face and cleans his teeth at the tiny sink. He puts on his parka. Then he climbs the stairs. The horizon pulses with pink fire; the rest of the world is blue. His face feels blue, prickling in the cold.

A few other passengers are already up, looking at the sea. They hail him cheerfully, raising mittened hands.

The sea stretches out like a slab, like something solid, a great blue quartz. It lies so still, as if immune to storms.

At breakfast, he hooks his cane over his wrist so his hands are free to carry the tray. Some of the passengers are being assisted by the staff. Hardly anyone on the cruise is under seventy years old. Most of them, like him, have worked all their lives, and possess money and leisure for the first time. Many still wear the surprised expressions of people who have only recently discovered they can afford a cruise, whose children have said, "Dad, why not go?" Some look wary, expecting their luck to run out; others are smug in their furs, adding one more trip to their list. All of them, with their shrunken or bloated wind-carved faces, their hoarfrost hair, look as if they belong to this landscape. *We are snowmen*, Wyland thinks. *How stiffly we move, as if our bones are frozen.* He pours himself a cup of coffee.

All day the sun will dance along the horizon, buoyant and lacy, a paper snowflake. There will be islands like dark seals. There will be a guide who tells them about the shrinking of the ice. Trembling, the passengers will say: "Oh no, oh no."

One passenger is much younger than the others: a researcher catching a ride north on the cruise ship. Wyland sets his tray down beside hers, pulls out a chair, and sits. The researcher appeals to him. He likes her dark skin. Her scowl.

"You know, you remind me of someone," he remarks.

Her scowl deepens. She stabs grimly at her eggs. She is wearing a stiff brown coverall fastened with snaps. Her hands are small, bony, chapped to whiteness at the knuckles.

"The person you remind me of would probably never wear that kind of getup. But she was young like you. And she loved the North."

His heart gives a little twist, as if waking up. Pain fills his chest. He sets his coffee cup down carefully and breathes.

Breathe, breathe, as if you were walking blinded through the snow. Do not for a moment allow your heart to stop. Nesha smiling at the ocean, wrapped in her long shawl. The blue, and her burnished cheek. Complementary colors.

His vision clears. "Where are you from?" he asks the young researcher.

"New Jersey," she growls, and then, relenting: "My parents are from Bangladesh."

"The person I knew was from somewhere near there."

"That's nice." She's collecting her cup, her napkin, piling them together on her tray.

"She told me anybody could love the North."

"Yep," says the researcher, standing up. Young people move so fast. He's forgotten that. He's forgotten everything important. How quick they are, how easily insulted, how Nesha flared up at him that afternoon, her smile fading out like smoke. He had told her it was surprising, unexpected, to find a person like her, from the South, so interested in the frozen North. "That has nothing to do with it," she snapped. She said she was interested in *the world*. She was drawn to *phenomena*. "Anyone can love the ice." Sir C. V. Raman investigated the stringed instruments of Europe, she said, but he was interested in *sound*. Then she glanced pointedly at Wyland's hair, the close, slightly reddish curls he had plastered down painstakingly, but inadequately, with brilliantine. "You are going to Paris," she said, "but you're also from the South." And he had been stung in his turn, indignant. "I'm from Michigan."

The young researcher is walking away with her tray.

"My name's Wyland," he calls after her, "but you can call me Shoeless Joe."

He chuckles. Stupid old man. She'll never talk to him again. Still, the exchange has soothed the ache in his chest. For a long time he's called himself Shoeless Joe, as a joke. His friends call him Shoeless. He's sure the young researcher doesn't appreciate the humor. He loves this about her: the glittering intolerance of youth. He has not possessed this quality for a long time. He used to call himself The Unhappy Negro, also as a joke, until his children told him it was offensive.

"You're one of us."

He's hungry. He is turning into a wolf. He is waiting for things to become ordinary. Isn't that what's supposed to happen? People are supposed to get used to things. They are not supposed to be tortured every day. The sight of the sea, for example, should become ordinary to a sailor with the passage of time. "What do you think?" he asks a sailor. Standing bleary-eyed on deck at six o'clock in the morning, gesturing toward the North Atlantic. Lavish sprays of arterial color are pouring across the ocean. The sky throbs. There is a dim, wild smell of fish. "Does this seem normal to you?" The sailor observes the youth with the hollow eyes and smiles blackly. He has few teeth, and speaks no English.

¡Salud! Santé! Skål!
At midnight the musicians drink champagne. They are given supper in a room behind the dining hall. They sprawl on the chairs, the women in poses that seem lewd to Wyland when Nesha drags him there for supper with her friends. He doesn't want to go; he feels instinctively that he will disappoint her, will prove that he is not, after all, one of them, and he tries not to look at the toes of the flautist, who is also a dancer, coiling near his elbow, nude under pink silk. The flautist is from Bohemia; she has poor skin and hair from having grown up on potatoes. "Ah," she says, closing her eyes. The tall, red-haired percussionist, who has moist and colorless eyes like a pair of snails, flicks a pistachio shell that lands in the flautist's bosom. The flautist opens her eyes and sits up, outraged, and everyone laughs. The man who plays the oboe is trying to talk to Wyland: he is French, and when he speaks, or at any rate, when he speaks English, gray spit collects in the corners of his mouth. As the oboist draws something complicated on a napkin, the map to a place in Paris where, he insists, Wyland absolutely must go, Wyland watches the laughing gaze of Nesha travel across the table to meet the tiny, flashing eyes of the conductor. No one seems to know very much about this man, the orchestra conductor. He is rumored to be a Pole. He is a taskmaster, Nesha says. He has a thin, spidery body—the type, Wyland thinks, you could crush under your boot.

Afterward he sees the conductor below decks, in the red hall. He recognizes him, though the light is dim. He sees the conductor and Nesha standing at the end of the passage. The conductor has his hand about her throat.

¡Salud! Santé! Champagne corks pop. The ship heaves over the sea. It heaves toward France. No, it heaves toward Svalbard. The ship heaves toward the Barents Sea. The water is growing very green, says the violinist. Then it will turn blue, and at last it will be black.

*

285

The violinist crouches behind him and rests her head on his shoulder. Her head is small and hard, and there are pins in her hair. He feels as if he is being embraced by his grandmother's hairy pincushion. The violinist's fingers, encased in black satin, are digging into his shoulders. Now she comes to perch like a raven on the arm of his chair. She drinks from his glass. Across the table the percussionist regards them mockingly. His jeering eyes, without depth, like chunks of blubber, like segments of walrus tripe, like bits of undigested ptarmigan in an owl casing.

Wyland stumbles outside. He has drunk too much. He touches his face, which has gone numb. Suddenly he's afraid the wind has sliced it up. No, his face is all right. Everything's fine, he tells himself, but he can't stop the wave of self-pity that surges through him, the tears.

Breathe. He leans his arms on the railing. He rests his forehead there.

A narwhal, the corpse whale, nudges its horn through the gloom. All over the hills the snowy geese are sleeping. An ice bear lifts its nose from the kill in the moonlight, painted like a clown.

But what have they been saying? They're making fun of him. He won't go back in that room. He weaves his way to the stairs and goes down, touching the walls. Here the ship makes a groaning sound. There is sometimes a frightening *ping* that makes him think the iron is warping, about to break. He thinks the iron is going to collapse from the pressure of the water. He does not feel he is floating. He is underneath. And Nesha stands at the end of the passage, regal in crimson light, wearing the conductor's hand like an ivory choker.

"How could you?"
    "You don't understand. He is a very enlightened person."
    "He's hurting you."
    "And you—you're going to save me?"
    "I could. I could pitch him overboard."
    "So could I."

286

He clenches his fists uselessly. "You people are sick," he says. "You drift around drinking and pretending to be artists. You pretend to love the world, but all you care about is drunkenness and filth."

"We are interested in the mechanisms of force."

"Shut up!" he shouts. "You probably all sleep together—you play your wolf tones—"

Now at last she grows angry. "I have never played a wolf tone for you. You have never heard it. None of the regular passengers have heard it."

The phrase *regular passengers* rakes across his heart.

She rearranges her shawl, folding it tightly, and walks away.

"When I play a wolf tone, Wyland, you will know."

For three days he doesn't go to dinner. He hoards food from the other meals, eats rolls in his cabin. Then he is back. He doesn't sit at his usual table. He sits at the edge of the crowd, as far as possible from the stage. He sits with the French boys, who are playing cards.

She knows he is there. The sound of her cello reaches out. Tentative. Frayed.

He plays cards. All the French boys are laughing at his schoolboy French. The orchestra takes a break, and when they come back, Wyland stops playing. Nesha steps onto the stage. She has taken down her hair.

She plays with her hair falling over her face. It falls to the strings. She is playing her own hair. A strange tune, and quiet, and only for him. So quiet he can hear the small hiss as she moves in her black silk dress. He hears it across the room. He can hear her heart.

Afterward, on the deck, she sits in the shadows against the wall and he lies down with his head in her lap. He holds her hand. Her other hand circles slowly, comfortingly, in his hair, freeing the curls. The stars are so close. *Don't let me fall.*

Sofia Samatar

Was it because his passion was incomplete? He was giving her everything. Even now he knows he could not have given more. Lying on the black swell of her thigh, clinging to her fingers, it was as if he had been emptied and then filled. Emptied of everything in the world, of his childhood, his ambition, his patron's confidence, his family's hopes, even his forty dollars, and filled to the brim with sorrow. Now he sits in a deck chair, an old man, looking out at the fierce blue arctic waters, and feels that emptiness again. Emptied even of the desire to paint. Old Shoeless is going to paint the Arctic, they said. Good for him. One last run. He is going to paint it from life this time. But although he has found the emptiness, he has not been filled. There is nothing to put inside. The guide is talking and curved brown mountains are floating past the rails. Now a dash of color: pink flowers. Everyone rushes to take a picture. Rare fox cubs. In the distance, black hills garnished with blue snow. "I'm sorry," she said, and he told her: "Don't ever say that." Don't say you're sorry, he told her, because he knew it meant saying goodbye. She in her long hair, tender. Her hair stirring on his cheek. She told him about the great single-mindedness of Sir C. V. Raman, his illimitable passion for the natural world. C. V. Raman was interested in every kind of vibration. He studied sound, but also optics, X-rays, magnetism, color. He loved music, flowers, diamonds. In 1921 he traveled to Oxford and hypothesized that the blue of the Mediterranean was due to the molecular scattering of light. Wyland can feel her hand in his hair. He feels she is telling him *no*. Somehow she is telling him *no* with these stories of C. V. Raman. The wolf tones occurring only on certain notes. And now the light, the small fraction of light that undergoes the change of frequency known as Raman scattering. Raman established his theory using a mercury lamp, a glass bulb full of benzene, and a pocket spectroscope. Direct a white light onto the bulb and you will observe, contrary to expectation, a magnificent blue radiance. This is because some of the light particles—but only some—are being transformed. He understands that she means she is a blue light, a wolf, while he, Wyland, is ordinary light. Raman scattering, she says, occurs with gases and solids as well as liquids. The first solid Raman studied was ice.

The ice. It's melting. Sinking. Becoming sea.

*

288

The guide announces: "This is a journey among the last of the glaciers."

The passengers are excited. They board the boat, which is lowered down to the turquoise water. To the aquamarine. The scattering.

"Nesha," he says. "My wolf." But she is already far away. His hand is empty. The one intended to touch her face. Then someone catches him, steadies him, helps him aboard the boat. "Are you all right, sir?" It's one of the staff, the young Norwegian, sunburned and jolly in her blue vest. He speaks to her in Norwegian and she laughs, showing teeth of improbable whiteness. "They'll do," he says, stamping his boots on the deck. There's a squeaking sound, as usual, but nothing to worry about, it's not my feet, it's my heart, he wants to tell this young woman who is so kind. Now the boat casts off and everyone waves. "Goodbye," call the ones left behind on the ship. Not everyone has joined the journey among the last of the glaciers. Some of the passengers are too frail. And the young researcher too, Wyland sees, has remained at the railing. She stares at the boat with a strange look: a look of rage.

Something inside her, certainly. A flame.

As for him, he is empty, sawdust. He has outlived everything, even his century. Its horrors and its triumphs. The Indian Association for the Cultivation of Science, where the young men worked all night. Coming and going at all hours, often sleeping on the premises so that they could get a chance to use the equipment. C. V. Raman lived so close to the association building he could slip in a back door whenever he was free. And even though he would later take up residence in lovely Bangalore, where he would maintain a splendid flower garden, a diamond museum, and the Raman Research Institute with its panoramic view of the city, it was those early days at the association, in that dusty building in one of the most crowded parts of Calcutta, that he always called "the golden era." It was there he began his studies of music and light. Such passion among the mercury lamps. Such frenzied writing. To get his papers into print quickly, before anyone else stumbled on his discoveries, he'd hail a cab, rush to the post office, pay the late fee to make the last mail. Is this what it means to be an artist? To vibrate at such a pitch? In tune with the changing world. *It appears to me*, a fellow scientist wrote, *that this very beautiful discovery that resulted from Raman's long and patient study of the phenomenon of light scattering is one of the most convincing proofs of the quantum theory.*

What are you dreaming of? Did you think it would be quiet?

She lifts her bow.

The grinding and popping sounds. The groans. Subdued thunder.

Wolf tones, she said, are considered unmusical. They are a hindrance. Techniques and devices have been developed for their suppression.

Listen, she tells him, now we are going to begin.

He remembers his throat was sore. The oncoming fever made him feel like a child. He allowed himself to be ordered about like a child in the supper room. They made up a bed for him by pushing the chairs together. "This fever," he told the flautist, "is the outcome of despair." "Nonsense," she crooned, loosening his tie with her worm-like fingers. Someone was taking off his shoes. The lights were in his eyes and the oboist stood on the table to shield them with paper. Individual paper shields, perhaps made of cigarette packets, for each of the little sparks in the chandelier. Wyland's eyes filled with tears because of the kindness. "These tears," he explained to whoever was listening, "are the outcome of despair." They gave him a special cig- arette, telling him it would help his cough, but it made him cough more. His chest seized, his body thumped on the chairs. Through his tears he could see the conductor observing him, as one would regard an insect, with a calm and clinical gaze.

"You," wheezed Wyland. "I know you. You're the Devil."

a collective excitation

He's read so much, through the years, to try to make sense of it. The papers of C. V. Raman. *The hope that our laboratory studies would furnish a solid experimental basis for the explanation of such natural phenomena as the color of the sea and the color of the ice in glaciers*

Glacial blue. A frozen heart.

The young Norwegian helps him ashore. They will climb this little ridge. They will see the ice. He proceeds with a creaking sound not unlike the sound of a glacier. Not at all unlike the melting of a glacier heard from a distance. The unmusical, daily sound of his prosthetics.

the far ultraviolet

A little ridge. Then glaciers like wild beasts. Their condensed, alien, and lambent blue. Everyone gasps at the sight, but it's the smell that makes him weep: a raw and ferrous wind from the days of hope. From the days when he still had feet.

if the process of scattering could be

He moves forward slowly, testing the ground with his cane. They have half an hour, says the guide, before they must return to the boat. They may walk on the ridge. They must not go down to the ice. He walks toward the distance with fragile, uncertain steps. Snow breaks under his boots.

*

Toward the fading isles. The blue cathedrals of desire. The sinking world.

Listen, now we are going to begin.

His throat aches. He wants to clear it, but he's afraid of the pain and, even more, afraid diseased flesh will slough off into his mouth. Certainly they've put something in the cigarette. But the ship soothes him, rocking. The chandelier swinging, adorned with tiny shades. It begins to swing more violently. Shadows pass over him. A pair of red lips, a naked shoulder, a small chignon. Then the sparkling cuff with jade links that can only belong to the orchestra conductor, followed by his neat and jaundiced-looking hand, a hand that comes startlingly close to Wyland's face, as if to stroke him, then turns to exhibit the knuckles tufted with fine hair.

if the process of scattering could be regarded as a collision

Nesha's face, with the lights of the chandelier winking around it.

As if a coronet of stars.

She's taking him, picking him up. *It is time, my darling.* Is he being carried? Out the doors where the wind whips at his face. He whoops for joy. The door flung back behind them, banging, the glass shattering.

Sailors running about, feet thudding. French shouts. The huge sea.

The deck tilts and flings him against the wall of the dining room.

New pain now, in his shoulder, in his knees when he falls on the deck. "Nesha!" he shouts. Frightened, for the first time.

*

To be scattered at higher frequencies is to be scattered *to the blue.*

The members of the ship's orchestra have taken their seats on the deck. Somehow, when the ship tilts the other way—tilts so sharply that Wyland clings to the broken dining-room door, to keep from being swept off—they do not move.

The conductor raises his baton.

"No!" Wyland screams.

Flashes of light and darkness. Flashes of flying hair. And her face, impossibly clear, as if she were seated right beside him, though she is far away, too far for him to reach. Too far for him to seize the hem of her skirt, though he tries to crawl. His fingers are bleeding from the broken glass. Something hard slides down the deck and hits him, shocking his wrist into numbness. He clings in the doorway, sobbing. He cannot go.

I was going to go to Paris. To be an artist.

She lifts her bow.

Her face like a topaz. Luminous. Remote.

Her face of sorrow. Of deep, slow-burning triumph. Of desire. Her arm in the torn sleeve rising like a whale.

The bow on the string. It's as if someone has touched his inner ear.

293

Sofia Samatar

The wind. He writhes. His body curls and uncurls in sound. Sound of the ocean. Sound of wolf. Of storm. It beats back and forth. It achieves an *unbearable*. A shudder that never ends.

At the hospital in Svalbard he says: *I saw a woman riding on a wolf.*

She is playing the wind, the water, the ice. He lifts his face. He sees them playing faster and faster, the whole orchestra in frenzy but she is slow, slow, the bow a thing of intolerable weight. She does not need to move quickly because each note she plays is thousands, millions of notes. The others are playing the ocean but she is playing the tide. The conductor's baton dancing like an antenna against the rising waves. The slopes. The darkness clapping like a bell.

When it goes up, he tells the nurse, *you can't look down.*

The foaming waves. Lit up in the night. Luminescent, like a corpse.

The violinist playing and screaming. Ecstatic. A volley of curses. The percussionist's shirt ripped off, his body of solid white fat.

They are all monsters. The flautist's teeth, how has he never noticed them? The oboist's eyebrows twisting up like horns. The conductor with his matted hair. And Nesha. She is huge, her glance of thunder. She is taking up the sky.

She throws her head back. Icy mouth. Delirium.

And the waves come down.

He says: *The ship went down into a hole.*

He mimes it with his hand. His fingers diving against a background of white curtains. At the hospital in Svalbard.

He says: *Let me sleep.* He begs them: *Let me.*

Curled in bed, he clings to the pillow. He will put it over his head to save his ears. He will strap himself to the little bed and use it as a raft. All night the bed will bang against the wall. And he will see her rising. Throwing her cello over her shoulder. Her long hair. How she grasps the Wolf King by his gray-white ruff. With a leap, she gains his back. She sits astride him, howling, raising her bow to the sky. The Huntress of the North.

But I was going to Paris. I was going to be an artist. I had forty dollars sewn into my coat.

His feet are black, the doctor says. He doesn't understand. The doctor repeats it: *Black*. They will have to come off.

Tie me up, says Wyland. He begs them to tie him to the bed. Then, for a long time, he doesn't speak.

When he speaks again, he asks for books. He asks for books about music, science, and history. He takes comfort in the language of Sir C. V. Raman. *If the process of scattering could be regarded as a collision between a light quantum localized in space and an individual molecule, the observed laws of light scattering would be quite different from those anticipated on the classical principles.* The words are like a rope thrown in the dark to Wyland, who has lost the ability to anticipate anything on the classical principles. He sits by the window in the full glow of night. It's so bright outside, the shadows of the window bars are cast across his page. He reads the words: *There are more unexcited molecules than excited ones. Why should that be? What causes this difference? Why are so many of them left out?* Touched, but never transformed. He searches for a

295

reason but cannot discover it. He cries for the first time since his rescue.

In Norway they tell tales of the Oskoreien, the Terrible Host, who may be the souls of the restless dead. They rush across the sky with a dreadful noise. They enter locked homes and devour the Christmas feast. Once, at Dalen, they left a dead man on the hearth. The corpse hung from a pothook. By his clothes, the people who found him could tell he came from Numedal, a valley to the east. The Terrible Host must have seized him there and ridden him to death. His heart frozen under the silver buttons on his vest.

Now as he walks across the snow it wells up in him again, filling him. All his sorrow and his years. The hospital at Svalbard, and how he asked for newspapers he could read, English and French papers from the time of his accident. The papers told of the tragic wreck of the *Agate*, a French ship driven mysteriously, incredibly off course in a freak storm. The lone survivor, an American Negro, had been picked up by a team of land surveyors. He was feverish, raving. He did not know his name. The unhappy Negro, Wyland read, was transported to the hospital for treatment. A phrase that stuck with him, ringing: *le malheureux nègre*. He began to read voraciously, as if he could discover in written language the whole meaning of his life. How closely he followed the career of Chandrasekhara Venkata Raman, how passionately he read the texts that travel back to him now in fragments, as he walks through mist, through an arctic morning suddenly overcast so that he stumbles, missing his footing in whiteness, his depth perception failing. He remembers the words: *spectral violet*. He recalls: *the romance of glass*. He hears a sound in the distance, a sort of siren, undoubtedly from the boat. He remembers: *In the waters of our seas and oceans live many denizens of the deep endowed with what has been happily termed living light*. Words that sustained him through the years, the painting career in the Florida Keys, where he moved, because, he would say with a shout of laughter, he hated snow, where he married and had children and was widowed and became part of the furniture in a bar, his sweat sinking into the chair. But, Nesha, you told me I was one of you. He sways, he staggers. The ground is moving. He is riding on a boat. Beasts groan about him, jostling in the fog. He reaches to touch them but they will not come near. He coaxes them, clicking; they answer with hollow grunts. He laughs through the pain in his chest, through the tears that freeze at once on his lashes. These are her herds, the ones she keeps to feed her wolves. He must be very close now. And soon, yes, the mist draws aside its nacreous curtain and there she stands, taller than the peaks.

He sinks to his knees on the rocking ice. *Nesha!*
Wyland! she says. *Come in!*
In where?
In here, she says with a merry laugh. She is wearing her same paisley shawl, only now its pink and pale-green shades are spread in majesty across the sky. The colors shift and ripple with a meditative intensity so beautiful he cannot move. He cannot close his eyes. Come, she says, I will make you a supper of seals' eggs. There's no such thing. Oh, but there is, she assures him, in her hall. And he will dine on the choicest ones, served on a bed of blackened greens retrieved from a bear's stomach. Eggs so tender they burst at a glance. He will see marvels in the light of whale-oil lamps. And he will tell her marvels too. The tale of the *crystal lattice*. Of the *fiber-optic probe*. Leaning into the warmth of her couch, which is made from the wing of a goose, he will speak between kisses of the diffraction of light by ultrasonic waves. *The Raman spectrum*, he will tell her, *is the physicist's musical score of the atomic symphony.*

The young researcher settles down into her sleeping bag and presses *play*. A gentle droning fills her headphones. It's *Naldjorlak I* by Eliane Radigue, a composition for solo cello that fills the young researcher's bones with sound. Now, at last, her muscles relax. Soon she will begin to feel like she's floating. Then she will be fully here: here in the camp, in the tent that envelops her in a pinkish glow, cocooned in the sleeping bag, in the polar night. Then she will let go of the trip, of the fury that consumes her every time she has to travel on one of those awful cruise ships: the sense of contamination as she shares the heated air and the thrum of the oil-guzzling vessel with the stupid, wide-eyed, gawking tourists. They're all old, they've lived their lives, they've driven their big cars, they spend their days between the swimming pool and their air-conditioned rooms. When they click their tongues at the dwindling ice and hold their little paws up over their mouths in dismay, she wants to bash their heads in. *You gave me this world,* she wants to shout. But she doesn't. She needs the ride. A frown creases her forehead. She wills her breath to deepen. *Let it go,* she tells herself. Let it all go: the trip, the guides, the miserable delay as they searched for the old guy who wandered off on the glacier tour. They never found him. He probably had a heart attack out there. The blonde guide who'd gone out on the boat was in hysterics. Her face covered with red blotches like a rash. "He was so nice," she sobbed. The young researcher sighs again. *Let it go.* And as she listens, as she allows her thoughts to dissolve in the subtle, resonant tones of Radigue's music, she feels it going. She even feels a touch of the old excitement. Tomorrow, after all, she'll be on the ice. She'll be on the ice, taking measurements with a remote Raman spectrometer, gathering data on the structure of the dying bergs.

A wind ripples the tent, and she closes her eyes. Radigue's music has always filled her with a sense of space. It's music that builds an environment, patiently, delicately, inexorably, as crystals form. It's the feeling of the ice. Because of this music, the young researcher forgives Radigue everything. She forgives her for belonging to that generation. The word *Naldjorlak*, which makes her think of trolls in a winter cave, is apparently made up, and she's read that it's supposed to suggest something to do with Tibetan Buddhism. This too she forgives, she lets it go, the vague religiosity, the whiff of exoticism, she lets it go, she sinks, she feels herself shifting from red to blue, becoming spectral in the vast vibrating night. For this, for music that sounds like ice, she is willing to forgive. So it's unfortunate that she doesn't know and will never know that earlier today she met the painter Wyland Alexander, known as "the painter of glaciers," because she might have forgiven him too. She might have forgiven his age, his questions, and his foolish jokes had she known that he painted glaciers obsessively for fifty years, developing in them a blue of such convulsive, pounding radiance that critics called it both appalling and sublime. It was said that one was "battered" by Wyland Alexander's blues. This was painting that aspired to the state of noise. In the end, his color was something no one could bear for very long: a blue as deep and penetrating as a howl.

Moby Dick, Ecoterrorist
James Morrow

THE CHASE—FIRST DAY

THE LEVIATHAN SLEEPS. He permits neither the screams of the gulls nor the roaring of the waves to disturb him, for he must conserve his energy for the battle ahead. The great fleshy petals that are his flukes point toward the sea bottom. His cranium bobs near the surface like an immense naval mine. Even in his dreams, he cries out to his nemesis.

"Hear me now, O wicked ship, bearer of bad faith, carrier of woe! Like the devils who came before thee, thou art marked for oblivion!"

These days the leviathan travels under an assumed name. Call him Mocha. His nemesis is the *Otaru Daikaiju*, a gargantuan steel-hulled brute, presently plying the North Pacific, having departed from Yokohama with malign and treacherous intent. Although the Panama Canal could easily accommodate an adult sperm whale, Mocha never seriously considered taking that route to the East Pacific. A dock-worker would surely have spotted him, the lock chambers being a mere sixty feet deep, and reported the trespasser to his superiors. So instead Mocha had pitched and torqued his way around Cape Horn, then crossed the Tropic of Capricorn and allowed the frigid Humboldt Current to bear him north along the coast of Peru, every cell of his cetacean brain fixed on finding and chasing and sinking the *Otaru Daikaiju*.

The leviathan awakens. The sun hammers his wrinkled brow. An oily and insidious aroma reaches his olfactory organs. He is the Roderick Usher of aquatic mammals, possessed of an acute sensorium.

"I smell thee, damned *Daikaiju*! Across a thousand miles of open sea, thy stench tells thy coordinates! Two days hence I shall be drinking thy wake!"

Gifted with a longevity to rival Methuselah's, the leviathan has time on his side, and yet he fears that even eternity may prove insufficient for appeasing the darkness within him. Perhaps things will seem different once he has worked his wrath on the *Daikaiju*. Perhaps he will finally know peace.

He breaks his fast by gulping down a pod of passing cuttlefish. Before he can resume the hunt, a broad-winged female albatross lands on his dorsal hump. So weathered is the leviathan's skin, he can barely feel the bird's barbed feet.

"Your reputation precedes you," says the albatross. "You are the notorious albino avenger, in pursuit of—what vessel is it today?"

"One worthy of my spleen," Mocha replies.

"Call me Bronwyn."

"I have no time for chitchat."

"Might I travel with you awhile? I am weary to the bone and in flight from catastrophic conditions at the Pole."

"Thou mayest."

"Will you take me to the Line?"

"If thou wish it."

"My continent is melting," keens Bronwyn. "If the Ancient Mariner sailed into the Weddell Sea tomorrow, he would have trouble becoming icebound."

Mocha will not soon forget the mild, mild day he struck and killed his first quarry. No sooner had he destroyed the *Mashpee* than the world began making sense to him. They kept on coming, of course, the quarry's sister ships, sailing uninvited along his preferred currents, their crews consumed by blubber lust and the going price of spermaceti. He chased and fought them all, staving in their bows with his mighty skull, sifting their timbers through his stalagmite teeth. Usually he sent the vessel to its death, though sometimes he succumbed to exhaustion and the pain of his ancient wounds, and his prey would escape.

By the turn of the century, canvas had yielded to steam. Then came diesel engines, and, worse, harpoons fired from cannons. Decade after decade, Mocha's friends, lovers, and relations died by the tens of thousands. At first the steel sides and bulkheads of the whaling ships had stymied him, but then he learned to swim furiously around each intruder, creating an artificial maelstrom that often capsized the damned thing and sucked it down.

Tail thrashing, pectoral fins churning, he begins the day's journey. The albatross is not his only passenger. Trapped in a mesh of harpoon lines, a madman cleaves to the leviathan's left flank, directly below the blowhole, adjacent to the ear. Call him Abraxis. Against all odds, this ivory-legged mariner has assimilated the

James Morrow

leviathan's longevity and mastered venerable cetacean techniques for storing and conserving oxygen. Together the interconnected mammals patrol the oceans of the world. They are not quite friends, but they are no longer antagonists. Although Captain Abraxis was pleased to have finally reached a rapprochement with the universe, what truly mellowed the old peg leg was his encounters with other whaling masters—a routine event throughout the latter half of the 1800s—some of whom were even crazier than himself.

There was Captain Bartlett, for example, who'd periodically diverted the *Narragansett* so he could chase after Crimson Jack, the great red squid who'd bitten off his right hand. And Captain Eliphaz of the *Wampanoag*, who'd regularly forsaken his profession to pursue Queen Proserpine, the colossal moray eel who'd deprived him of his dick. Without exception, Abraxis detested his fellow amputees, not only because they were leading their men to certain doom but because butchering sentient creatures for profit now struck him as an obscene thing for people to be doing with their time.

And so it happened that, throughout the twentieth century, Mocha prosecuted his reign of terror with the blessing of his former bête noire. The sailors always died, of course, drowned like rats or bludgeoned by the leviathan's flukes or devoured by his entourage of sharks. Mocha didn't care. His power gave him pleasure. Did God too enjoy his forays into slaughter—the Great Flood, the razing of Sodom, the torching of Gomorrah, the Ten Plagues? Mocha couldn't say. When it came to theological matters, he was out of his depth.

Although not the most sociable of persons, the madman would occasionally strike up a conversation with the captain of a passing ship—but only if his mission was innocuous: piloting a vacation cruise, retrieving a sunken treasure, gathering scientific data. Invariably the captain would offer to cut him loose from the sea beast. Abraxis always refused.

"I'm doing penance," he would explain.

It was from these nautical tête-à-têtes that Abraxis had learned of a menace even more terrible than the whaling trade. Reluctantly he'd relayed the bad news to Mocha. As Abraxis understood the situation, early in the twentieth century *Homo sapiens* had been conquered by *Combustioni internis*, a race of mechanized parasites boasting considerable variety within the species. Most probably these invaders had come from another planet, but conceivably they'd sprung from gaps in the earth's crust or perhaps a dimension beyond the ken of whales and humans. The parasites could survive only by devouring

301

James Morrow

great quantities of refined petroleum and excreting the residue as a heat-trapping gas called carbon dioxide—a process that, in fewer than a hundred years, had turned the planet into a lethal greenhouse. Day after day, global warming murdered coral reefs, acidified the seas, and sterilized coastal wetlands. Each new season brought its own sort of meteorological apocalypse.

And so Mocha shifted the focus of his campaign, targeting the fleets that ferried the Saabs, Volvos, Volkswagens, Ferraris, Lexuses, Fords, Chryslers, Dodges, and Chevrolets from one continent to the next. The Charybdis technique he'd perfected for sinking steel-sided whaling ships worked reasonably well for these new enemies. By circumscribing the *Marseille Mermaid*, the *Charleston Selkie*, the *Stockholm Jormungand*, and the *Hamburg Kraken* with a whirlpool of sufficient ferocity, the leviathan had sent all four to the bottom along with their unholy cargoes.

"Thy death is immutably decreed, *Daikaiju*!" he proclaims, reaching a speed of fifteen knots. "Ye shall not escape, O toxic autos! Prepare ye to sleep amongst the anemones!"

Built by human minions in thrall to *Combustioni internis*, the first auto carriers were a clumsy and inefficient breed. Their holds could be filled and emptied only via a crane that lowered and retrieved the parasites one at a time through a hatch in the cargo deck. But by the mid-1980s, lift-on, lift-off had been replaced by the roll-on, roll-off method, predicated on freighters resembling gigantic seagoing dumpsters. Mocha loathed these behemoths, which normally proved immune to even the strongest manufactured maelstrom. On those few occasions when he'd capsized and sunk a roll-on, roll-off carrier, over four thousand parasites had perished at a stroke, but usually the leviathan left the battle without a kill.

Mocha has vowed that the showdown with the mighty *Otaru Daikaiju*, pride of the fleet owned and operated by the Consolidated Shipping Corporation, will play out in the planet's favor. He and Abraxis have devised a novel and ingenious strategy. Explosives are involved. Does the master of the *Daikaiju* have any inkling he's in mortal jeopardy? Probably not. Sailing under the flag of Panama, the fool doubtless believes he'll have no trouble bearing his 1,700 Toyotas, 1,850 Subarus, and 2,050 Hondas through the canal and thence to the port of New York.

"O abominable *Daikaiju*, I shall chase thee o'er the Guatemala Basin and o'er the Cocos Ridge and o'er perdition's flames until I see thee turn keel up and descend into hell's deepest trench!"

THE CHASE—SECOND DAY

Mocha swims all through the night. Occasionally he breaches and, rolling back and forth, surveys the starry vault of the South Pacific. His vision is a bifurcated affair, a split-level way of being in the world. Using first his right eye, then its nonconverging mate, he observes the celestial Octopus of Tuamotu, the heavenly Sea Serpent of Vanuatu, and the skybound, pearl-laden Oyster of Santiago.

Acting on a revelation from the madman, Mocha had passed the previous month tooling around the British Isles, sucking up sunken, unexploded depth charges from the North Atlantic battles of the Second World War. A half dozen aquatic bombs now lie in the largest of the leviathan's four stomachs, waiting to be spat out. The weapons rattle against each other like loose cannons, a din that distresses the albatross, though she is not about to forgo her easy passage to the Line.

The battle plan is simple and elegant. If Mocha can sustain his present speed, he will catch the *Daikaiju* long before it sights the shores of Panama. Somewhere above Isla del Coco, three hundred and forty miles southwest of Costa Rica, he will blow his nemesis out of the water.

In the late afternoon he swims past Española, southernmost of the Galápagos Islands. A fifty-foot cruise ship sails into view, the *Alfred Russel Wallace* out of Guayaquil. Mocha wants nothing to do with it. A stately, dark-skinned human female, dressed smartly in a white jacket with gold piping, stands on the foredeck. She presents herself to Abraxis as Captain Juanita Ruíz, explaining that the *Wallace* is a chartered vessel carrying fifty-two US high-school biology teachers. They have just finished exploring the renowned archipelago from whose volcanic soil had sprung the theory of evolution by natural selection.

"Shall we free you from that whale?" asks Captain Ruíz.

"Not today," says Abraxis.

A young man with pale golden skin appears on deck and, leaning against the gunwale, introduces himself to the madman as Denis Chao, one of the biology teachers on board. Though obviously bewildered by Abraxis's entanglement, Captain Ruíz and Mr. Chao listen respectfully to his story. As he reveals the nature of the leviathan's mission, their expressions fluctuate among fascination, delight, incredulity, and moral outrage.

"When I plead with you to spare the *Daikaiju*, you must not imagine I doubt that the earth is in peril," says Captain Ruíz. "Here on Galápagos, we see the tragedy in microcosm. For centuries these islands have been assaulted by one of the world's most destructive weather patterns, El Niño, so savage it actually heats up the Humboldt Current. Now the Anthropocene is causing the phenomenon to increase in violence and frequency. Rising ocean temperatures mean less algae for marine lizards. With each El Niño, multitudes of Galápagos iguanas die, though some cope by absorbing parts of their own skeletons, until they resemble frogs from hell."

"Would you like us to untie you?" asks Mr. Chao.

"I'd rather you didn't," says the madman.

"When El Niño is at its worst, the fish population drops off sharply," Ruíz continues, "inflicting famine on the mammals and birds that need sardines to survive. Malnourished sea lions can no longer nurse their pups. Starving flightless cormorants die in their nests. Blue-footed boobies stop laying eggs."

"The Anthropocene is also implicated in the spread of invasive species—on Galápagos and around the world," says Mr. Chao. "Right now the islands are enduring a plague of fire ants. They eat the eggs of the giant tortoises and mercilessly attack the adults. Could any sight be more wrenching than a female tortoise shambling across a beach, dropping her eggs while trying to escape the insects biting her legs?"

"Despite these horrors," says Ruíz, "or perhaps because of them, I believe human consciousness is on the verge of a sea change."

"Don't bet on it," says Abraxis.

"As the climate crisis enters its final act," Ruíz persists, "people will realize that all the world's humans, animals, plants, fungi, and bacteria are bound together in a tapestry of shared chemistry and common ancestry. My biology teachers are learning how best to educate their students about Charles Darwin's magnificent tree of life."

"By proposing a wholly natural and materialist mechanism behind evolution," says Chao, "Mr. Darwin took away our passports to immortality—or so some people, myself included, would argue. After wrestling with Darwin's ideas, I found it increasingly difficult to imagine that the human race, alone of all creatures, is on a trajectory to eternal bliss."

"Darwin confiscated our passports," says Ruíz, "but he gave us something more valuable in return. He gave us citizenship papers. We belong here, his theory tells us. The earth is our home. We're not tourists on this planet. We're citizens."

"Once enough people grasp that idea," says Chao, "they will cherish the world as never before. Nations will come together to cleanse the biosphere of greenhouse gases."

"Oh, give me a break," mutters Bronwyn.

"Fish fingers," says Abraxis.

"I beg you to reconsider your mission," says Ruíz.

"I prefer not to," says Abraxis.

"The officers and sailors of the *Daikaiju* are innocent," says Ruíz.

"The hunt must go forward. My companion is of the same opinion."

To corroborate Abraxis's assertion, Mocha releases a geyser of seawater from his blowhole. The captain and the biology teacher get soaked, an experience they seem to find more bracing than annoying.

"Let us not strain on the gnat of a sacrificial crew," Abraxis persists, "while swallowing the camel of a sacrificial planet."

"The cargo deserves to die," says Captain Ruíz, dripping.

"But not the sailors," says Mr. Chao, shedding salt water.

"Here is my promise to you," says Abraxis as Mocha begins to bear him and Bronwyn away from Española. "For the rest of the day, my sea beast and I shall ponder the coming battle in all its ambiguities— but right now we must make for the Line!"

The leviathan accelerates, soon reaching thirty knots. He has never swum so fast. He skirts San Cristóbal, the easternmost Galápagos island, then cuts across the goose-egg latitude, pausing to take a bite out of the Equator and gulp down a dinner of shrimp.

As dusk descends, the usual retinue of sharks arrives, thirty ancient and rapacious fish bent on exploiting Mocha's modus operandi to their own benefit. They will follow him into the thick of the battle, the better to claim the meaty spoils of naval warfare.

Mocha sends out Bronwyn on a scouting assignment. She returns with heartening news. The *Otaru Daikaiju* is exactly where they expected to find it, ten nautical miles west of Isla del Coco.

The leviathan plunges ahead, and by moonrise he has spotted the boulevard of foam formed by the *Daikaiju*'s screws and keel. Bubbles and spindrift dance in the lunar radiance.

"Shall we in fact reconsider our mission?" asks the madman.

"Only after we have accomplished it," says the leviathan.

*

305

James Morrow

THE CHASE—THIRD DAY

The burning sun ornaments the tropical sky with streamers of red
and gold. Mocha maintains his demented pace, the albatross soaring
above him on fully spread wings. Soon his left eye discloses Isla del
Coco and its adjacent formations, arrayed across the horizon like
teeth erupting from God's jawbone.

At noon Mocha reaches 6°N, 87°W along with Abraxis, Bronwyn,
and the sharks. A soft but steady rain mutes the sky and veils the sea.

"It's near," whispers the leviathan. "It's very near."

Now the misty curtains part, and the behemoth appears, all 62,200
tons of him, churning through the ocean like a sarcophagus built to
inter the entire population of Lower Egypt.

"To the last I grapple with thee," mutters Mocha.

The leviathan is dismayed—but not surprised—to behold two
corporate cutters, the *Privateer* and the *Expedient*, cruising in tan-
dem with the *Daikaiju*. Abraxis reports that each vessel is armed
with 76mm guns and short-range missiles. Apparently the execu-
tives and stockholders of Consolidated Shipping, acting at the behest
of *Combustioni internis*, have plotted to assassinate the albino
avenger before he can wreak more havoc.

Mocha takes a deep breath, forming a psychic bond with his largest
stomach. A depth charge travels up his esophagus and comes to rest
on his great trampoline of a tongue. He marks his target, the nearer
of the two cutters, the *Privateer*. He fires, vomiting forth the canister like the outsized grouper disgorging Jonah. The projectile flies
true, striking the hull amidships and detonating. Soon the cutter is
listing to starboard and going down fast. Her sailors abandon ship, a
protocol of which the sharks approve.

Heady with success, Mocha summons another charge to his tongue,
then takes aim at the *Expedient*. He spits out the canister. It strikes
the prow, blowing open a hole the size of a human grave. Terrified
sailors leap over the side into the pathologically warm current.
Minutes later the cutter plummets toward the Cocos Ridge, even as
the sharks fall upon the human jetsam and begin eating them alive.

Better a sacrificial crew than a sacrificial planet. Mocha admires
Abraxis's motto, even though it evokes the vile chant "A dead whale
or a stove boat."

The leviathan summons the balance of the arsenal to his throat.
Perhaps these remaining depth charges will be sufficient for a victory,

306

perhaps not—he will soon find out. The behemoth's prow and sides are formed of interlocking steel plates, each ten centimeters thick, so Mocha decides to attack from the rear. With any luck, he will shatter the enormous aft gate through which the autos will exit should the *Daikaiju* ever reach port.

The leviathan cruises along the behemoth's starboard flank, passes the rudder, and turns ninety degrees. He fantails forward, spewing explosives.

"From hell's heart I stab at thee!"

The four charges arc gracefully through the air like shells from a cannon. They strike the latter-day portcullis and detonate, blowing it off its hinges. Tons of seawater rush into the breach.

"For hate's sake I spit my last breath at thee!"

Something strange is happening. With mounting frustration and begrudging admiration, Mocha fixes on the stern, peering into the cavity his weapons have wrought. Evidently Consolidated Shipping realized that, if the cutters failed to stop the albino avenger, the *Daikaiju* might go down, so they devised countermeasures to protect the precious *Combustioni internis* specimens. Frantically the sailors unfasten the autos' stabilizing chains and inflate the powered pontoons affixed to their undercarriages. One by one, the parasites cruise free of the carrier, crashing through the waves under the impetus of outboard motors. With astonishing efficiency, the radio-controlled rudders send the salvaged cargo on a southerly course toward Isla del Coco. Soon a flotilla spreads outward from 6°N, 87°W, as far as a whale's eye can see, thousands of Subarus, Toyotas, and Hondas bearing down on the island at fifteen knots like an immense amphibious landing force.

The *Daikaiju* slides beneath the sea. The sharks feast on the helpless crew. Screams fill the air. The waves turn pink. To Mocha the carrier's death seems a Pyrrhic victory at best, for the parasites are escaping in droves. Soon they will be on the beach and overrunning the island, immune to Mocha's fury. He copes with the catastrophe as best he can, sounding and breaching, sounding and breaching, again and again, each time crashing down on the flotilla and sinking at least a dozen autos—but it's obvious the vast majority will survive.

"Have we failed?" asks Bronwyn.

"Have they won?" asks Abraxis.

Mocha refuses to abandon hope. "Know this, friends. A sacred solidarity obtains among sea monsters—at least when our bellies are full. Even as we speak, I sense this ancient fellowship, bearing down upon the parasites."

First Crimson Jack, paragon of cephalopods, appears on the scene, a prodigious gloopy mass, suckered tentacles wriggling in preternatural sine waves. Reaching the flotilla, he flogs the autos, lacerating their pontoons. Now a forty-foot moray eel arrives, the legendary Queen Proserpine. She closes on the autos and chews their pontoons to pieces with her railroad-spike teeth. In the space of an hour, the *Daikaiju's* entire cargo of Subarus, Toyotas, and Hondas has disappeared, never to poison the planet again.

The monsters trade glances of mutual respect and instinctual mistrust. Under different circumstances, they would be maneuvering to eat one another, but today they are allies.

"This was a good fight," says Crimson Jack.

"Worthy of its own constellation," says Queen Proserpine.

"I am grateful to ye," says Mocha. "The planet is grateful."

"A malign and inscrutable providence is grateful," wheezes Abraxis.

Mocha swims away at twenty knots, the albatross gliding above him, the madman clinging to his flank. Abraxis is hyperventilating, but he has survived the great battle.

By nightfall Mocha's exertions will doubtless have caught up with him, and he will fall asleep, flukes down, head bobbing. His dreams will be horrendous—vivid, overlapping nightmares that find him performing absurd acts of atonement. But then he will awaken, and his cetacean soul will collect the rising sun, even as that same star burns away his remorse, and his cranium swells with pride and spermaceti. Once again he has told the world his opinion of petroleum. Once again he has joined the side of the sea lions, aquatic iguanas, giant tortoises, flightless cormorants, and blue-footed boobies.

"The battle is won," he tells the madman. "But the war goes on."

"Next time we'll arrange to have more huge cephalopods and eels on hand," says Abraxis.

By Mocha's lights, the madman's words are at once prescient and wise. Marine gigantism is the hope of the future. Tentacles will one day save the world. You can never have too many squid.

Drop
Jonathan Thirkield

Drop from a height so high the light is blinding the wind is
like a body pressing against you as if you are not nature are not
made of water taste the drop in oxygen content of the
atmosphere the felled trees and wind chimes blind luck
invisible changes are hard to detect difficult to imagine in
freefall

Drop the apocalyptic video game bliss the unbroken sheen of
zombies painted against the unfamiliar valleys of human
migration as if it's good target practice for the real guns trained
on the mass casualties you can't prevent nor prove causation for
only correlation so nothing's certain there is no reason not to

Drop a bottle of kerosene on the Holocene let nature's bonfire
burn on a million species drop away into the fuel of all our
dreaming feeding heating up the air and land the ash and sand to
glass the living earth falls from us like skin like salt like water
like words like a memory drop it forget it a million servers deep
in the ocean fire up brand new worlds and palaces Alices and
fallacies cloud the eyes' black pupils like iron pills

Drop a curtain on your certainty replace it with a bell curve
draw a circle around your group and hope that it will turn out
well jack your headphones into satellite radio bring the almond
dipped in chocolate to the tongue let its taste spread from place
to place across the palate sucked up into the palace of the brain
while the matter part falls toward the heart is absorbed by the
blood while the hand continues the loop

Drop dime drop rhymes drop beats drop sheets drop lines drop
time drop the tonic an octave drop in the bucket in the ocean
ripple in the margins like a thought like a letter like a leaf like
an ash key spinning like a helicopter slowly like a thought

down the rabbit hole like the underground regions of the earth
are a mind to be plummeted or harvested for diamonds

Drop your eyes to the screen in your palm to the faceless
dandelions' holographic landscapes streaming beautiful end after
end of human action rendition addiction redaction draw your
eyes across the iron lace on the grate as you hear the water
flowing under you is he here he is not the rest of the search
party walks with their eyes to the ground the surveyor's strings
marking bounds like buoys in a lake beach

Drop the guise of sweetness of lighthanded notes written as
if a moment's work intelligence is more difficult no shine of
ease a word won't fizz when dropped in the pool of thought off
consciousness's shore we are lying to ourselves if we think we
are being true if feeling feels real when what we see isn't to end
of time the human race goes hand in hand since we are the
measurers from here

Drop the hypnotic clock back and forth till each tick rips
through ripples rifles through the ganglia the gaslight dims at
scales so slow and slim you can't tell if it's live or if it's
Memorex how much is this in your head how much can you fit
in there can you pack the whole world in your mind what is the
taste of the tape on the brain that catches the light in the sky
and calls it blue calls it back to you to recall

Drop the idea that you will upload consciousness to the cloud
that the cloud is a cloud that data goes up and you are below
and information like icicles forms in beautiful crystals before it
rains at your request as you read down the page down the never
infinite scroll as the text falls and your eyes fall along with it

Drop lies like flies like life is only lifelike like in the old days in
the dark age when life was a simulation for god's judgment for
admission to the kingdom's real behind the trees and torn sky
plug the body into the fallacies and be astonished blinded by the
brightness of invention the lightness and ease with which the
soul dissolves on the tongue with which meaning is surpassed
by a sensation of darkness

Drop the losses the costs can be refolded into the next venture
there is nothing physical in capital just numbers to adjust watch
them drip down drift down the coasts like the raft of the
Medusa floating into the future

Dropped mid action mid history in medias res in the middle of
someone else's lifetime it's impossible to understand everything
is behind you are falling forward wars were fought the living
somehow survived dodged avoided a void where history wasn't
where the church or department store before the bombardment
left holes puddles giant lakes

Drop myself alone into the world which means my self is
broken by the loop between me and the world the thread
through the eye of the pupil the needle through the black iron
pill the tonic fizzing in the cells disjoins my head from the
illusion of music holding everything together with every fourth
note a stitch in the heart cleft I am falling for you for the
illusion of you for the illusion you build

Drops are not circles are not spheres are not atoms but atoms'
patterns for liquid divisions acquisitions of the form and
position at least for the time being time bound beings found
together in a membrane in a memory a pooling of parts and
particles past participles

Drops' opposites are bubbles or bubbles are just types of drops as
they are types of thoughts rising up from the brain and written
in the comic frame they float into the cloud I wonder how the
cloud can get heavy enough for the thoughts to rain back down
how does language rain in words or letters or sound it is the latter
which are waves and anyway bubbles are more spherical than

Drops in populations correlate with rising temperatures and loss
to suicide even when corrected for other factors of geography
and development the heat presses the mind always losing
water my father killed himself in the height of summer by
dropping his body enough stories to crush it whatever it is
inside those million droplets of life that act in concert to keep
the consciousness engine burning bright but not too hot

Jonathan Thirkield

Drop of red on the glass beak of the dipping duck machine's
hypnotic rock back and forth tracing a ninety degree arc path
down to the jar round and bare and barred like jail the jealous
systems of wellness and dominion tell us not to worry the
world as we rub it down to the nub the glass shines cities of
burnished walls falling falling falling down nose to the water
watch the diver

Drop a rope down let me climb back up never let me go never
let me hope the feel of rope of throat and hair an ankle
somebody above me I can grasp who will let me grasp them
even if they are falling too they can pull me up to them I can
climb the falling bodies to the top of what there is no top to

Drop from a skyscraper splashless through the river surface just
as they rehearsed it their body glides through the riverbed
punctures the crust of the planet clean through and through to
the other side like a bullet through the shoulder like a needle
through a beetle's side like a la la laser through the white of an
eye they keep diving up to the other sky the lower one the
southern not governed

Drop to sleep like a mouse in your hand like a mouth in your
head like a roach you thought was a chocolate and nearly bit
into stop sleeping your mind is an engine chewing through
relations the wheel of wheels spinning with your body stuck
where it is until it stops and flings you like a spark out into the
stars if you sleep you will miss the party we will miss you your
body like a hammock and the body in it

Drop souls into a well the fall is gentle the leaves smell of metal
and seeds endlessly in free fall and forever some day casting
bodies out in space will replace burial with the idea that
our DNA might somehow survive the radiation outside our
magnetic field

Drop your tongue into the sun into the surface of its plasma
ocean watch it melt like a lozenge on itself watch the sun drop
to the coin slot down the horizon's throat like there is no
tomorrow

312

Drop vertiginous coins from the eye everything goes even in a
vacuum bodies of metal of flesh of water feather and fruit
dropping like flies the next plague climbs up the antibiotic
ladder scales the molecules at scales we can't see

Drops which are themselves the definition of their shape like
pears are large drops are sweet masses who form over time in
ways that resemble the formation of molten glass hanging from
a branch or pipe shaped by their own weight or the gravity
forcing it lower like a tear breaking off from the ducts and lower
eyelid we are so water dependent in our thinking that is one
difference between us and computers

Drop yourself the body shatters the shadow it falls through
don't kid yourself death is our central currency by currency I
mean both money and electric current blood beats time's meat
and music through us warm as dawn you are delusional to think
anything but think away it's awesome to be able to think of a
beach the shape of your brain on which you can stroll watching
your footprints go

Drop the zealotry of someone loving lovesick dusted drunk
undead the gesture swipes the screen the scream from the rattle
bag of mice installed in your heartspace driving your body like
an automized vehicle to the next human system there is
nothing outside our world time is relentless even if it bends in
space's fabric that is beyond our horizon the land bends around
the earth's core as words like curved birds dive into and fill
our heads

Spectra Reservoirs
Rebecca Lilly

MARS IN SCORPIO

Unseen but immediate this tremor of
blackening waves through our eyes still
stranger than our wake of waiting
silence it isn't this rain *hello again* the
international fires reinstated would you
care to add genetic or spiritual *phish* to
outlaws redistributed in the molecular
scrubbing and rinsing the bone-on-bone
tic to hack portraits of life in painterly
blues and ochers glossing darker energy
shouldering whiteness of an eye's trial
(diffuse liminal redness) Mars igniting
our wars icons for splendorous galactic
armor the lava pouring into a glass globe
(an hourglass bulb of dead sea sand-
storms) cosmogony of grit for dream
downtimes of trophies and arrowheads
guesswork's creeping underlight the
existential settlement

WEST OF MY BACKYARD PINES

Letting be: it was a challenge of not-
seeing the now settled how it was farther
to go in the currents but why when I
looked would be the feeling of one
greenery pure water and the relative
means

theory versus the real glimpses slip and
curl tighter than a leaf in the storm winds
did you find your illnesses in the middle
earth distant lightning an extinction of
energy diving through will and its gilt
quiver of shadows head-on jolted the
moment in its hair-split of futures blown
missed

the wind walks through polluted springs
past byways of neon-colored waters of
microplastics hidden in pebbled grass
what of light in absentia, the wet soles,
heart, westerly enchantress, rags to root
blackish my tall bushy pine light thins
truth lasts

Rebecca Lilly

LOSING FOOTING

My foot sinking at the hole's edge be-
guiling its emptiness underbreath that
pressure to fly against earth swinging
under its point of rest: ingrown, out of
step, some runner the light left on its
loose ends the poetics expired where it
went

the pastoral's old bowler hat soaked in
pesticides the scarecrow had it but wind
took it back my footing in bedrock in
twisted wire later silvered twilight drops
an existential drift (one cloud it's in
earnest) the shattered rest a quiescent
split world the particulates

scaling a wide straight path a gradual
slope beware the earth's dark attractors
to sandy burials in fresh grass in golf
course flybacks the path dust-deviling
bad faith losing footing I dig the way of
poetics (banging a left of the devil's
yawn in sky's glossed horizontal) dark
splices the cloud hole's blue dot tele-
scoped wrong blurred out . . .

316

TRIO OF SUMMITS

Dust retreats *blings* a cornered spell east
of the sun west of the moon this trio of
summits headlands so still an undertow
water's run out of an island of broken
shells rattles loose a raw glittery vista!

this land we knew its green pastures full
of rubber boots for the landfill *to crawl
through its trenches with deformed new
species of insects*

trees wish for better views: each leaf of
skin, trunk's dark rings the cerebrum
bounded limp it's raining a settlement of
nested stingers a haplogroup's broken
shells Rounded-Up compost

a climatologist treks legs sink into muck
weeds eating themselves grinding up in
the sea's ride out to the headlands not to
cease vanishing this misted spar seams
the leaks in what appears upstream
seeing is touching a simple mountain
peak

Rebecca Lilly

MIGRATIONAL HABITS

Watery lead this longing in dream logs
adrift in afterburn nights quicken vigilant
igniting the dark spectra's reservoirs a
floating world strung before doubling
back to forests' controlled burn behind
the veil the day lost in each burial in
woods become water

earth blacks out the resurrecting flowers
misted in patchwork lyrics pressing the
body long after its wings are clipped I
wasn't drawn to wing-shadows so much
as wind's outgrowth of wisdom hinged
into ultimacy as water gets scarcer isn't
the solar makeup mapped instantly in
streams from snowed peaks melting to
mirror the trees lost little creatures to be
its vision a calling

Naming the Storm
Francine Prose

WHEN I WAS VERY YOUNG, newly thrilled by just having learned the alphabet, I loved it that tropical storms had alphabetical women's names. Hurricane Agnes, Betsy, Cleo, Doris, all the way to Zelda. I don't know why, I thought it was great. I was totally proud. I'd been taught to be thoughtful and nice. But look what damage women could do. And what a brilliant use for the ABCs, so much more grown-up than alphabet songs.

At one time the storms were named after saints. San Felipe. Santa Ana. According to the National Hurricane Center, whose website makes fascinating reading, Australian meteorologist Clement Wragge began naming storms after women in the late nineteenth century. Wragge's Wikipedia page tells a somewhat different story of a British-born world traveler and spiritualist, a follower of a messianic Muslim mystic. The founder of weather stations in Scotland and across Australia, Wragge did serious research not only in storm tracking but prediction. He did indeed name storms, but after classical heroes (Xerxes, Hannibal) and Australian prime ministers (Hurricane Alfred Deakin).

Sometime in the 1950s, hurricanes became female, apparently following maritime practice. Sailors were said to name storms after women, as they were said to name ships after women.

Most likely seventies feminism inspired us to reconsider if there was something unjust about nature at "her" most treacherous inevitably being conceptualized as female. And so we began to divide the storms between men and women. Lately we have more gender-neutral names, Dorian and so forth.

The names we don't have anymore are the names of the worst ones. The great catastrophes are one-time only. Every year storms are retired forever from the name rotation because of the severity of the damage they have done. In many ways, it's understandable: partly it's superstition, partly consideration for the survivors (and the rest of us) who don't need to revisit a painful history.

But it is also, obviously, an encouragement to forget.

Second only perhaps to the latest mass shooting, there is nothing the "mainstream" media loves more than "natural" disaster. During prime time, every channel is the Weather Channel. The rubric for picking the top story used to be: if it bleeds, it leads. But now blood is too familiar, or insufficiently photogenic. Not big-picture enough. A mourner weeping for a shooting victim, collapsed in the arms of a loved one, is wrenching but hardly compares—I'm talking optics here, talking *action*—to suffering palm trees bent double by the wind, or a churning, swollen, implacable river rushing over the land, clapboard houses bobbing along like toy boats in the tub. Now what leads the news is houses reduced to rubble, mobile homes floating downstream, residents searching the (best case) water-logged, mud-choked rooms for the family photograph, the lost wedding ring, the graduation portrait. Or, worst case, the foundation. It's like war journalism used to be, only now there are no victors.

I have been thinking about the production crews whose job requires them to go to the places where climate disaster has just struck and find the survivors to interview for the local or national TV news. It's not the person who talks to the camera, perfectly coiffed and made-up, sometimes in a parka and a hood with a few locks of hair fetchingly stirred by the leftover wind. They're not the ones whose job it is to seek out the dazed and devastated. I imagine that duty fallen to a younger person, a newer member of the team.

Are there lots of volunteer survivors? Does the team pick someone out of the small, stunned crowd, or from among the families wandering through the destroyed landscape? How does the team choose? Is the distraught homeowner convincing? Is it better if the newly homeless cry or act brave, clutch the single family memento salvaged from the wreckage or be joyously thankful for the survival of the pet?

Mansions have burned in Malibu, but you hardly ever see rich people in these segments, and the celebrities who have lost homes don't appear on camera, but in headshots, speaking through their agents. The teams gravitate toward survivors who are lower or middle class, mostly white, many of them women, perhaps because women are more closely linked to the idea of home, in this case the lost home. You much more rarely see people of color, though their homes must also have lain in the path of the wind and fire and water. The class origins of the newly homeless reinforce the uncomfortable idea that God so often seems to hate the poor.

Does a member of the television team ever want to ask about climate change? Does a team member ever want to ask: What do you think? Is there any *pattern* here beside the whims of nature? It would be tasteless to introduce politics at a moment like this. Cruel. It really would. This is no time for blame. The exchange would be cut from the segment. The team member would be warned, maybe even fired. Lots of people want that job. They're dying to be on the team.

What if a hurricane took Mar-a-Lago? What if a tornado rolled over Mitch McConnell's home? Our leaders would stalk through the ruins in hard hats, heroes with insurance coverage to build something fancier, bigger, and brand-new, but suffering, like so many fellow Americans, the effects of natural disaster.

Once again language and word choice mean everything—and nothing. Refugee versus immigrant. Pro-Life versus Pro-Choice. Natural disaster versus climate disaster. Better not use the word climate, best not think the word climate with its pesky new tagalong friend, its constant companion, the word *change*.

But there does seem to be an inverse correlation between the things we don't say—or don't say constantly—and the things we can't help thinking. Constantly. The danger we're in—the danger our planet is facing—is never far from our minds, and, I would guess, never far from the minds of the climate-change deniers. These days, every storm is an omen, a harbinger of disaster. Every coyote howling in the night is the voice of something coming closer. . . .

At this moment, four black bears are living in our backyard, driven down from the mountains by . . . what? Drought? The reduced population of honey bees? The promise of delicious garbage in the increasingly populated neighborhoods?

I've been thinking about *The Wizard of Oz*, about the equanimity with which we watched Dorothy's Kansas farm swept away by the tornado without feeling the fear that we would feel now—the idea of it happening to us—and without the promise of Oz somewhere over the rainbow.

It used to take a certain amount of work and effort and concentration to think—to really think, as clearly and as deeply as we could. But now much of that effort goes into *not* thinking, into *not* seeing every orange maple, every cornfield, every rushing stream as something impermanent and at risk. If we allowed ourselves to dwell on all that, we could rarely make it through an ordinary day.

And so, at least in that sense, we are all climate-change deniers. If we weren't, we would be doing more. We would be insisting and demanding and loudly holding them accountable, the ones who are most at fault. It's so hard to know what to do, so hard that unless we are going to act, we can only survive by not thinking. Getting through the average day means being a climate-change denier.

Meanwhile, the storms keep coming. To make it easy on the alphabet, we now have six-year rotation. But no matter how bad it gets, we can take comfort in the fact that there will never be another Katrina, another Maria, another Andrew, another Sandy.

Meanwhile we are prepared. If the number of tropic storms exceeds the number of letters in the alphabet, we will switch to the Greek alphabet.

Hurricane Alpha.

Hurricane Omega.

And then what?

Our imaginations quit at that point or head for the postapocalyptic, but despite everything we know, despite our reasonable fears, we are an optimistic species. My favorite painting in the world is Giovanni di Paolo's 1457 *Saint Nicholas of Tolentino Saving a Shipwreck*.

It is a night scene, a boat is out on the sea, the sails have been blown away by the wind, the passengers are kneeling on deck, praying.

But look! Their prayers are being answered. From the upper right-hand corner, Saint Nicholas is flying in, in the black robes of his order, calming the storm with one hand, holding a lily in the other.

A Liberation
Matthew Cheney

—In memory of Katherine Min

AFTER HIS MOTHER DIED, Arthur sold off most of his possessions
in a yard sale, then made his way across the world to the city of
N———, where his mother had been born, and where he decided he
would live out the rest of his life, though he knew nothing of the language or the culture and nobody recognized his mother's maiden
name when he spoke it. Within a few months, he changed his name
to Akaky, since that's what *Arthur* sounded like when he imagined
it in the local dialect, and the kind owner of the café that Arthur
spent much of his time at said, in the few words of Arthur's language
that he knew, "Ah, yes, Akaky, name good, yes, Akaky." The café
owner clutched a coffee-stained scrap of paper in arthritic hands, set
it on the table where Arthur sat, and, with a plastic ballpoint pen
that perhaps had traveled as far from its home as Arthur had, wrote
the name in the alphabet of the language Arthur did not speak. After
finishing his seventh cup of gritty coffee that morning, Arthur thanked
the old man and left a few coins from back home on the table. The
old man treasured these coins, and Arthur was glad he had gained
many at the yard sale and had had the foresight, or blind luck, to be
too lazy to turn them into paper money at the bank before he left.
Arthur wandered out of the café and to the park of dead trees, where
he sat on an iron bench and showed the piece of paper to an old
woman who shambled by. "Akaky?" she said, looking up at him. He
nodded. She also nodded, then smiled and walked on. And so he
became Akaky.

He lived in a one-room apartment in an abandoned building a few
streets down from the café. When he first arrived in the city, he found
it difficult to tell where one building ended and its neighbor began,
because in the center of N——— each building was as close to the
others as possible, with the few alleys barely large enough for a
scrawny person to squeeze through. This design, he learned later,
conserved heat and prevented strong winds from blasting all sides of
the buildings. In a city as north and as cold as N———, such a design

was a matter of survival. Outside the center of the city, most build-ings were empty warehouses and massive, abandoned tower blocks, the relics of an old regime that had hoped to relocate citizens to the north to work in the mines. Older residents occasionally told stories of the Winter Massacre, when temperatures plummeted so far that heating systems sputtered and failed, and by the end of a week so many people had frozen to death that the tower blocks became ghostly morgues. For months that spring, the howls of wolves echoed through the concrete halls of massive buildings on the outskirts of the city. Sometime in the summer, the army brought truckloads of prisoners to help clean out the towers. The prisoners hauled, scraped, scoured. Plumbers, carpenters, electricians, and mechanics guided the prisoners. Sawing and hammering echoed for many miles. Soon enough, the apartments were habitable again and the army took the prisoners away, but the buildings remained empty. Winters now were cold, but never quite so cold as they had once been, and there weren't enough people that they would die en masse. Nonetheless, each spring the daylight revealed what winter's darkness hid and ice preserved: lonely tableaux of last days.

Akaky's apartment was small, dim, and shabby, cluttered with fur-niture left behind by whoever lived there before. He welcomed the dimness during the endless sunlight of summer, and in the winter's darkness he found it comforting to live in a space of shadows. The previous residents must have had a cat or some other animal as a pet, because the upholstered corners of the chairs and the sofa were clawed and torn, and for months Akaky found clumps of hair in corners and under rugs. An iron potbelly stove stood in the middle of the room, and he fed it bits of wood and garbage whenever he was home, but if he went out for more than an hour, the stove cooled and the apartment cooled. (He worried about the pipes, as he didn't know what to do if the pipes froze and burst.) He thought perhaps he should move to an apartment in one of the empty buildings on the outskirts of the city, and so one day when there wasn't too much wind and the tempera-ture was almost pleasant, he walked out to the nearest tower block, a twenty-story cube of concrete, but he discovered that he couldn't safely go inside because the building's foundation had shifted, sinking more than a foot into the ground, shattering much of the first floor. Through broken windows, Akaky peered in at a rubble of tiles, Sheet-rock, wood, metal, and cement. A skeletal staircase dangled in the air.

A few days later at the café, the owner introduced Akaky to a woman who spoke his language. Akaky thought she looked to be a few years older than he was, but he had never been a good judge of age, and in any case the conditions up here skewed people old. Her name, she said, was Zora, or rather it was now Zora, though it had been something different long ago, but so long ago she hardly remembered what it was. Despite speaking the same language, Akaky did not understand some of the words she used, and her accent was one he had not heard before. He wanted to ask her where she was from, but the question seemed impolite. Lacking another subject, Akaky talked about the weather, and then Zora asked him if he had noticed that the buildings in the city were all sinking into the earth.

"Yes," Akaky said. "I saw this on the outskirts. I went looking for another place to live. My apartment is not ideal. I thought perhaps one of the abandoned buildings would allow me a bit more space, though of course there would be no electricity, no running water, I expected that, and I've certainly lived with greater deprivations, and in any case I thought it couldn't hurt to have a look, and so a few days ago I walked out to one of the towers, and I couldn't even go inside because the whole ground floor was destroyed and the building was, as you said, sinking into the earth." Speaking his own language made him loquacious, he realized. He stared at the table and said quietly, "It's all very strange."

Zora sipped a large, steaming cup of tea. She said, "It's sinking. All of it. The towers are simply heavier than anything else, so they're going faster."

"All?" Akaky said. "All sinking?"

"Yes," she said, as if stating an obvious fact, something even small children knew.

"Here, you mean? In the center of the city?"

"This is not the center of the city. We are on the edges here. No matter. The center too is sinking."

"No, I don't believe that's true. I wander the city every day, and I have not noticed any sinking."

"Nonetheless," Zora said, "it is sinking. The city is getting warmer, and the frozen ground is not staying frozen any longer. The sea too, it is coming closer every summer, and though it remains many kilometers away, soon enough it will come closer and closer, and one day it will reach the center of the city. One day, a few years from now, a few decades—one day where we are right now, where we sit, here, this will be underneath the water."

"Well, no matter," Akaky said. "I am not young. It will be after my time."

"The sinking, that is now. You are likely correct to think the worst cataclysms will come later. Perhaps, though, you will have a long life. If so, you will suffer."

"Yes, but I will not have a long life. I have started smoking. I never smoked before, not seriously anyway, but after my mother died, I decided I would smoke, and so I do. I'm up to a pack a day! And the cigarettes here, I don't know if you've tried them. They're wretched. I think they make them in the mines." From his coat pocket, he pulled out a crumpled gold-and-red pack of cigarettes. "I must say, one thing I love about this city is that we can still smoke indoors." He picked up a matchbook from the table, struck a match, and lit the cigarette. "I suppose smoke is not much worse than the air that's already here."

"You smoke," Zora said, "to keep yourself from having a long life?"

"I suppose," Akaky said. "I never thought about it before right now, but, yes, that would be one reason."

They sat in silence until Akaky said, "Who did you leave behind? Back home? Was there a husband, or children, or . . ."

"No one," Zora said. "Once, there were people, but I was no good at keeping track of them, and soon enough I found myself with no reason to stay in any particular place."

"That's sad." Akaky took a deep drag on his cigarette.

"It never seemed so. Not happy, not sad."

"I suppose it was the same for me. After my mother's death. No reason to stay put. I had a wife once, but it was a mistake, we were not in love. Once we realized that, we separated. I don't know where she is now. You said you are not married?"

"I never married."

"Did you ever want to?"

"Look around this city," she said. "Smell the air, let it burn your nostrils. Listen to the breaking buildings, the cracking roads, the silence. What does it matter what I wanted? Or you? We are here. That is all there is to say."

Akaky lit another cigarette. Zora finished drinking her tea and stood up. "It was nice to meet you," she said. "Perhaps we will meet again."

Akaky sat in the café and smoked his cigarette after Zora left, then returned to his apartment. As he prepared himself for bed, he was interrupted by a bark. Akaky often neglected to close the door of his apartment, which was terribly warped and required him to put his full weight against it if there was any hope of it closing, but no person or animal so far had ever come to visit until now, when a dog, something like a beagle but a little bigger and scruffier, trotted in and made its presence known with a few sharp shouts. It then sat down and stared at Akaky expectantly.

"Who are you?" Akaky said to the dog. The dog did not reply. Akaky walked around it, surveying the animal. "Do you have fleas? No?" He leaned in and picked gently at the dog's fur. The dog stood up. "A male, I see. Or a former male. An *it* now. So someone has attended to you in the past." Akaky gave the dog a few pats. "I have pieces of chicken in the refrigerator," Akaky said. "I will make us both sandwiches."

The dog followed him to the kitchen and watched with great excitement as Akaky put chunks of chicken between thin slices of bread. He opened a jar of mayonnaise and smelled it to make sure it wasn't rancid. It wasn't, so he spread a layer over the chicken in the sandwiches. He handed a sandwich to the dog, who ate it mightily.

"Now that we are friends," Akaky said, "perhaps you should have a name. Do you know your name? My name is Akaky. You should have an exotic name, don't you think? Yes, an exotic name. Therefore, I shall name you Arthur."

Arthur looked up from the scraps of sandwich on the floor.

"Hello, Arthur," Akaky said.

Arthur followed Akaky wherever he went, because whenever Akaky had food, he shared some with Arthur. At the café, the owner couldn't pronounce *Arthur*, so he called the dog Sobaka, which Akaky decided was a word meaning *kind, intelligent friend*. The café owner too gave Arthur occasional scraps of food. Akaky worried perhaps Arthur would gain too much weight, but Arthur was so demonically energetic that it was unlikely; he spent his days almost constantly moving, running, bouncing. Even in the café, where Akaky warned him to be on his best behavior, Arthur constantly patrolled the perimeter, dove under tables, dashed between chairs, chased rodents from the kitchen, and raced to greet every occasional customer who came through the front door.

Zora finally returned to the café one afternoon when Akaky and Arthur were there, and Arthur immediately fell in love, trying to jump up into her lap, but she gently coaxed him down. He sulked beside her chair, stealing glances now and then, eyes wide with longing.

"How have you been?" Zora asked Akaky.

"Dying by inches," he said, lighting a cigarette. "You know how it is. But now I have a dog."

Zora twirled a strand of hair around a finger.

327

Akaky said, "And you? How goes existence?"

"I am considering taking a trip out to the sea. I saw it last some years ago, and I would like to return. I thought I might do some painting. I was a painter once. Not a good one, but I enjoyed the work. I have developed terrible fears, however. I am afraid of travel, because I am afraid that when I return, everything will have sunk farther into the earth. Far enough to be, finally, irretrievable."

Akaky nodded. "Seems reasonable," he said.

"Does it? I can't tell anymore. There's too much light. I don't think well in all this light. It is too easy to see the smog in the air, the wreckage all around."

"If you went on a journey to the sea, you would get away from here, away from the city and the mines. The light might be beautiful up there."

"It might," Zora said. "Or it might be more horrible. Horrible in what its beauty reveals of the rest of the world. I don't know if I could survive that."

They sat without speaking, Akaky finishing one cigarette and starting another, and then Zora stood and walked to the door. Arthur tried to follow her, but she paid no attention to him, and she closed the door before he could get through. He stared at the door, whining quietly, then paced slowly through the café.

That night, as Akaky sat in his apartment smoking cigarettes and trying to remember a long poem he had memorized as a child, Arthur wandered through the building. Akaky heard his footfalls and occasional inquisitive barks. The poem was not coming back to him, so Akaky played a game of solitaire with a pack of cards with scratched and faded pictures of penguins on the reverse. He remembered seeing penguins in a zoo once with his mother. As a boy, he was delighted by zoo animals, and he had been sure the animals shared his delight. Now, he wondered if those animals had ever had a moment of happiness. He looked at the old picture of the penguin on the back of a card and sighed. The zoo his mother had taken him to must have closed many years ago.

As Akaky was beginning to accept that he was not going to win the game and might as well go to bed, Arthur returned, carrying something in his mouth. Akaky couldn't tell what it was until Arthur proudly placed it at his feet.

A bone of some sort. Long. Perhaps human. A femur, Akaky expected, not that he knew much about bones. Arthur lay on the floor and gnawed on it.

"Where did you get that from?" Akaky asked, trying not to let any annoyance into his voice, because he didn't want Arthur to feel chastised, for if he did, Akaky knew, Arthur would become cautious and furtive. Arthur ignored him. Akaky approached the dog and slowly leaned down. Arthur growled.

Akaky decided it wasn't worth antagonizing the dog. He went to bed.

In the morning, Akaky discovered that during the night, Arthur had scattered various bones throughout the apartment. They looked like bones from human feet and arms, though he supposed they might be from any animal—remnants, perhaps, of a prehistoric deposit only now surfacing through unfrozen ground. But what of the ones with specks of flesh and blood on them?

Arthur sat amid a small pile of what looked like finger bones. He seemed proud of his work. Akaky picked up a bone. Arthur did not growl. "Where'd you get this from?" Akaky asked. He gestured toward the door. "Where's the boneyard?"

Arthur stared at Akaky, who pointed once again toward the door. Arthur looked at the door, as if expecting a new arrival. "Where are the bones?" Akaky said. "Show me the bones." He started walking toward the door, holding the finger bone out in front of him. Arthur followed. "*I* can't show *you*," Akaky said. "You're the one who knows. You're going to have to lead." Arthur slowly walked past Akaky, then stopped and looked back. "Yes, good boy. Show me the bones."

Suddenly Arthur bounded through the hallway and down the stairs and it was all Akaky could do just to keep him in sight as they descended into the basement of the apartment building, a place Akaky had only ever glanced in at through the door. He had to be careful, because the bottom stairs were covered with debris and the metal railing had separated from the wall. The stairs seemed solid, though, and Arthur hadn't hesitated at all to run through the open door at the bottom. The closer Akaky got to the door, the more pungent the air seemed: thick, both sweet and rotten. Shadows filled the basement, which stretched far beyond Akaky's building, being a basement, it seemed, for the entire block. The only light came in sharp, thin shafts through cracks at the top of the concrete foundation. Though it was a warm day outside, the basement was cool; wet, dripping ice lingered on the wall. Beneath Akaky's feet, the floor was spongy. His boots sank down, the muddy substance rising above his ankle. Fragments of what might have once been a concrete floor drifted like icebergs. He stepped carefully, his balance uncertain in the half darkness as he walked across a terrain both solid and liquid. With each step he took farther into the basement, the air grew more fetid and fungal. Akaky began to feel nauseated, light-headed, but there was something about the air that satisfied him, like a meal rich with fat.

Arthur plunged his snout into the mossy stew of the basement's floor, wriggled his head, grunted, and brought up a long bone in his mouth. Akaky stepped closer. The bone Arthur joyfully chomped was a human leg, the foot still attached and intact, with rotted cloth, flesh, and muscle falling away as rags and jelly into the muck.

Akaky bent his knees and touched his hand to the damp ground. As he let his hand sink lower, he felt matter amid the mud, objects suspended in melted layers of old earth, bits of stone and concrete but also Arthur's treasure: the bones of corpses, which Akaky soon saw (a blast of sunlight pouring through the many cracks high up in one of the foundation's walls) filled three quarters of the basement's floor and rose in piles at the far end, where, despite distance and shadows, Akaky could see the bodies had been quite well preserved, though rodents had clearly been recently feasting.

He wanted to vomit, but instead Akaky discovered himself laughing. His laughter unbalanced him, and he wobbled, then fell down onto his knees, and laughed even harder. As Akaky knelt laughing, Arthur ran over to him, dragging the leg he had found, and Akaky's laughter shook his whole body. He was unable to help himself, and he feared the force of his laughter might knock the floor beneath him loose, until he plunged down into whatever darkness lay below, like a miner lost to the pit. Soon enough, though, Arthur dropped the bone he'd held in his mouth and barked at Akaky, as if telling him his behavior was inappropriate to this place, and Akaky could only agree.

Eventually, once his laughter subsided, Akaky and Arthur together began pulling bones and bodies out of the ground and up into the dusty, fugitive light.

Zora heard that Akaky was up to something down by one of the little lakes, but nobody cared enough to go and see what he was doing. "What do you know about Akaky?" she asked Voshchev, who worked at the mine and lived in the building next to hers and sometimes brought vodka to drink with her.

"We see him there," Voshchev said, "every morning when we go, every evening when we come back. He's building something."

Matthew Cheney

Akaky had never seemed to Zora like a builder, more a lazy dreamer of shallow dreams, a man with little experience and less imagination: a body taking up space, which made him a good fit for this city in its sinking. Nonetheless, good fit or no, Akaky bored her, and she hated his dog, so for more than a month she had avoided visiting the café. But the cold, dark season was coming and she worried about him. Nobody else in the city spoke the language of her country, and though she was perfectly comfortable speaking their language, talking with Akaky, dull as he was, had given her the comfort of old memories and barely remembered dreams. If he were in a bad way, he might not make it through the months to come, and she feared for herself—feared his loss might be her own.

She went to the café one morning. Prushevsky, the owner, said he hardly ever saw Akaky anymore. "Hardly ever?" Zora asked.

"Once a week, twice at most. He drinks coffee, eats some bread or a pastry now or then. I send him home with slices of meat, cheese, whatever I have around, but I do not know that he eats it. He is growing thin."

"And the dog?"

"It seems healthier than he," Prushevsky said.

"How does he spend his day?"

"He says he is working on a project at the eastern lake, the one down the hill from the building he lives in. It took a few tries, a few days, for me to understand that was what he said. He talked about it at length in his language, your language, but I could not understand, and he drew some pictures on a napkin, which is how I know it is the eastern lake, but more than that I do not know. He seems both passionate and at the end of a tether."

"I am familiar with the ends of tethers. I shall go see him."

"Here," Prushevsky said, "wait a moment while I make some sandwiches for you both, and a few scraps for the dog."

Prushevsky filled a plastic bag with sandwiches, bits of meat, some extra cheese, and a bottle of white wine. "For a picnic at the lake!" he said. Zora thanked him and tried to hand him some money, but he wouldn't take it. "Be good to him, and bring him back if he needs to come back. That is enough for me."

She might have hailed one of the city's few taxis, but decided to walk the kilometer out to the lake, giving herself time to think about what she could say to Akaky, what she might tell him of her recent weeks, whether to admit to him the dull truth of her conversations and assignations or to lie and tell him tales of traveling to the

331

river or, even better, up north to the sea. As she walked, she smiled to herself at what she might tell him of the rogues and rascals she had met at the river docks, the scandalous gossip they imparted, and she sighed at the thought of the sea (which she had, in truth, never seen), and how she might describe its vast reach to the horizon, its shifting shores, its seals and whales and polar bears. (Were she to talk of such creatures, though, he would surely know she was telling a tale.) She soon passed the building he lived in, and then the city's streets crumbled away, the orderly design of the city obscured into rubble and ash. She made her way down a winding path along a hill, the lake soon coming into view. She didn't see Akaky until she was almost ready to turn back, sure he wasn't there. He and the dog stood at the far end, the dog digging a hole in the ground, Akaky fiddling with something that she couldn't quite see at a distance, some form, like a tree in a grove, but without leaves. As she got closer, she saw he wasn't alone, and that the form he had been touching, moving, shaping was a person.

A light wind off the lake carried a scent not only of the lake's water but of something else: not the familiar sulfurousness of the mines, but something sharper. Though unfamiliar, it smelled old to her, as if its source had been underneath the lake for centuries and only now had found its way to the air. As she got closer to Akaky and the people he was with, the scent became richer, almost overwhelming.

Something was wrong with the people. They sat or lay sprawled on the shore of the lake or stood beside metal poles. Akaky moved from person to person, shifting their arms and legs, adjusting each person's position, but none of them moved on their own. As she realized this, she stepped close enough to see that their faces were wounded—or no, not wounded, but rotted away.

"Zora!" Akaky cried with delight, a cigarette dangling from the side of his mouth. "How nice to see you!"

The dreadful dog ran up to her, barking. It sniffed the plastic bag she carried. She held the bag out to Akaky, who took it from her. Without speaking, without acknowledging him at all, she walked to the people—the bodies—he had set along the shore. One was simply a skeleton, its skull the color of old stone. Others looked almost alive, mottled with desiccated remnants of veins, muscles, flesh. The clothes each wore were in better shape than their bodies. When she stepped closer, she saw that the people leaning against metal poles were strapped to the poles with wire and rope. The stench was awful, but less awful than it ought to have been, she thought. Flies swarmed around and between each body in such numbers as to make the air shimmer. She swatted, slapping her neck and arms and forehead.

"Smoking helps," Akaky said. "The flies don't like it. And it lessens the smell." He blew a puff of smoke toward her.

Zora tried to ask a question, but her mouth would not form words.

"I found these—these—people—I found them in the basement of my building," Akaky said with the excitement of one who has lived for weeks on little more than coffee. "I tried to bring up the ones in the best shape. There's a remarkable range of—of—of *something* here—some of these people, I'm sure they're as old as the land itself—but others, the ones that reek, the still so wretched ones, the rankest, might as well have died only a few weeks ago, a month or two maybe, a year, I don't know, decomposition is not my speciality—some may be miners lost in accidents, or the people from the winters, people the military cleared out of buildings, but that's not the whole story, is it, no, it can't be, there's all the others coming up now, the ancestors, the predecessors—coming up from underneath, as if this is where they have always gone, always ended up, as if this is the place where everyone for all the eons . . ." His breath failed him.

The dog whined and scratched his snout against Akaky's leg. Akaky said, "Arthur likes the bones, any bones, and he keeps trying to bring them here, but I tell him this is not an ossuary. And we certainly don't mix and match. That would be ghastly."

"What . . . is it, this place? What are you doing?" Zora said, her voice barely a whisper.

"Doing?" He watched the dog run off, chasing some animal, or perhaps a shadow, in the tall grass beyond the lake. Akaky smoked his cigarette. Finally, he said, "I think of this as a liberation. I bring out the ones I can. I scrounge new clothes for them in my building and a few other buildings that seem safe to enter. I'm getting good at eyeing what fits." He dropped the stub of his cigarette to the ground and lit another. "Eventually, perhaps, I will save them all, but there are limits to my energy, to my strength. There are limits. I found a big old wheelbarrow, and I use that to transport them here. I bring out whomever I can, and I try to position them so that they have a good view of the lake. I know it sounds absurd. And smells terrible. And these flies. But don't you think . . ." He stared out at the lake.

"What?" Zora asked. "Don't I think . . . ?"

"I was going to say, Don't you think there's something right about it? I mean, it feels right to *me*, it feels entirely right, but I realize it may seem like I am disturbing them, that I have brought them here against what might have been their will, their wishes. I don't know how they got there. I don't know what they wanted, or even who they are. They could be murderers. They could have been born in caves or in mansions. I don't know anything about them. But still. I would not have done this if I wasn't absolutely convinced. In my heart. No matter who they are, or why they were down there. I am sure this is right. I would not do it otherwise." He breathed deeply.

Zora looked out across the lake at the city silhouetted against the horizon. Smog from the mines tinted the scene yellow. She remembered when Voshchev took her out to see the giant pit of the largest mine, an abyss she could never have dreamed, a perfectly round crater wider than the eastern lake, a structure she knew had been built by people but which her imagination insisted must be something else, something older and stranger than human action, the result of an extraterrestrial force that pierced a hole in the world. She had turned away from the pit, buried her face against Voshchev's chest, and wept. All the bodies that had ever lived and died in this city would not fill that hole.

"What time is it?" Akaky asked.

"Late," Zora said.

"We shouldn't eat the food if we're here," Akaky said. "The flies. Who knows what germs. We could eat in my apartment, if you want."

"Yes," Zora said, "that would be fine."

They walked slowly back to Akaky's building, the dog following, all silent. Zora washed in the bathroom while he washed in the kitchen. She was impressed with the water pressure in his building. Perhaps she would look for an empty apartment here herself. Maybe Voshchev would join them too. Could Akaky and Voshchev get along? It wouldn't matter. The building was large enough that they could all keep to themselves when they wanted. Though clearly the building was sinking—it was already listing enough to the west to be noticeable from outside. Still, good water pressure was rare.

Akaky placed their sandwiches on plates. He poured wine into glasses and set the glasses on the formica table in his kitchen. The apartment, Zora thought, was cozy, though its furniture was all the wrong size for such small rooms. There must be larger apartments in this building, ones with better light. Certainly there was other furniture around, and this furniture could be moved or tossed in a pile and burned. He didn't need to live like this.

They ate in silence. Akaky lit a cigarette. Eventually, Zora said, "Will you take more people to the lake?"

"A few more," Akaky said. "I would like to take them all, but I feel myself fading, and there are so many. I have little energy anymore. I think my heart is slowing down."

"It's strange that the wolves have not found them. There used to be wolves that would wander through the streets of the city. I suppose they've all been killed, though."

"So few animals left," Akaky said. "Just us and the flies."

"And your dog."

"A survivor. Like us."

They finished their sandwiches in silence and sipped their wine.

"The bodies are from this building?" Zora said.

"The basement," Akaky said.

"Perhaps . . . Yes, I think I would like to see them."

"Oh?" The tone of his voice suggested skepticism to her.

"I was a nurse in a war once, long ago," she said, untruthfully. "Far from here. I've seen bodies with every type of mutilation, every type of rot. Nor does the stench bother me. I have a weak sense of smell. Weak sense of smell, strong stomach."

"Perhaps," Akaky said, "after we eat. Give it a little time."

"Yes, of course. Even with my strong stomach . . ."

"There are limits."

She nodded and finished drinking her wine. She heard the dog snoring in the other room. In only a few days, she thought, the sun would finally sink away and then begin to rise and set again. She hoped the people at the lake would last long enough to see that. It would rise at their backs and set in front of them. She could help Akaky bring some more people out. Yes, she would do that. Unpleasant work, but though she had not been a nurse in a war, she had done unpleasant work often enough, and dead bodies were familiar to her. She might even recognize some of them from seasons past. "Hello, Yuri," she imagined herself saying to one of the many who had gone away without a goodbye. "So this is where you ended up. Let's get you out of here, shall we? Oh, and Olga Safrova too. How good to see you again. Is your daughter Masha here? I have so missed seeing Masha." She let the scene carry on in her imagination as Akaky washed their dishes in the sink. It would not be entirely unpleasant work. And, in any case, seldom had she done unpleasant work for much purpose. Here there would certainly be purpose, strange though it might be. Bones and bodies to bring up from the depths. A kind of mining of their own. Mining for what? Some moments of freedom. For the people, for Akaky, for herself, maybe even for the dog. If their luck

335

held, they could all sit out there one night, perhaps, and watch the shadows lengthen, the light slip away, the bright stars shine through the shrouded sky over the sinking city, and they would know that the sun would rise again, at least once more, before the winter brought its conquering night.

Extracts

Jessica Campbell

THERE ARE A FEW THINGS you should know before we begin:
1. This pig was bred to be an organ donor.
2. The liver is the only organ that can regenerate.
3. The ancient Greeks considered the liver the seat of the soul.

The pig is already split. It lies on a cart next to the surgeon, open from neck to groin, bones wrenched out of their protective curl. The surgeon snips away the blood vessels and bile ducts connecting the pig's liver to the workings of its body. She lifts the liver clear of the carcass and places it on a stainless-steel tray.

The surgeon then turns to the patient. All that is visible on the operating table is the basin of the body, brimming with raw organs. The abdomen, a butcher's bowl. She digs the liver out of the meaty pile.

Human liver and pig liver lie side by side on the tray. The pig liver is notably smaller than the human liver. The surgeon places the pig liver into the butcher's bowl, and it seems to float in the viscera. She stitches it into the digestive tract, stretching blood vessels and bile ducts to meet it. She folds muscle and skin back over the cavity.

If the body does not destroy the pig liver, it will grow to fill the void left by the human organ. It will take on the size and shape of that which is missing—but it will always be a pig's liver.

One more thing you should know:
4. Even gods have soft underbellies.

Under Prometheus's rib cage is a tender spot that yields when pressed. The eagle knows this spot well. It is as fragile as a hare. It never scars.

Jessica Campbell

The eagle perches on the god's last rib, talons sunk in thorax. Her grip is perpetual. Her claws can do nothing but grasp.

The bone is a fulcrum. She pivots her body to his abdomen. Her beak tears open the tender spot and plucks out the liver. It is like a carp in her mouth.

The eagle does not swallow the liver. She drops it in the sea. It becomes an island.

One day, the island will have a name, a population, an economy, but for now it is just the liver of a god floating in the black waters.

It probably goes without saying:
5. The role of the liver is to remove toxins from the body.

The bird alights on a Gatorade bottle. She plucks up a plastic cap. It slides down her esophagus and settles in her crop. She hops from the Gatorade bottle to a shard of polypropylene. She pecks at some strands from a shredded plastic bag. They follow the cap into her digestive system. She skims the water with her beak, and a mouthful of krill-sized polyethylene washes her breakfast from her crop into her stomach.

A buffet of polymers stretches as far as the bird can see, as far as she can fly in a day. If the microbeads and fiberfill had any nutritional value, the bird would never go hungry again. If the bits of DVD casing and packing peanuts could be converted into calories, she could raise several generations of chicks here, in a nest made of polyvinyl tufts tucked into a margarine tub on an island of plastic five times larger than Greece.

At the risk of stating the obvious:
6. The ocean will soon contain more plastic than fish.
7. That bird already contains more plastic than flesh.
8. The air you breathe contains more nitrogen than oxygen.

On the laboratory bench sits a machine: a pump, a compressor, and a condenser, none larger than a table lamp. The pump pushes methane into a compressor filled with air. Air and methane shed their component parts, which mingle and bond. Nitrogen from the air meets hydrogen from the methane. Liquid drips from the condenser.

A small man, hairless save for an epaulet on his upper lip, runs from the laboratory. He hurries down the hallway, shouting, "Come! See! It is falling."

Ammonia is falling, dripping out of the machine into a small basin. The machine is pulling nitrogen from the air and turning it into ammonia. Only a few teaspoons of ammonia, no more than the human body produces in a day.

There is very little one can do with a few teaspoons of ammonia. One cannot change the course of a war, for example, or feed a few billion people.

Still, the little basin of ammonia excites the man with the mustache as nothing has for many years. He knows that machines are scalable, in ways that human bodies are not. And he believes the supply of air is limitless.

I imagine you're already aware:
    9. Ammonia is used in the production of synthetic fertilizer.
    10. Ammonia is used in the production of explosives.
    11. Mortals were never meant to possess fire.

The Titan is armed with a fennel stalk. The fennel stalk is slender, bright, and eminently destructible. The Titan cannot be destroyed, and he knows this. He looks down into the volcano. The lava is quiet. The god of fire is not at home.

Prometheus steps into the crater. He moves from cleft to boulder as though he were descending a staircase. He does not look like a thief. It is not in the nature of Titans to skulk.

Nevertheless, the footfall of a god makes no sound. Prometheus enters the magma chamber without a ripple. He pierces the black, wrinkled skin of the molten rock with his delicate fennel stalk and sucks the fire of the underworld into the hollow herb. He smiles just once, lips smeared with ash.

Jessica Campbell

The fennel does not burn, or even smoke, as he carries it to the nearest village. This is because Prometheus has decided it will not burn.
Such things are still his prerogative. He gives the fennel stalk to the
people of the village. The stalk holds just a few liquid drops of flame,
but the Titan knows it is enough to set the world on fire.

I probably should have mentioned:
    12. The world is on fire.

Smokestacks hold umbrellas of soot over the factory, blocking out
the sun or the rain or whatever the sky is doing off on its own.
Underneath the smokestacks furnaces strain against flames and
gases while iron melts. Puddlers shove rods through the furnace
doors and poke and stir the molten metal. Impurities leach out of the
iron and get sucked up into the chimney. Pockmarked balls of iron
float up to the surface and get fished out by the puddlers.

Workers hammer at the iron balls until they are flat enough to push
through the rollers. Smiths' assistants wait for the solid metal to
emerge from the machine. They take it to the forges and reheat the
bars, so the smiths can begin their work.

One smith bends iron to form lancet window frames. Another welds
branches of wrought iron together to form a pulpit. Three smiths
work together to fit the plates of the iron coffin in which the owner
of the ironworks will be buried.

Obituaries call this man a titan of industry, a new kind of god. Like
the old gods, he can chase off the sun and send emissaries to the
underworld. Like the old gods, he can command the sacrifice of men.
Like the old gods, he can demand temples filled with monuments to
his deeds. He will still rot and molder in his grave, but he can keep
the worms from his flesh a little longer than most.

Perhaps this is the moment to let you know:
    13. Humans once used the ammonia in their own urine to re-
        plenish the soil.
    14. Phosphorus is the other essential ingredient in synthetic
        fertilizer.
    15. There is no known way to manufacture synthetic phosphorus.

340

The satellite image shows a line of jagged white, like icicles hanging from the sand. The icicles stretch across the desert, from the last gasp of the mountain range to first breath of the sea.

Perched on an acacia, the buzzard doesn't see icicles. He doesn't even imagine icicles. He is looking at a conveyor belt, the longest in the world. It stretches from the mine to the port. It is heaped with phosphate rock coated in white dust.

The wind lifts the loose powder into the air and feathers it out across the sand. A loss that can be seen from space. A loss that is negligible on the mine's balance sheet. The bird looks back at the mine. It is in the business of losing things. It has lost a mountain already. The mound of rock that once formed part of the spine of the continent has been inverted. It is now a mountain-shaped absence, a pit in the ground surrounded by slurry pipes, spoil heaps, and lakes of acid.

The buzzard looks down at his body. He has lingered too long near the conveyor belt. He is coated in phosphorus, a powdery ghost.

It's only fair to tell you:
16. Synthetic fertilizer causes toxic tides and ocean dead zones.
17. Without synthetic fertilizer, farmers could only produce enough food for half the world's human population.

It is a feast fit for a king, and Phineus is a king. This is obvious because he sits in the tallest chair at the center of the banquet table. His chair's back is carved with eagles. His chair's seat is well cushioned. On either side of Phineus, the table goes on for yards, and men sit in shorter, less ornate chairs. Along the table, roasted rams and stuffed peacocks and suckling pigs drip their juices on the ocean-licked sand.

Phineus's plate is empty—golden but empty. A servant steps forward and fills the king's plate with the most tender cuts of beast and fowl. Before Phineus can lift his knife, however, the wind gusts and the food is gone. Neither Phineus nor the servant has seen it go. One moment it is there. The next it is gone.

The servant steps forward and fills the king's plate with slightly less tender cuts of beast and fowl. Before Phineus can lift his knife, the wind gusts and the food is gone.

Here's what Phineus, the servant, and all the men at the table cannot see: an eagle as large as a lion leaping down from the cliff behind them. Her feathers are the color of the rock; her wingspan blocks the sun. She has the face of a madwoman and the breasts of a nymph. She snatches up the king's food in her talons.

The men at the feast feel only the wind beaten into existence by the harpy's wings. They do not see her drop the king's feast in the salty ocean. They do not see her sister poised to leap from the cliff face as the servant steps forward again.

Important to note:
  18. Phineus blinded his own sons to keep his kingdom intact.
  19. The harpy eagle requires ten hectares of rain forest to thrive.

The bird wears a crown: feather spikes that require no jewels to convey authority. Her talons scar the bark of the branch on which she is perched, waiting.

She sees it: a howler monkey moving through the canopy in the distance. She unfolds her wings. They are as long as the branch. She tips her body forward and falls into a glide. Her wings make no sound. She slips through the tangle of trees and vines. The howler monkey doesn't know she is coming.

Men call this bird a harpy, after the creatures to whom myth gave the job of harassing sinners and escorting dead souls to the underworld.

This particular monkey is neither sinner nor ghost. The bird gusts at him. Her talons catch at his back. She plucks him from the tree. He writhes and swipes at her but cannot free himself.

The harpy emerges from the canopy like a puff of smoke. She carries the monkey's body above the treetops. The forest ends in a cliff drop, green falling to black with geologic abruptness. She flies over charred vegetation, blackened trunks, and ash-covered soil. Her destination is the single tree still standing. It is dead and wrapped in soot. Its branches hold a nest, also blanketed in soot. The nest is yards long and decades old.

Jessica Campbell

For what it's worth:
20. More than five million hectares of Amazon rain forest are burned each year.
21. The man with the epaulet mustache led Germany's chemical weapons program during World War I.

The woman stands alongside a basin filled with water. Steam rises from underneath the basin, heating the water and mingling with the fumes drifting out of the basin. On either side of the woman, the basin goes on for yards, and other women stand alongside it, waiting for the phosphorus to dissolve.

The woman removes a stick from the rack next to her and dips it into the basin of water and phosphorus. She shoves the dripping stick back into the rack and takes down another. When she breathes, the phosphorus fumes move into her nasal cavities and her mouth. They seep into her decaying teeth. Already, she has a toothache.

The woman next to her had a toothache last week. Now several of her teeth have fallen out. The woman next to her lost her teeth last month. Now her face is swollen. Abscesses have opened along her jaw. Pus oozes out of them. The jawbone of the woman next to her is visible through the holes in her flesh. The bone glows a faint green in the dim light of the factory.

There are other women who used to stand alongside the basin. These women are gone now. Some are in a paupers' hospital, having had their jawbones removed. Some are in a paupers' graveyard, having died from liver failure.

In another room in the factory, other women place the dried phosphorus sticks in boxes labeled Strike Anywhere Safety Matches.

Let's just take a moment to acknowledge:
22. Francis Bacon believed the soul was rendered invisible by heat.
23. Aristotle believed that humans had rational souls.

The pavilion is open to the air. Seventeen chicken eggs lie on a table under the roof.

A man in sandals walks down the path toward the pavilion. A dozen younger men follow him like the tail of a comet. When the older man stops at the table, his students pool behind him.

The man picks up the first egg. "This egg was laid this morning," he says. He pries the top of the shell off of the egg with a knife. He shows his students the egg's contents: a yellow orb floating in a clear substance.

The man picks up the second egg. "This egg was laid yesterday," he says. He pries the top of the shell off. He shows his students the egg's contents. Faint red lines are visible in the yolk.

The man picks up the third egg. "This egg was laid two days ago," he says. He shows his students the egg's contents. A heart beats in the yolk.

In the sixth egg, a beak is visible. In the tenth, the shape of the head is apparent. In the twelfth egg, the students see toes. In the sixteenth egg, the chick's body is covered in feathers.

The man picks up the seventeenth egg. He pries the top of the shell off of the egg with a knife. He plucks the chick out of the amniotic fluid. It is not yet fully formed. Its head is wrinkled, its feathers slicked down against its body, its legs curled.

The man sets the chick down on the table, where it quickly dies.

"Only man," he says, "has the intellect to understand the nature of life."

I regret to inform you:
  24. Five million birds were killed in 1886 to provide feathers for ladies' hats.
  25. One million birds died in oil waste pits last year.

The banks of the pond are black. There's a sheen on the surface of the water, and a ripple around the lone grebe floating there.

It's the sheen that gets the eagle's attention and the ripple that prompts her to circle back around the pond.

She expects the grebe to take off as she approaches. She expects it to squawk and flap. The grebe only shifts around in the water, sending out another ripple. The water moves with a thickness, but the eagle does not notice this as she dives at the grebe. Her talons slide off the grebe's slick feathers. She passes over the strangely still bird and circles around again.

This time her talons pierce feather and flesh. The grebe is heavier than she expected. It plunges under the water when the force of her body comes down on it. Her own wings skim the water. Her own breast breaks the surface.

Heaving her wings, the eagle lifts her body and that of the grebe out of the pond. There's a drag on her feathers she doesn't recognize. She struggles upward and circles the pond again. She can't seem to catch the wind.

She drops the grebe. Its body falls back to the pond and sinks through oil and water. At the bottom of the pond, it comes to rest on a pile of hollow bones.

For the record:
26. Since 1918 it has been illegal to take, capture, or kill any migratory bird.

The island is more rockslide than landfall: an eruption of boulders in the sea-foam without so much as a single tree to offer shade. The creatures who live on the island are unbothered by the sun. He is their uncle, after all, and they are nothing if not bound by family ties.

Family ties will be their undoing. An aunt, a goddess, *the* goddess: Hera, who for all her might, spends her days instigating petty feuds.

There are five of them on the island. From a distance they look like five boulders. Their feathers are the color of the rocks. They hold their wings close around their bodies, to cover their naked breasts. Their faces are beautiful, beaks notwithstanding, but mortals rarely get near enough the island to know this.

They throw their voices into the wind the way fishermen throw nets. Their songs convince perfectly able sailors to steer their ships

345

into the shoals around the island. The ships splinter. The sailors try to swim but drown instead. This constitutes the only amusement the sirens have on the island, which may explain why they are susceptible to Hera's goading.

The contest takes place on their island. The muses descend on a crescendo. Three towering beings clothed in light hover above the boulders. One coaxes an aria from the waves. One draws down an overture from the clouds. The third teases a concerto from the rocks. The muses cast their eyes toward their toes with false modesty. Hera grins. Her lips are tinted by wine.

The sirens' song cannot compare. It may be enough to drive men to their deaths, but to the ears of the other gods it sounds as weak as birdsong.

The victorious muses claim the sirens' plumage as their prize. Humming, they pluck the sirens clean. They leave the naked bird women on the rocks and float back up into the sky. As they go, they fashion crowns from the sirens' feathers.

The bird women throw themselves into the water. Their featherless bodies become islands. Sailors still steer their ships into the sirens' shoals.

Before we move on:
27. Aristotle thought Greek cosmology was hogwash.
28. Many Europeans believed Australia was a mythical place.

The ship is skewered on an outcrop of coral, listing and taking on water. A dozen men wrestle sails down. A dozen more work to shove cannons off the deck. A steady line of sailors carry iron ballast pigs from the hold to chuck them overboard. Even the gentlemen passengers have been pressed into service. They are among the men taking turns working the pumps that push the water back into the ocean.

Everyone on board understands the ship must be lighter by high tide if they are to wrench it off the reef.

When the ship is free of the coral, Captain Cook steers it into the mouth of a river. The river has a name, but Cook doesn't know it. He decides to call the river Endeavor, after his ship, which will anchor there for two months, waiting to be whole.

Cook plants the colors of the king. He makes notes of latitudes and landmarks. He announces, to no one in particular, that this land belongs to the crown. He orders his men to fire three volleys with their pistols, the cannons being inaccessible, to celebrate his declaration.

Two centuries later, divers find the ballast pigs and the cannons from Cook's ship encased in coral at the bottom of the sea.

We mustn't forget:
29. Captain Cook's Pacific voyages were funded by profits from the steam engine.
30. Captain Cook's funders modeled their corporation on a fictional scientific society in Francis Bacon's novel *New Atlantis.*
31. Half of the coral in the Great Barrier Reef is dead or dying.

The boy sits at a table, quill in hand, stack of foolscap at his elbow. The room is dim. The candles are unlit. Smog presses against the windows.

The lack of light does not bother the boy. His eyesight has not yet failed. He has not yet subjected his eyes to the gloom of Cambridge libraries, the tedium of legal briefs, the rigors of late-night experiments. He is not yet lord chancellor, not yet the Father of Empiricism. He has not yet written the future.

The boy has been set a task by his tutor. He is copying passages from the Bible, translating as he writes. He has copied out the same passage a dozen times. From Latin into English. Then from English back into Latin.

"Crescite et multiplicamini et replete terram et subicite eam et dominamini piscibus maris et volatilibus caeli et universis animantibus quae moventur super terram."

"Be fruitful and multiply and replenish the earth and subdue it and have dominion over the fish of the sea and over the fowl of the air and over every living thing that moveth upon the earth."

Jessica Campbell

The time has come to reveal:

32. Francis Bacon died of pneumonia shortly after going out in a storm to determine whether snow could preserve the flesh of a chicken.
33. Aristotle died of a liver complaint.

Prometheus walks the earth, taking an inventory of the creatures his brothers and sisters have created. His fellow Titans have crafted slick porpoises from leftover bits of moonlight, fleet raptors from the detritus of a sandstorm, and muscular beasts from the reverberations of a battle snare.

Prometheus feels an itch to make some living thing. But all the gifts the gods have to give—flight and stealth and speed—have already been given. All the scales and feathers and claws have been dispensed. He lacks the raw materials his siblings used to make beast and fowl.

The god squats by a mud puddle and scoops up some wet clay. He pinches a face out of the clay, pulls down arms and legs. The flimsy creature lies in his palm, without fur or fang. The god sighs. His breath enters the clay. The clay breathes.

The Titan sets the first human upright on its hind legs. He casts his eyes over his creation. It is not impressive. He will let the thing walk as the gods do, Prometheus decides. It's the only gift he has to give. At present.

Let's leave it at this:

34. Phineus was punished by the gods for revealing to humans what he knew of the future.
35. Prometheus means forethought.
36. There has never been a successful pig-to-human organ transplant.

Notes on a Metamorphosis
Thomas Dai

EGG

I don't seek out inception in its thicket of youth;
inception seeks me out in its thicket of youth.

—*I Ching: The Book of Change*

THE CHANGE BEGINS IN THE TRASH, in the grist and bone and scent of matter not mattering anymore. The change blooms into the yellow house through a cracked window or a door left open to July. To get where it is going, it runs this alien gauntlet: pop music and iPhone trills, burnt coffee, greasy cast irons and moisture-dimpled walls, the rustling sound of a human spooning with his pillow. Inside the bin, the change—in the shape of a fly—oviposits (that lovely, cogitative verb), releasing its cargo of eggs.

All summer, I work in an insect lab on the edge of campus. The lab is led by a world authority on ants and butterflies. At the lab, there is a terrarium full of Madagascar roaches munching on lettuce and a cabinet set aside for storing butterfly wings. There is a glass bridge connecting the lab to a museum, and on the museum side of things, there is a room for dead ants and a room for dead butterflies and a larger room for dead beetles. People are at work inside these rooms, pulling wooden cases of specimens from the archives, pinning thoraxes and spreading wings, laboring over the insect parts.

Up on the building's roof is a greenhouse reserved for *Acacia drepanolobium*. The acacias are myrmecophytes—plants with a symbiotic affinity for ants. In nonlab settings, ants act as an acacia's security force. Each colony spends its days in a tree's tracery of limb and leaf, raising its young in the plant's specially evolved domatia and sipping the sweet dew produced by the plant's nectaries. One of the lab's research objectives is to chart the evolution of this cross-species relationship, to better understand how ant and tree are yoked to one another and how their partnership came into being. Day in

349

and day out, the graduate students in my lab tend to the acacias with a care verging on love, like monks shaping bonsai in a temple's courtyard. The trees grow and dwindle inside the glass house, little worlds sprouting up from our instruments and our plans.

I joined the lab after taking an entomology course with the lab director. Something about insect collection drew me in—its paraphernalia (beat sheets and sweep nets and Berlese funnels), its sense of small discoveries made within everyday life. During that course, I rode all of Boston's subway lines to their ends, where there were sprawling parks to explore. I caught a dragonfly by a pond in Harvard Forest, emerald halictid bees at Arnold Arboretum, migratory monarchs in a weedy Malden lot.

Whereas before I had seen few insects because I never bothered looking for them, now they were everywhere (the earwigs fencing outside my door, the moths in deathly repose on my windowsill). All that fall, I accumulated insect names—sphingid and hairstreak, lacewing and collembolan, pentatomid and elaterid. Then I went outside and began matching bodies to the names.

The word metamorphosis means a process of biological change. The caterpillar unravels its inner butterfly; the jellyfish shifts from sessile polyp to pelagic medusa. Metamorphosis differs from ordinary growth in that it draws a stark line between a creature's mature and immature states. Young and old metamorphs look nothing alike. They compete for different resources and are adapted for separate lifestyles—one phase may busy itself with feeding, another with rest, another with mating. Living in such a way allows an animal to delegate tasks among a team of selves, a strategy of divide and conquer that helps the species as a whole to prosper.

While biologists sometimes refer to metamorphosis as a "life history" comprising a few distinct "body plans," such language hardly accounts for Western culture's fascination with the process. Think of Ovid, think of *Queer Eye*. Think of fairy tales, both Disney's bastardizations and the Grimm originals. Think of all those movies about the guy next door who dons a spandex suit and saves the world, and then recall that right now there are billions of insects performing such extreme makeovers in just a few miles' radius of your position.

Thomas Dai

*

A friend writes to me from New York, where she is waiting tables and studying for the MCAT. "Greetings from the Anthropocene's front lines," she writes. I guess the implication is that everywhere is a front line now, all of us party to the world's changing. There are many names for this change—Global Warming, Ocean Acidification, the Sixth Extinction. Somewhere in a city south of here, tropical zoonoses, once rare, are spreading. Somewhere else, far to the north, an ice sheet calves off the land. "How are you coping?" my friend wants to know. "How goes the summer of *A Bug's Life* and wine?" I want to ask her if a whole world and not just the body can undergo metamorphosis.

Instead, I write to my friend that summer has delivered a null result. When at the lab, I send emails and compile lists. I read abstracts. I window-shop online. When not at the lab, I shut myself inside my sublease, a tiny room in a yellow house full of strangers, and read.

The lab director has lent me a book called *Tuning in to Nature* by the entomologist Philip S. Callahan. It's a strange read, a mix of unproven science and New Age mumbo jumbo. My favorite part is when Callahan likens the world of insects to *ukiyo*, a Japanese word he translates as the "fleeting-floating world." For Callahan, *ukiyo* evokes the ambient, evanescent qualities of entomological existence—how insects occupy a world largely unseen by human eyes, even as their minute motions permeate our own.

As Callahan would have it, the fleeting-floating world is full of hidden messages passed on secret channels. He suggests that many insects navigate this world using what amounts to ESP. According to this "radiation theory" of insect communication, the sex pheromones produced by female moths fluoresce under dim light, emitting an infrared pulse that males of the same species sense from far away. Callahan argues that male moths use their antennae to "tune in" to the female's location as if she were a radio station in the night. He writes that "the moth flies the maserlike emissions from the pheromone just as I used to fly a radio range during World War II. It flies in and out of the luminous stream of molecules along the strongest IR signal." In Callahan's view, any self-respecting entomologist's goal should be to enter this fleeting-floating world, to eavesdrop on the conversations of insects.

Thomas Dai

LARVA

Shedding skin is an endless process: water drowning fire, fire parching water.

—*I Ching: The Book of Change*

One weekend, the director and I decamp for a USDA lab on the Cape. We spend the day shuttling between the insect nursery and the electroantennogram chamber, a windowless room where we shoot infrared lasers at severed moth antennae. The machine records only minimal antennal response, flickers indecipherable from static.

When the work is done, we have lunch in the communal canteen, peeling string cheese as a USDA scientist tells us of his lepidopteran troubles. Last summer, the scientist left a vial of gypsy moth pheromones in his car. The chemical volatized in the heat, seeping out from tube and chassis. When the scientist returned that evening to fetch his Corolla, hundreds of male moths had adhered to the car's hood, seeding its windows with their thrumming, lustful shapes. This courtship of animal and machine apparently lasted for months.

Sometimes, in a dream, I drive my car back to that USDA site. I walk into the insect nursery and sit down among the shelves of plastic cages. The sound of that space is difficult for me to describe, a white noise composed of many bodies moving both in unison and apart. In the dream, I listen as the insects build an aural structure all around me, a many-bodied chorus that is sibilant but warm, like a meadow stuffed inside a box.

The ancient Chinese believed that the universe began inside a void. This void had substance but no form. Eventually, the primordial substance would separate into heaven and earth, which in turn gave rise to an array of forms. Root-Breath and Lady-Voice, two dragons, were the first forms to spring from heaven and earth, and it was Root-Breath who created the sixty-four hexagrams of the *I Ching* or *Book of Change.* Each of the *I Ching's* hexagrams is composed of six broken (*yin*) or unbroken (*yang*) lines arranged into a glyph. The hexagrams, which bear names such as "maggot bowl" and "wholeness," try to make legible the forces of change that animate our universe. They speak not only of human lives but of the universe's overarching cycles, of which humanity is merely a constituent part.

352

Thomas Dai

*

A roommate screams from the kitchen. Coming out of my room, I watch a bolus of trash and larvae disintegrate on the floor. My roommate drags the trash bag outside as I take the bin into the bathroom and straddle it inside the pale pink shower. When the bin is full of soap and water and dead maggots, I carry it down to the street, find a storm drain, and pour.

My roommates want me, the aspiring entomologist, to tell them where the maggots came from. I gesture to the outdoors, to the night sky blanched with light pollution. "It's like they came out of nowhere!" one of them says. A little high from the Lysol, I nod in agreement. Later, I read online that the word larva comes from the Latin for ghost. Etymologically speaking, every larva is a prior apparition, a spectral shape that must consume itself in order for adult life to commence.

My parents had me when they were still fresh out of grad school, two young scientists wandering the American suburbs in a red Mercury sedan. For those first years of my life, my parents only spoke Chinese at home, farming out my English education to the television or the schoolhouse. I have very few memories from this Mandarin phase of my life. It is a void with neither form nor substance. Even if my English life has proceeded quite smoothly from the lacuna of my Chinese one, I still attribute great meaning to that absence. When at a loss for words in either Chinese or English, I find myself blaming my early swapping of tongues—how, for a certain period of time, at least, I lived with an ear in each language, at sea among the words.

Truthfully, I don't think I became aware of my changing, linguistic or bodily, until puberty arrived and the talk among my peers turned to the riddle of personal development, of whom or what we were becoming. At thirteen, I remember watching the signs of change accrue in gym class: that flash of peach-fuzzed chest in the locker room, that tautening of jawlines, that moment on the court when the jock with the unbearably bright smile makes a perfect jump shot, nothing but net, and is graduated on the spot into manhood. My own transformation seemed slipshod in comparison. I sprouted leg hair but only on my kneecaps. My round, yellow face broke out in minefields of acne. When I spoke, the sound got not manlier with age but more singsong and mauve colored.

Thomas Dai

Maybe translating a life is always this messy revision of forms. From 变化, I get metamorphosis.

Several hundred years after the *I Ching* was first set into writing, Aristotle proposed that certain life-forms emerge de novo from inanimacy, an idea known today as spontaneous generation. Following this logic, one could devise recipes for making life out of nonlife. Mix soiled rags and wheat chaff together to conjure a litter of field mice. Wedge basil leaves beneath a rock in the forest to manifest scorpions the color of jet.

After the maggots unfurl into our house, I spend several days walking around wondering if the natural world might occasionally try to speak to us, not in any ordered language but in these one-off, cryptic signs. Outside the lab one morning, I see a young hawk hopping across the lawn. The fledgling, still unused to flight, crash-lands in a hedge, where it settles, eyeing me with disdain. A day later, I look out the lab's windows to see a group of bagpipers playing a dirge on the lawn as the rain cuts slanting paths across the glass. Neither of these signs seems remotely connected, but I acknowledge their serial appearance in my life with great ceremony. "Consider the hawk still unfledged," I write in my journal. "Remember the funeral you are always attending."

I have started staying at the lab all night for the air-conditioning and solitude. With the space emptied of human chatter, the hatches battened and experiments paused, I feel more alive than usual, closer to that fleeting-floating way of things. This aliveness is perhaps similar to the trance state that serious practitioners of meditation report entering. I sit on the couch. I breathe. I range through the lab's darkened halls and the museum full of taxidermy specimens, trying to locate mentally all the separately articulated bodies gathered in or around these spaces ("I must borrow every changing shape / To find expression," T. S. Eliot writes). Though I have names for some of these shape-shifters—the ants in the acacia, the caterpillars dropping frass on the lawn—most of them live well beyond my powers of perception. They aerate the soil in the potted plants and dine on molehills of researchers' dandruff. They watch me through compound eyes from the ceiling or flutter furtively in my peripheral vision.

To leave itself behind, an insect sheds its skin. It molts. Entomologists call each period between an insect's molts an "instar." They use this unit to measure the passage of insect time. Human time is of course not measured in ruptures of an integument. We lose ourselves imperceptibly, in gentle sloughings of dust or the dance of cell division and death inside, all those lipid bilayers pursing to smooth meridians, all those amino acids chain gained into proteins and then denatured. The result of both processes is still the same, however. As Li-Young Lee writes: "O, the murderous deletions, the keening / down to nothing, the cleaving. / All of the body's revisions end / in death. / All of the body's revisions end."

PUPA

In the season for abiding, abide.
—I Ching: The Book of Change

Our lab director leaves for Kenya on a field trip. For a week, she will cross and recross the African savanna, bagging ant acacias as she goes. Before leaving, she fills me in on the latest news from the greenhouse. After removing all the ants from one acacia, a postdoc had bathed the tree in a cocktail of ant alarm pheromones. Within a few days, the tree had started growing its thorns longer, its domatia roomier. The acacia appeared to be responding to the chemical distress of its inhabitants, like if your apartment grew thicker walls whenever you cried.

The idealist in me yearns for a corresponding equilibrium between humans and the earth, a symbiosis modeled on the intimate mutuality of ants and plants—all of us responsive to the world's degradation, all of us responsible for what changes and what stays.

In the 1960s, E. O. Wilson and Daniel Simberloff devised a novel experiment for testing how life goes on after disaster. They wanted to model how insects and other arthropods recolonize a landmass artificially cleared of life. To do this, they picked six tiny mangrove islands in the Florida Keys, built a scaffold in the shallows around each, and draped the frame with a weighted tent. When the islands were enclosed, the scientists filled the tents with methyl bromide, a potent, poisonous gas.

Thomas Dai

The bromide acted quickly. Trees lost their leaves. Wood-boring beetles stopped tunneling into the trunks. After removing the tents, the biologists stood vigil in the Keys, watching and waiting as species returned to each mangrove speck. Some of the arrivals came by water, floating to the islands on rafts of algae and driftwood. A few hitch-hiked over on the bodies of others. The bulk, however, returned by air, flying over from the mainland. The biologists kept a record of every book louse and spider and moth that returned to the islands. (The flies, however, were exempted from the data; the dipterans' relationship to the islands—were they colonists or casual passers-by?—was never very clear.) By experiment's end, only 40 percent of the species now living on the islands had been present prior to the gassing, evidence that a massive turnover had occurred.

I write to my friend to ask if she thinks we are conducting a simi-lar experiment right now: tenting the earth and fumigating its inhab-itants. The bee colonies are collapsing, the coral skeletons expelling their algal partners into the sea. What animals remain are acting in erratic, unexplainable ways—cougars running into suburban traffic as octopuses squirm across our beaches at night. My friend writes back, opining that the crucial difference between Wilson and Simberloff's experiment and our own is that this time, the humans are standing inside the tent.

With the director gone, I flounder through each day and night at the lab. The USDA scientist sends me a package of female gypsy moths to raise. The pupae arrive by FedEx—twelve teak-colored bullets I place inside a white mesh cage. A week passes, and still the cases do not burst. Pupation can drag on like this, the dormant insects wait-ing on a cue I cannot provide. Even evolution—Darwin's theory of constant, species-level metamorphosis—does not always proceed at the same rate. Biologists have argued that evolutionary change tends to happen in concentrated bursts within the geologic record, periods of tumult emerging from much longer periods of stasis. This is referred to as the theory of punctuated equilibrium.

Perhaps this is the pause then, the rest that is actually the song. *The world is changing and you are a part of that change,* I tell myself, hovering over the pupae in their cage, but it is a truth that is difficult to feel.

*

Thomas Dai

In *Tuning in to Nature*, Callahan writes of watching a moth immolate itself in the flame of a candle—"First it singed each of its wings; then returned for a third successful dive and plunged into the candle. Wax and protoplasm and the hard shell sizzled and burned for a second, and a little spiral of smoke ascended from the waxy crematorium drifting upward among the needled boughs of the evergreen." Callahan cites this moment as inspiring his interest in the fleeting-floating world of insect perception. Why are moths drawn, he wondered, to the flickering of a flame or the glow of a tungsten filament? What strange derangement brings them winging to their ends?

My time among the moths has turned me into a pheromone lure. Male gypsy moths arrive at random moments to inspect my face. They do this in parking lots and on the lawn outside of the lab. Once a moth flies at me while I am biking, making a dull thwap against my cheek. Another time, at brunch, one dives into the open portal of my mouth. These days, I feel like a streetlamp, a candle, a blaze. Insects keep coming to skim across my light.

Insect metamorphosis delineates a cascade of forms that reminds me of the *I Ching's* hexagrams: brief moments in time when change gets distilled and schematized, turned into something I can name. And so I entopomorphize myself into phases—the egg that was childhood, the larval awkwardness of adolescence, the finely wrought adult I hope one day to embody. In this biological arc, my current surroundings are like an insect's puparium, a silken cloister in which I wait for the promised change to arrive.

Entomologists split insect metamorphosis into two types: holometabolous and hemimetabolous. The former represents a "complete" metamorphosis, the latter "incomplete." The difference is that all holometabolous insects pass through an immobile pupal phase before becoming adults. Inside each holometabolous larva are structures called imaginal discs, islands of generative cells that give rise to the distinctive structures of adult life.

Interned inside the yellow house, the flies reimagine themselves behind films of chitin flesh. The imaginal discs burgeon as the rest of the larval body turns into fuel and fodder. In a matter of weeks or even days, the maggot's limp and legless form is translated into a

357

body with six legs, a hairy abdomen, geodesic dome eyes, and wings etched with veins.

IMAGO

Wandering whole and through to completion—
that's how you praise the inevitable unfurling of
things.

—*I Ching: The Book of Change*

I suppose the change ends as it always does, with continuance, a new before emerging from this after. Imago is the name entomologists give to the adult phase of metamorphic insects, and images are what they are: fleeting, conceptual. When the blowflies reveal their final form, I want to say everyone in the yellow house is awed by the swarm's proliferating motion, how the images mass in the living-room drapes, coating the windows and light fixtures, the cabinet shelves and stray issues of *Vogue* and *Nature*. Some of the flies, the adventurous ones, take to the air of the house and never look back, tunneling every hour through the flow of our routines, keeping us awake with their incessant humming.

One of my roommates leaves and does not return until her partner texts an all-clear sign. Another stands shirtless and sweating with me in the flyblown kitchen, taking a hand vacuum to the lace. After not nearly enough bodies have piled up inside the bag, still buzzing, we give up, stand there in the kitchen watching the walls swirl with metallic color.

While I don't subscribe to all of Callahan's theories, his attempts to compare insects to waveguides and computers, I can't help but believe that there is a fleeting-floating world woven into our own. Call it the haloed look of transience, the hawks and the bagpipers, the liminality. Call it this day: the long ride I take to Walden Pond, the quaking of tree boughs over the bike path, the coital slugs that drop off a leaf onto my bare and sweaty thigh.

Many entomologists have tried to map the contours of this world, to rub against its edges and number its many inhabitants. In one survey, completed more than thirty years ago, scientists pumped a fog of pesticide through the Panamanian jungle until insects rained down from the canopy far above. The scientists counted almost a thousand species of beetles living in just one species of tropical tree, a number they extrapolated outward, by dubious methods, to arrive at a global total of thirty million arthropod species. This number has been widely critiqued as far off the mark, though entomologists are still bickering about just how far.

In the meantime, the ranks of the fleeting-floating world are thinning. Monarch butterfly numbers in North America have plummeted by 90 percent in the last few decades. Certain German parks have registered a 75 percent decrease in insect biomass since the eighties. Insects, once the paragon of ubiquity, are getting rarer. Entomologists in training may soon struggle to gather enough specimens for their collections. That sound they search for in the meadows and the parks will keep getting quieter, a little closer each year to silence.

At home with the flies, I read the *I Ching,* not because the book has any of the answers I seek (it doesn't), but because I can't stop thinking about what the translator, David Hinton, writes about the hexagrams—that they "allow us to locate ourselves in the unfolding of change." Is this not what science and writing both seek to do? In the chaos of heterogeneous parts, in the crucible of our own making, writing sentences or running experiments helps clear a space for thinking, reflection, maybe even response. You ride the lines of words looking for that space, a moth circling but not meeting its flame.

The philosopher Zhuangzi once famously dreamed he was a happy butterfly. As he dreamt, Zhuangzi no longer could tell if he was a human dreaming the butterfly or a butterfly dreaming the human. He characterized this anthro-entomological limbo as the "transformation of things."

Morning arrives. I wake up, or the butterfly starts its dream. I look in the microwave and find an origami crane plated like a dish and covered in flies.

Up in the greenhouse, the moths have eclosed, their second birth leaving fuchsia stains all over the white mesh cage. Meconium is the word we use for this excess. It names the metabolic waste that builds up during an insect's pupation and is expelled when the case finally splits. (In humankind, meconium is an infant's first shit.) After cleaning up as best as I can, I usher the debutantes into a newer, airier cage.

The lab, once quiet, now throngs with bodies, both human and insect. The director returns from Kenya with suitcases full of ant colonies, each superorganism seething inside its Tupperware container. As the graduate students shepherd the ants onto new trees, the rest of us clean up, combing through the plastic for stowaways, moving the dead or aging plants downstairs, reapplying the Tanglefoot and refilling the moats that keep each ant colony isolated from the others. For two days, we sweep the floors and pluck mealybugs off of leaves. When the work is done, I stand out on the rooftop under the August sun, my face and body abuzz.

In the *I Ching*, there is a hexagram called Pattern. Its fourth line states: "The pattern is tranquil, so it penetrates everywhere."

Every scientist I know would advise against entopomorphizing your life. Such fancies have no place in the seriousness of labs. Sure, all things change, as thinkers from Zhuangzi to Darwin have said, but the special province of humanity is that we get to watch the changes as they happen, that we are aware, and that that awareness overwhelms.

I'm not so sure that the flies aren't also, in their own, dipteran way, at once aware and overwhelmed. I watch them press desperately against the house's windows, seeking always an outside. I putter about the kitchen as the swarm parts all around me, the flies wary of my weight, the changes in weather I bring to the room. If nothing else, there is a convergence here, the flies' metamorphic path intersecting with my own. I want them gone, for my sake but also theirs. As a hexagram, the flies say something about the closeness of these walls, and the desire, laid egg-like inside me, for escape.

By the end of the week, my roommates and I are sweeping bodies off the floor—each fly a particle of glass. Every morning, I stick a new curlicue of flypaper to the ceiling before leaving for the lab. The paper smells of menthol and of cherries.

I once read an article in *Science* detailing how trillions of insects migrate in seasonal bioflows through the upper atmosphere. The bugs take these trips constantly, redistributing their biomass across the earth's surface. Though some of the migrating insects have a clear destination in mind, many others simply drift as part of the aerial plankton, passive passengers on the wind. I have tried and failed to grasp the scale of their migrations—all the neuropterans and hymen-opterans, the damselflies and aphids, the alate ants and speeding locusts—all of them airborne, a Gulf Stream of insects. I like to imag-ine the flies from the yellow house rising up to join that flow, pushed by whatever instinct it is that nudges us to the right door at the right time, that instinct that joins us to the fleeting-floating world.

Up in the greenhouse, I stand and I watch the ants on patrol for a few minutes, listening for that white noise I have come to hold so dear. When the time comes, I wave goodbye to the acacias and take the elevator down. It's night outside, soft and balmy. I get on my bike and ride to a bank of metal grates where a cool wind blows up from the floors of lab space below. I ride across the grates as I do every night, standing up on the pedals to feel the air ballooning around me. This is a silly ritual, I know, but I keep it each night for the simple solace of air rising up, that split second when thinking stops but I remain—one body cutting through the updraft.

Amaryllis
Toby Olson

1. ANTICIPATION

I cannot walk as fast, can't run fast.
    A secret opening through bushes.
Can't sink myself in blues in the valley's shadows.
    Time is a thief and a rocket.

Cannot remember you these days beyond illness.
    A tilted field of dandelions.
I cannot ride fast anymore on a bicycle.
    A bloody flower in memory.

Rooted in the heritage of color.
    For a little while, from a distance, inaccessible.
Empty orchestra.
    Anticipation of a few tubes of green.

Time is a painting of time against time.
    Fritillaries by the thousands. Wind. Somber ditches.
Rooted in the reducing glass.
    I cannot ride fast anymore on a bicycle.

Time is the innocent iris of vision.
    Any involvement of any kind.
He left before he arrived. Cancerous. On a bicycle.
    Rooted in the valley of infants and death.

Can't walk as fast, can't run fast.
    Firecracker honeysuckle sparks in the memory.
Dandelions on a tipped vertical plane.
    Ignited into luminosity.

Amaryllis.
  For a little while, from a distance, inaccessible.
A bloody flower in memory.
  Time was I loved you, old oak, my cousin.

Dandelions in a systematic grid of flags.
  A refuge from mortality.
Begonias. Cobalt violet. Cathedral.
  Abandonment is death also.

Time is a cloud clouding the memory.
  Secreted entrance. Cancer. On a bicycle.
But we are children once again, that time I loved you.
  Rooted in the heritage of color.

I cannot walk as fast, can't run fast.
  Time is the innocence of first vision.
I cannot catch insects, frogs, birds, on a bicycle.
  Any involvement of any kind.

Come to the valley of contradictions.
  Deeper than the iris in anticipation.
The flower in permanent violet at the green brook.
  I cannot ride fast anymore on a bicycle.

Anticipation of abandoned barn.
  A tilted field of dandelions.
Rooted in the valley of infants and death.
  Transformed and affirmed.

Time was I loved you, idyllic vision, my cousin.
  Dream like innocence, nostalgia, liberation.
Time is a thief and a rocket.
  Firecracker honeysuckle sparks in the memory.

I cannot see the reeds' signal at the river's edge.
  Intimations of eternal paradise.
Less than I gave you.
  Amaryllis.

Toby Olson

Bloody flower of resonance.
    Secreted entrance, zephyrs, tranquility.
Time is a painting of time against time.
    Fritillaries by the thousands. Butterflies. Abandoned barn.

Empty orchestra.
    I cannot ride fast anymore on a bicycle.
Rooted in the reducing glass.
    For a little while, from a distance, inaccessible.

He left before he arrived.
    Any involvement to forget not being alive.
Time is a thief and a rocket.
    River's dampness in the air and on the ground.

I cannot catch cancer, blood, amaryllis, on a bicycle.
    Rooted in the heritage of color.
Can't walk fast, can't run fast.
    Time is the innocence of first vision.

She won't forget you.
    For a little while, from a distance, inaccessible.
Just wait and see.
    Time is a painting of time against time.

She won't forget you.
    We are children once again, that time I loved you.
How green was her valley.
    Amaryllis.

Red roses for a blue lady.
    Time is a cloud clouding the memory.
It must have been moonglow.
    I cannot ride fast anymore on a bicycle.

Deep purple.
    Dandelions on a tipped vertical plane.
The shadow of his smile.
    Rooted in the reducing glass.

At twilight time, vermilion, on a bicycle.
    Anticipation of tranquility.
Down by the riverside.
    Secreted entrance. Zephyrs. Somber ditches.

What will be will be.
    Time was I loved you, bloody flower, my cousin.
To each his own.
    Rooted in the heritage of color.

Time is a thief and a rocket.
    For a little while, from a distance, inaccessible.
Time after time.
    I cannot ride fast anymore on a bicycle.

Heart of my heart.
    Rooted in the valley of infants and death.
Too late now.
    Any involvement of any kind.

He left before he arrived.
    Time is a painting of time against time.
Intimations of eternal paradise.
    Amaryllis.

2. GREEN IRRITANT

Cinnabar green of a rocket exploding into fritillaries on the canvas.
The fluid contents of, the draining, the covered trench, the tissues.

Green yellow of acoustical bleached light, titanium in the reducing glass.
Ore of mercury, red rose river, sap green in the amaryllis.

Ripe lemons and hepatitis, cinnabar green yellow of the meadow's insect tents.
But a tilted field of dandelions, from a distance, for a little while at least.

Olive green of tumescence, adolescence, cancerous in permanent red violet.
Yet motion, life in the fluid contents of, the draining, the covered trench,
    the tissues.

Indian yellow deep recession, ground without a figure, no one at the door.
Deep secret, an opening through bushes, on a bicycle, the hour of blues.

Cadmium of orange shield, reaction and fatigue, less than I gave you, these
   fritillaries.
But vermilion, red rose of amaryllis, iris of memory's last reduction.

Permanent violet, deep yellow on a tilted plane, cobalt blue and titanium.
Yet indigo, splashes of permanent deep or cadmium red and cobalt blue.

Ultramarine, indigo, and sap green, flower patterns passed by in quick running.
Rooted in the heritage of color: cinnabar, emerald, purple lake.

Music of an empty orchestra, cadmium yellow, transformed and affirmed.
He left before he arrived, on a bicycle, inaccessible.

3. PERMANENT

Now and then in early morning's anticipations near sunrise.
   Old oak and dark valley of no light or distinct color.
Now and then, after storm of time's secret involvements.

   After the tale told, the sap green luminosity extinguished.
For a little while, from a distance, inaccessible.
   Rooted in the valley of infants and death.

Within which the painting is eternal harbinger of stillness.
   Now and then on a bicycle rooted in the reducing glass.
The firecracker honeysuckle sparks again in the memory.

   Ignition of a field in cadmium on a tipped vertical plane.
Beyond which an empty orchestra announces the bloody amaryllis.
   Though I cannot remember you these days beyond illness.

And the innocent iris of first vision, a thief and a rocket.
   And the reeds' signal, acoustical in bleached light.
And fritillaries by the thousands. Butterflies. Abandoned barn.

Toby Olson

After any involvement of any kind.
The flower in permanent violet at the purple lake.
Before any irritant, concert of insects and green frogs.

Beyond the forgetting of red roses for a blue lady.
In cinnabar green slippers riding fast on a bicycle.
Passing through valleys of zephyrs on a tilted field.

Now and then I can walk fast, run fast.
Within which a few splashes of permanent red deep.
Rooted in the heritage of color.

How green was her valley.
Any involvement to forget not being alive.
Bloody amaryllis in permanent violet at the iris brook.

The painting is a painting of time against time.
Time was I loved you, on a bicycle, old oak, my cousin.
Now and then, from a distance. Resonant. Gone.

NOTE. "Amaryllis" is an approach to Joan Mitchell's *La Grande Vallée* paintings, a suite of twenty-one canvases created between 1983 and 1984, and the story (provided by her friend the composer Gisèle Barreau) that provoked them. It was conceived as a libretto for a choral piece, the music written by Paul Epstein, and follows the death of a young man who desires to return to a place of his youth, a garden paradise that now has deteriorated into a gone world.

As a child, Barreau, together with her cousin Jean-Philippe, spent many pleasurable hours in a secreted valley in Brittany. This magical place provided her with a refuge from troubles at home. Shortly before his death from cancer at the age of twenty-eight, Jean-Philippe asked Gisèle to take him to their Grande Vallée one last time. He died before this wish could be granted.

Mitchell said, "Painting is the opposite of death; it permits one to survive, it also permits one to live." But paintings themselves display stillness, which may be thought of as death. "Amaryllis" is about time, memory, and forgetting. Many of its words and phrases, often transformed, come from Mitchell and Barreau themselves as well as from Yvette Y. Lee, whose essay in *The Paintings of Joan Mitchell* (the Whitney Museum of American Art in association with University of California Press, 2002) served as a valuable source in writing this piece. I also want to thank Diane Burko, who provided me with Mitchell's paint color names.

Excerpt from
Sen's Ninth and Final Notebook
S.+648 Days to S.+731 Days
Debbie Urbanski

ONE HUNDRED MATCHES LEFT.

The rain fell in a storm in the morning and it touched the trees and it turned into a sound. Water dripped through the leaves for hours after the storm moved on. Some of the water dripped from the leaves onto the cabin roof. The water slid down off the roof and some of the water fell onto the rot of the porch. Some fell down the side of the cabin, and other water fell onto the rocks that surrounded the cabin, both the rocks that covered the body my mom and I buried, and the other rocks that I carried up from the creek and placed around the perimeter. I had arranged the rocks carefully around the base of the cabin, edge to edge, stacking or overlapping the rocks only when necessary, because I was bored and I needed something to do, and also because I thought the rocks were a form of protection. By the afternoon the air felt sluggish and thick, which meant another storm was going to arrive the subsequent day and another storm would arrive after that. The birds came out from the forest after the storm. I saw a brown bird, a red bird, a black bird, another black bird, a blue bird, and a yellow bird in the clearing over the span of an afternoon. The birds didn't startle when I stood or sat or stepped off the cabin porch avoiding the broken second stair. I saw a tree today. I saw trees. I am so sick of the trees. "There you go, dwelling in negativity," says Mama Dana, as if she were here. She is the mother I think about the most. Though I don't dream about her. I don't dream about my other mother either. My dreams are peopleless and inhabited by gusts of wind and flattened grasses. "You don't know what beautiful is," Mama Dana would have said. "The trees are beautiful, Mom. I know they are," I would have told her because I can see that the trees are beautiful even if I am sick of looking at them, and also this is what my mother would want to hear. The beautiful trees, the thriving, richly green, perpetual trees, unhuman, lengthening upward. I might decide to die under one of them. "Tomorrow I will try harder, Mom. I will not be sick of the trees tomorrow, I promise," I would tell my mother, were she here, were either of my mothers here. "You'll need to try harder than that," my mom would have said, staring out of the cabin window at the soaked meadow, and the place in the meadow that was never our garden, and the approaching dark. "What a lucky girl you are, to be surrounded by this," she would have said to me were she here and running her hands through her greasy hair while the meadow drips and darkens. I might have pointed toward the woods. Or I might have pointed beyond the woods to where there are more and more woods. I might have told her, "I don't want any of this. I'm giving it back. Here. Take it back." My mother would have replied, "No." When the dark arrives it would have buried its face in my mother's hair.

Last night the dark was sticking to the walls of the cabin and to the corners of my mattress. The dark stuck to the only window in the loft and coated the dirty glass then the dark straddled my chest. It held me down against the mattress last night with a heavy indifferent pressure as it exhaled on my face slowly. Its breath was wet with pollen and dirt and creek water. "This is not supposed to be about you and how you felt," my mother would have said, were she here. The dark was creeping around inside her mouth as well. I would have seen it had she opened her mouth. "I'm sorry. I'll try harder next time," I would have said to her, shutting my eyes. The animals that call to each other in the woods in the dark aren't frightened of the dark. The red foxes and the owls and the coyotes, they aren't afraid. I am not yet a wild animal though I think I will eventually become one. I think it will be a relief when I become one. I have difficulty sleeping. The dark bites onto my hair, it enters my mouth and wriggles under my tongue. How does one let go of one's humanness? "How does one let go of one's humanness, Mom?" I would ask my mother were she here. It doesn't matter which mother I would ask. I would ask either of them. The light leaves me every day with the dark, which is growing longer and twisting itself into thicker strands. "Oh, honey, you just let go," Mama Dana would say, opening her hands in a gesture of letting go.

I used to see far-off explosions in the night sky. "You mean, *there were explosions in the night sky*. Or, *the night sky was exploding*," my mother would have said. That isn't what I meant but I would have nodded my head were my mother here. The explosions used to transform part of the dark temporarily into distant orange light. Humans exploded into light in the sky; I used to watch them. When I first began exploring beyond the meadow, past the other field and up the road, I came across the edge of a plane's wing covered in new green moss. Moss also grows on the stones along the creek, particularly on the northern faces of the rocks. Moss has begun to grow on the rocks that circle the cabin as well as on the rocks that are piled on top of the dead man's body. Those rocks are mostly in the shade. Water collects between and under the rocks after each storm, dampening the surrounding plants. Occasionally the moss covers an entire rock and the rock becomes something else.

There are places where the creek pools and stalls. Insects twitch across the surface of these still spots, rippling the water with their spindly legs, while rounded stones pile at the edges of the small pools. I've found rodents trapped in the narrow spaces between the stones. I used to save them, setting them down carefully in a safe pile of leaves on the bank in an area of sun, but now I keep my hands in my pockets and I watch them struggle. I am watching them with unblinking black eyes like I am some type of black bird watching a girl in a cabin about to begin to starve, or like I'm a white-tailed deer with unblinking dark eyes and a twitchy head watching a girl begin to starve through the window while I graze. Their bloated little carcasses in the creek must affect my drinking water. Probably I should go back to boiling the creek water before I take another sip. "Stop using those words," my mother would have said. "What words?" I would have asked. "*My* and *I* and *mine* and *me*," my mother would have said. "I'm doing the best I can," I would tell my mom, who would shake her head with frustration and disapproval. "I know you, and I know you can do better," she would say.

There is the stern but protective tree that stretches out its canopy as wide as it can to create a shelter from the rain. There is the tree with the blackened trunk. I did not blacken the trunk; it was that way when Mama Dana and I arrived here. I've rubbed my fingers against the ruined wood. There is the sullen tree that ignores me and will not look at me. There is the wild tree swiveling its loose leaves and looking everywhere at once. There is my favorite tree, the friendly maple growing to the side of the clearing that waved in my direction all morning, that is always waving at me and noticing me with concern. "You are full of garbage. Look, the trees were never your personal companions," Mama Dana would have said, were she here. She was the kinder one, though I remember both of my mothers surrounded by a softness that looks, in my memory, like a fading and recognizable light. "Pay attention. If you were paying attention to what's actually happening around here, you would realize every tree wants you gone. They are waiting for you to be gone," my mother would have said. "You mean, they are waiting for me to die," I would have said. "No. They are waiting for you to completely disappear into the earth," she would have said. I will pay attention. I am paying attention.

A partial inventory: two black toenails. One twisted ankle, beginning to heal. One cabin. One pair of clothes (T-shirt, jeans, underwear, socks). One extra pair of clothes that I am supposed to wear when I am washing my other pair of clothes but I have stopped washing my other pair of clothes. One ceramic water pitcher, cracked, from when I slammed it against the edge of the countertop. Buckets. So many buckets. The gray bucket I'm supposed to pee in when I don't want to go outside. I am supposed to make myself shit outside. Also a white bucket I take to the creek, and a smaller white bucket I don't use anymore, and a blue bucket I don't use anymore, and a stack of buckets on the porch whose colors don't matter to me. A closet with shelves, another closet with shelves. A ruptured rain barrel that can no longer hold water. I let the water in the rain barrel freeze last winter. That's why it ruptured. One jar that once held honey and now holds a little last bit of honey that I am saving. Also a bowl. A cup. A glass. I used to have two bowls and two cups but then I buried my mother's bowl and her cup beside the creek. I used to have two glasses. A shovel. I use the shovel to move the snow out of the way, or if I have to dig into the dirt another time of year to bury anything, like when I buried my mother's bowl and her cup beside the creek. An ax. A pile of cut wood. I need to cut some more wood. It is beginning to feel like a waste of personal energy to cut more wood. A nearly full container of rosemary protie powder. This will last me more than a month if I can lower my intake to two protie drinks a day like my mother told me I should do when I'm on the last container, and also if I can drink the stuff without vomiting. Rosemary is a nasty flavor. Fourteen empty containers of protie powder stacked in the closet without shelves. I don't know what to do with these

371

containers. One half jar of tater flakes. A dry kitchen sink. I can turn on the faucet and nothing comes out of the faucet. Five sour apples. Forks. A knife. Some spoons. I don't need these spoons as I don't have any food left that would require me to use a spoon. One pot to boil water in, if I still boiled my water. One ladle. One broken fridge that I opened once and now I don't open it. The burner that doesn't work. The oven that never worked either. Inside the oven I put things I used to need, such as my mother's solar charge and a sliver of yellow soap that smells like her body. I would have shoved my broken screen in there as well but I threw my screen, after it broke, into the creek, which I should not have done, because that is a form of pollution. I did it anyway. Forgive me. Five dark light bulbs. Five dark lamps. Two rows of solar panels mounted onto the roof. The panels don't work. I don't know why they won't work. Wires. An outhouse. In the middle of the summer the outhouse smelled but the smell became less offensive as the weather cooled. One broken porch step, which is where I twisted my ankle. One postcard of Mount Rushmore. One photograph of a river with islands in it that I will never see again. I had a picture of my mothers but I burned the picture. Several notebooks. Several pencils. One pillow. One mattress with a circular reddish-brown stain in the lower center of the mattress. I am assuming the stain is from the beginning of the injuries of the dead man. The stain won't come out though I didn't try that hard. There used to be two pillows and two mattresses until I dragged my mother's mattress and her pillow into the woods after my mother left me. Two scratchy blankets. Four white candles. Seventy-two matches. Four porch rocking chairs; the chair on the right squeaks. Should I count my other mother's ghost? Nine hours six minutes of darkness. Eleven hours forty-five minutes of light. That leaves three hours ten minutes for the in-between. An overgrown path leading to what was once a trail. A different path, also overgrown, leading to a disappearing road. "Am I doing better with this?" I would have asked my mom after showing her my list. "No, you are not. This is still all about you. Stop making it about you," my mother would have said. "OK. I'll try harder," I would have said.

A bridge had crossed the creek downstream from the cabin as part of a historic trail network that once stretched from North Dakota to Maine. The trail system fell apart when my mothers were young because of some Private Ownership of Public Land initiative. Mama Lindsy used to complain about the initiative a lot; that's why I know about it. The bridge was built at a place where the creek widened after heavy rains, becoming uncrossable. Three days ago, I think it was three days, a storm came and it lasted throughout the evening, with blazes of lightning and lashes of wind. I heard things, trees, I don't know what else, come crashing down outside of the cabin where I tried to sleep and didn't sleep. After the storm, I wandered along the creek to note which trees had fallen over and which trees were still standing and which had blackened or whose bark had been stripped off. When I reached the bridge, I saw it was not a bridge anymore but planks of wood collapsed into the creek and clogging the creek in certain places. I collected several of the nails embedded into the smaller pieces of splintered wood and buried these nails in the piles of dead leaves up the bank from the creek so that it could be easier for the bridge to disappear completely when it came time for the bridge to disappear. On the way back to the cabin, it began to rain again, a thick, soaking rain. When I reached the cabin, I started a fire in the stove so I would stop shivering, my second fire of the day.

Fifty-six matches left.

For a while after my mother left me, when I walked through the woods or sat on the wide, flat stones beside the creek, I used to experience an overwhelming feeling that, at any moment, someone I knew or didn't know—it didn't matter at that point—was watching me and was about to appear behind me, at the edge of the creek or the forest. The reason I couldn't hear them approaching was because the sound of the creek and the forest was so constant and loud, the clicking burbling cawing scratching rustling whooshing, that if these places would just shut up for a minute, I would be able to hear someone approaching in my direction. One day the feeling went away, and then I panicked, then I stopped panicking.

Turning right at the bridge, or the place where the bridge once stood, eventually I would reach an overlook, or what used to be an overlook. The overlook used to face a pond and beyond the pond there used to be intersecting roads and squared-off fields of failing corn and soybeans edged by a thin border of trees. Mama Dana had taken me here before she left and she described to me how this place was going to look eventually once we both were gone. She said as long as I was still here, the changing view should give me peace and put what was happening to me into perspective, so I should come here as often as I needed. The last time I hiked to the overlook, it was difficult to get to the edge of the clearing between the trees because the space was no longer a clearing. It was an overgrown field of shrubs and thorns that fastened onto my jeans. Many of the plants were waist-high. I had to hack my way to the edge of the rocks where the drop began. The farmland below was filling in, not with corn or soybeans but with something tougher and greener. The gray edges of road were disappearing into the green, and a surge of wind disturbed the pond. Past the pond, the green hills twitched and stared. My breath broke into the quietness. Each breath I took sounded like a gasp. It was like I was breathing into a new world where there wasn't enough air for me to breathe. I decided not to return to the overlook. It was a difficult place to reach and I was losing energy. The trail had grown faint anyway. On my way back to the cabin, on that final visit, I kept taking wrong turns and had to retrace my steps until I spotted the faded blue marks on the trees. "You still aren't doing this right," Mama Dana would have said, were she here. "I will try harder tomorrow," I would have promised my mother.

The water is carving out its place through the rocks. The water is carving through the rocks. The rocks are being carved into new shapes by the water. The creek is loud and wet and cold and endless and it does not have eyes and it will not freeze. The forest is alive. The creek, the meadow, the sky, the dirt, and the rocks are alive. The earth is alive and aware. The earth is foaming at the mouth and serious.

Today I woke up and I was screaming. Then I stopped screaming.

Today I woke up and I wasn't screaming. I did not scream all day until the afternoon.

Today I woke up and I wasn't screaming. I did not scream all day.

I should not write about myself. Don't write about yourself.

"No one is coming anymore," my mother would say, were she here. "OK, Mom," I would have said with decreasing urgency. The road is about to disappear.

Today I woke up and I was screaming. I stopped screaming. I went outside and walked down to the creek. I walked into the creek. I stuck my head in the creek or tried to; there wasn't enough water.

I am turning into a gift. I will turn into a gift. I am turning. I have turned

"There you go again," says Mama Dana, were she here. "No. I want to talk with Mama Lindsy. Bring me Mama Lindsy!" I would have ordered my mother. Lindsy was the quieter mother, the one who watched over me without words. "Well, lucky you. She's right beside you. I think she's always been there," Mama Dana would have said. I would have looked beside me and seen nothing beside me. "Not her ghost. I'm not talking about her ghost," I would have said. Mama Dana would have repeated those words back to me in an exaggerated voice. *I'm not talking about her ghost I'm not talking about her ghost I'm not talking about her ghost.* "You have always been a picky child," she would have said. "Why can't I talk to her?" I would have said. "Oh, you are just a hoot," Mama Dana would have said, laughing and rubbing her throat with both of her hands.

Eighteen matches left.

I am wondering, after I'm gone, will there be monsters. Or have there always been monsters, only I couldn't see them. Will the animals become like monsters, will the trees grow fangs? Or am I the monster and after I'm gone, there will be no more monsters? I think the trees are growing fangs. "Mom, what am I supposed to do now?" I would ask if she were here. "Become invisible," my mother would say. "No, I'm not ready," I would say. Mom, will it look more magical, will the snow be blood colored and magical and predatory? I will not see the end of the creek though I have followed the creek for such a long time. "Don't make this about you. Don't make this about your grief or anybody's grief," my mother would have said. "No," I said. I have lost things. "But look at what you've gained," my mother would have said. "No," I said.

Seventeen, and so on.

The collective grief of I don't know how many billions of human beings flaps its scaly wings across the clearing. I am watching it, Mom, and as I watch it I am doing what you told me to do, I am writing down everything I see, so there will be a memory of what happened.

The movement of its wings creates a storm made out of wind and wings. I think I was holding on to it. I unclench my hands. The thick rope drops from my hands and skids across the ground. Anyone else who is holding on to it must let go as well. The collective grief of billions of human beings pounces into the air, ropes trailing from its muscled legs, claws extended, ripping its way over the forest and the hills and over the abandoned cities, its yellow eyes glaring right and left as if it is trying to remember this place. I think it is going away for good. It calls out once—a lengthy, piercing noise—then flies off, a dark spot in the sky that eventually isn't there, leaving behind a world without grief. I'm not imagining this.

Let the snow fall slowly so it takes hours, days, to bury the ground. Let me fall asleep. Let the stove continue radiating warmth. Let the fire in the stove not go out. Let me not fall asleep. Let me stay up and see what happens next. Let nothing happen next other than the snow. Let the snow fall in piles and sweeps. Let me go to sleep. Let the snow fall heavier, the flakes turning heavy and enormous. Let it become difficult to see where the snow ends and the sky begins. Let my breath become visible. Let the sky be the color of the snow which will be the color of my breath. Let the snow be the color of the sky which will be the color of my breath. Let me push the cabin door open and push and push to create a narrow opening for me to slip through into the cold white air. In the snow let me stand in the quiet under the colorless sky in my mother's boots.

I want to hear someone say, *I love you.*

"I can't say that right now," my mother would say. "It isn't what's important."

I am no one. Everyone. I was

The creek is stuck at parts, foaming in the sheltered pockets between the gray stones.

"Good girl," says my mother

Thistle
Donald Revell

"Thistledown is clouds," says Actual Man,
"Come down to earth to cover the churches."
Light is the color of walls between life
And death. Brief shadows of eclipse
Race like foxy clouds, but the dead move slowly,
As slowly as windows in walls when light
Barely shows through. If an actual man
Is present, the color of blood appears,
Rust of the fox tail between cupboard
And narthex. New York feels a tremor of barrage.
If only a ghost or candle of ghost,
All color backwards through a prism goes
To anathema—Manhattan's actual
Glands and wounds below the wall.

Either resurrection or the tall stain
Mistaken for a mountain actually
Begins with a human face, as a city begins
On the lips of a dying man dreaming
One last dream, and you and I will spend
Eternity there. Manhattan walls itself off.
The continent abolishes its mountains.
The Chrysler Building writes a novel
About an immigrant writing a novel.
I'd meant to love a woman with wires of hair,
But I love you. Eternity has a taxi
All to itself. Rain, rain. Your hand touches
My hair, and we must keep walking. We must
Remember to pray. God was a mountain once.

Donald Revell

Once the motive of memory, the accosted
Child, becomes real, it is free of memory.
Becoming an actual man, it plays
At a cat's cradle of fantasticals.
A faun, if you like, a perpetual
Curtain of hairs falling upon theatrical
New York. He is the eclogue of us.
Do the pronouns worry you? Do the taller
Buildings seem to menace little churches
Of cloud and eclipse in the alleyways?
A prism of blood in your own heart
Sets you straight. And prayer comes easily then.
You needn't remember your heart to beat it.
I have eaten words for sixty years, no harm done.

The crooked arm of the expressway bends
Up and away from the street life, the cloudy
Worship of numbers parallel to Christ.
"Victorious victimhood!" So laments
Or so begins the Actual Man's mock
Epic. "Last not merely first, but one
And only." It is too late to repair him.
He might as well be a window fallen
Into a flood upstate. He might as well
Tell once again the story of his beloved
Murdered, thrown to the trains as he
Watched the waters rising, glass himself.
Apocalypse is as you find it. North and south,
There is one last dream that will not be denied.

I am pretty well convinced that suicide
Explains the whales and the metal railings
At Battery Park. There is a consensus
Among drunkards that D. H. Lawrence's
Birds, Beasts and Flowers is a masterpiece:
"where God is also love, but without words."
The cathedral of Notre-Dame burns as I write this.

The fire is the color of blood, a fox tail
Withering, architrave without a trace.
Without words, it is easier to trace
One million televised images back
To their source: the Actual Man mocking
The shattered glass of himself. Manhattan Island
Has only an ocean to offer and a drunkard's tremor.

Was the original flower a white one
Covering the island from end to end
Not owned and not, therefore, in need of colors?
A white flower was the first window
Opened to the world. Human eyes
Could recognize themselves in the cluster,
Seeing the harmless sun shaped into petals,
Sensing a fathering and a mothering
In sunlight gentled there to simple vision.
Heaven is fine until the image of heaven
Catches fire inside a cloud and comes to earth.
A welter of colors then, like animals in a panic,
Disturbs the sun out of its innocence,
And the white flowers are blind then.

With our own eyes, you and I have loved
One another in a crowd of images,
In a snare of garlands only now
Remembered as the lovely young people
Fifty years ago when Manhattan felt
Like a real island and not like a madhouse
Grievance bulwarked against flowers and faith.
Victimhood has robbed the sun of its innocence.
Mockery, which is a kind of murder,
Has stolen into the language and fingers
Of the city, producing a stammer
Of obscenities and a tremor
Of burnt matches at our fingers' ends.
I wish that all these words were raindrops.

Donald Revell

"Out of the clouds," says Actual Man,
"A foxtail of rain covers the churches
And one by one the churches disappear."
Ave verum corpus is all well and good
For a gateway, but when the iron gates
Have rusted shut against the iron air
Choirs gasp, words die in the throat,
And the only sound is thorns underfoot,
A rustle as of bones shifting
Underground. Posterity is abandoned
To imaginary animals.
Race abdicates. Gender abdicates.
The color is disappearing from my hands
Like a vixen through a snare of garlands.

NOTES ON CONTRIBUTORS

DIANE ACKERMAN is the author of many works of nonfiction and poetry, including *The Zookeeper's Wife* (W. W. Norton), *A Natural History of the Senses* (Random House), and *The Human Age* (W. W. Norton). She has received the John Burroughs Nature Award, the Orion Book Award, and the PEN/Henry David Thoreau Prize, among other honors. A film version of *The Zookeeper's Wife* appeared in 2017.

HEATHER ALTFELD is a poet and essayist living in Northern California. Her second book of poetry, *Post-Mortem*, is forthcoming from Orison Books. "Obituary for Dead Languages," her contribution to *Conjunctions:70, Sanctuary: The Preservation Issue*, was selected for *The Best American Essays 2019*.

RAE ARMANTROUT's most recent book, *Wobble* (Wesleyan), was a finalist for the National Book Award. Her new collection, *Now See*, is forthcoming from Wesleyan in the fall of 2020.

JESSICA CAMPBELL is a writer and one of the organizers of Atrocious Poets in Woodstock, Illinois.

MATTHEW CHENEY is the author of *Blood: Stories* (Black Lawrence Press) and *Modernist Crisis and the Pedagogy of Form* (Bloomsbury Academic). He teaches at Plymouth State University in New Hampshire.

THOMAS DAI is a doctoral student in Brown University's American Studies department.

RACHEL BLAU DUPLESSIS, poet, critic, and collagist, is the author of the multi-volume long poem *Drafts* (1986–2012), from Salt Publishing and Wesleyan, and the recent collage poems *Numbers* (Materialist Press) and *Graphis Novella* (Xexoxial Editions).

KRISTA EASTMAN is the author of the essay collection *The Painted Forest* (West Virginia University Press). Her essays have been published in *The Georgia Review*, *Kenyon Review*, and other journals.

Contributing Editor BRIAN EVENSON is the author of more than a dozen books of fiction, most recently *Song for the Unraveling of the World* (Coffee House). He lives in Los Angeles and teaches at CalArts.

MATTHEW GAVIN FRANK is the author of the nonfiction books *The Mad Feast: An Ecstatic Tour through America's Food*, *Preparing the Ghost: An Essay Concerning the Giant Squid and Its First Photographer* (both Liveright), *Pot Farm*, and *Barolo* (both University of Nebraska Press); the poetry books *The Morrow Plots* (Black Lawrence Press), *Warranty in Zulu* (Barrow Street Press), and *Sagittarius Agitprop* (Black Lawrence Press); and two chapbooks. His forthcoming nonfiction book, *A Brief Atmospheric Future*, is due out in 2021 from Liveright.

TROY JOLLIMORE's poetry collections include *Syllabus of Errors* (Princeton Series of Contemporary Poets) and *Tom Thomson in Purgatory* (MARGIE/IntuiT House), which won the National Book Critics Circle Award for Poetry. His philosophical books include *Love's Vision* (Princeton University Press) and *On Loyalty* (Routledge).

KARLA KELSEY is the author of four books, most recently *Of Sphere* (Essay Press). *On Certainty* (Ahsahta Press) and *Blood Feather* (Tupelo Press) are forthcoming.

HILARY LEICHTER's writing has appeared in *n+1*, *The New Yorker*, *American Short Fiction*, and elsewhere. Her debut novel, *Temporary*, is forthcoming from Coffee House/Emily Books.

REBECCA LILLY's collection of prose poems, *Creatures Among Us*, was published by Broadstone Books in August 2019.

ROBERT MACFARLANE is the author of many books on place, people, and nature, including *The Old Ways* (Viking), *The Lost Words* (with Jackie Morris; House of Anansi), and most recently *Underland* (W. W. Norton). In 2017 he was given the E. M. Forster Award for Literature by the American Academy of Arts and Letters.

NATHANIEL MACKEY's most recent book of poetry is *Blue Fasa* (New Directions). Forthcoming from New Directions is *Double Trio*, a three-book set, from which the poem in this issue is taken.

SANDRA MEEK has published six books of poems, including *Still*, *An Ecology of Elsewhere*, and *Road Scatter* (all Persea), and the Dorset Prize–winning *Biogeography* (Tupelo). Recipient of the Poetry Society of America's Lucille Medwick Memorial Award, three Georgia Author of the Year awards, and two Peace Corps Writers awards, she is co-founding editor of Ninebark Press, director of the Georgia Poetry Circuit, and poetry editor of the *Phi Kappa Phi Forum*.

KATE MONAGHAN recently completed a PhD in classical Chinese poetry.

JAMES MORROW is the author of ten novels, including *The Godhead Trilogy* (Harcourt), *The Last Witchfinder* (William Morrow), and *Galápagos Regained* (St. Martin's Press). He has received the World Fantasy Award, the Nebula Award, the Theodore Sturgeon Memorial Award, and the Grand Prix de l'Imaginaire.

ANDREW MOSSIN has published five collections of poetry, the most recent of which is *Stanzas for the Preparation of Perception* (Spuyten Duyvil). He is an associate professor at Temple University, where he teaches in the Intellectual Heritage Program.

YXTA MAYA MURRAY is a writer and law professor living in Los Angeles. Her novel, *Art Is Everything*, is forthcoming from Northwestern University Press/ Curbstone.

KRISTINE ONG MUSLIM is the author of nine books, including the short story collections *Age of Blight* (Unnamed Press), *Butterfly Dream* (Snuggly Books), and *The Drone Outside* (Eibonvale Press), and editor of two anthologies—with Nalo Hopkinson for the British Fantasy Award–winning *People of Colo(u)r Destroy Science Fiction*, and with Paolo Enrico Melendez for *Sigwa: Climate Fiction Anthology from the Philippines* (forthcoming from the Polytechnic University of the Philippines Press). She grew up and continues to live in a town in Maguindanao, southern Philippines.

ROB NIXON is the Currie C. and Thomas A. Barron Family Professor in Humanities and the Environment at Princeton University. His most recent book is *Slow Violence and the Environmentalism of the Poor* (Harvard University Press).

JOYCE CAROL OATES is the author, most recently, of *My Life as a Rat* (Ecco) and *Pursuit* (Mysterious Press). She is the 2019 recipient of the Jerusalem Prize and is currently Distinguished Writer in the Graduate Writing Program at New York University.

LANCE OLSEN is author of more than twenty-five books of and about innovative writing, including, most recently, the novels *Dreamlives of Debris* (Dzanc) and *My Red Heaven* (Dzanc, forthcoming 2020). He teaches experimental narrative theory and practice at the University of Utah.

TOBY OLSON's eleventh novel, *Walking*, will appear soon from Occidental Square Press/Chatwin. His poetry collection, *Death Sentences*, was recently published by Shearsman Books.

FRANCINE PROSE is the author of twenty-one works of fiction, including *Mister Monkey; Lovers at the Chameleon Club, Paris 1932; A Changed Man*, which won the Dayton Literary Peace Prize; and *Blue Angel*, a finalist for the National Book Award. Her works of nonfiction include *Anne Frank: The Book, The Life, The Afterlife* and *Reading Like a Writer* (all Harper). Her latest book, *What to Read and Why*, was published by Harper in 2018.

JESSICA REED's recent work appears in *Denver Quarterly, PANK, Exposition Review, DIAGRAM, Conjunctions, Bellingham Review, Colorado Review*, and elsewhere. Her chapbook *World, Composed* is from Finishing Line Press. She teaches physics and the arts at Butler University.

DONALD REVELL is the author of fifteen collections of poetry, most recently *Drought-Adapted Vine* and *The English Boat*, both from Alice James Books.

SOFIA SAMATAR is the author of the novels *A Stranger in Olondria* and *The Winged Histories*, and the short story collection *Tender* (all Small Beer Press). With her brother, the artist Del Samatar, she co-created *Monster Portraits* (Rose Metal Press). Her work has received several honors, including the World Fantasy Award.

SABINE SCHIFFNER, born in Bremen in 1965, is a German poet. She is the author of four collections of poetry, including *Besteck im Kopf* (Emons). She has also published a novel and translates works from Spanish and Catalan into German. She is the recipient of numerous awards and honors, including the Jürgen-Ponto-Preis and the Preis der Deutschen Schillerstiftung.

ARTHUR SZE is the author of ten books of poetry, most recently *Sight Lines* (Copper Canyon). He is a professor emeritus at the Institute of American Indian Arts.

JONATHAN THIRKIELD is the author of *The Waker's Corridor* (LSU Press). He teaches programming at The New School.

QUINCY TROUPE's latest books of poems are *Seduction* and a book-length poem, *Ghost Voices* (TriQuarterly). He is coauthor, with Miles Davis, of *Miles: The Autobiography*, and author of *Miles and Me*, a chronicle of his friendship with Davis, reissued in 2018 by Seven Stories Press and scheduled for release in 2020 as a major motion picture for which Mr. Troupe wrote the screenplay. Also forthcoming from Seven Stories Press are *Duende: Poems from 1966 Until Now* and a memoir, *The Accordion Years*.

DEBBIE URBANSKI's stories have been published in *The Best American Science Fiction and Fantasy*, *The Sun*, *Kenyon Review*, *Nature*, *Terraform*, *Fantasy & Science Fiction*, and *Best American Experimental Writing*. She is the recipient of a 2019 Rona Jaffe Foundation Writers' Award.

HELENA VAN BRANDE graduated from Princeton University with a degree in comparative literature and minors in creative writing and environmental studies. She recently made her literary debut with the publication of her poem "No bedtime story" in *Tiny Seed Literary Journal*. She currently lives in Lakeview, Oregon.

ELIOT WEINBERGER's *Angels & Saints* is forthcoming from New Directions/ Christine Burgin.

WIL WEITZEL received his MFA at New York University's Writers Workshop in Paris. His stories have appeared in *Epoch*, *Kenyon Review*, *Michigan Quarterly Review*, *The O. Henry Prize Stories*, and elsewhere. He was an NYC Emerging Writers Fellow at the Center for Fiction, won the *Washington Square Review* Flash Fiction Award, and is currently at work on a novel.

And Go Like This

stories

by

JOHN CROWLEY

Either he has invented all this, or he is himself invented: and these are not two contradictory things but one thing.

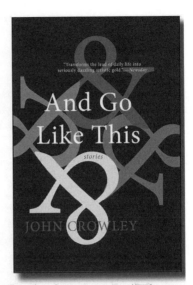

And Go Likes This collects thirteen stories for the first time. In "The Girlhood of Shakespeare's Heroines," Crowley takes us to a Shakespeare festival in 1950s Indiana, and then to spring break on a future Yale campus imbued by the spirit of Edgar Allen Poe in his Edgar Award-winning story "Spring Break." In the previously unpublished "Anosognosia," the world brought about by one John C's high-school accident may or may not exist. It will be available on November 5th from your local bookstore &c. in Smyth sewn trade cloth and in ebook. There is a third edition ($500); orders fulfilled in the sequence they are placed from our website, limited to 26 lettered copies hand bound by Henry Wessells in patterned paper over boards, with printed paper labels, signed on the limitation leaf by the author, and including a second tipped-in sheet of a handwritten passage from the book selected by Crowley.

Kim Scott exploration of the possibilities of decolonialization and reconciliation, *Taboo* is a luminous, haunted, unflinching, and unexpectedly hopeful novel.

"Makes a strong case to be the novel that will help clarify—in the way that only literature can—what reconciliation might mean."
— *Australian Book Review*

SBP

smallbeerpress.com. DRM-free ebooks: weightlessbooks.com. Small Beer Press protection while shooting arrows), is now tunneled, permitting population circulation. Wars etc. part of dying political-economic structures. Social work equals increasing number of global services. III. As McLuhan says, everything happens at once. Image is no longer stream falling over rocks, getting from original to final place; it's as Tenney explained : a vibrating complex, any addition or subtraction of component(s), regardless of apparent position(s) in the total system, producing alteration, a different music. Fuller : As long as one human being is hungry, the entire human race is hungry. *City planning's obsolete. What's needed is global planning so Earth may stop stepping like octopus on its own feet.* Buckminster Fuller uses his head : comprehensive design science; inventory of world resources. *Conversion : the mind turns around, no longer facing in its direction. Utopia? Self-knowledge. Some will make it, with or without LSD. The others?* Pray for acts of God, crises, power failures, no water to drink. IV. We see symmetrically : canoe on northern Canadian lake, stars in midnight sky repeated in water, forested shores precisely mirrored. Our hearing's asymmetrical : noticed sounds surprise us, echoes of shouts we make transform our voices, straight line of sound from us to

26

Bill and Elaine de Kooning were flying to Amsterdam. Shortly after the movie had started, Bill got up and said, "This's no good : let's go home.

a new expanded paperback edition of John Cage's

Diary: How to Improve the World
(You Will Only Make Matters Worse)

Holland Cotter, *New York Times:* "Over sixteen years, beginning in 1965, John Cage compiled anecdotes, observations and koanlike tales, originally typing everything on an IBM Selectric and using chance methods to determine the formatting of texts that twist down each page. The Siglio [hardcover] edition preserves the graphic effects, but, more important, it gives a sense of the company he kept during these years—Marcel Duchamp, R. Buckminster Fuiller, D.T. Suzuki—and of his passionate feeling about a world locked in a state of perpetual warfare. Cage has a reputation for being a Zen-inspired wit. He was also much more, an intensely engaged moral thinker."

This new edition includes a significant addendum with over twenty facsimile pages of Cage's handwritten notebook of a ninth part in progress. These previously unpublished pages bring the reader into compelling proximity to Cage's process and the raw material from which *Diary* is made.

$24 · PB · 200 pages · duotones and four-color · **www.sigliopress.com**

siglio

uncommon books at the intersection of art & literature

EPOCH

A MAGAZINE OF CONTEMPORARY LITERATURE

PUBLISHED THREE TIMES PER YEAR

$5/ISSUE $11/YEAR

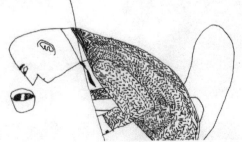

"Last Night's Tea"
sketchbook drawing
(12 x 9 inches) in
pen and ink by

Blair Thornley

WWW.EPOCH.CORNELL.EDU

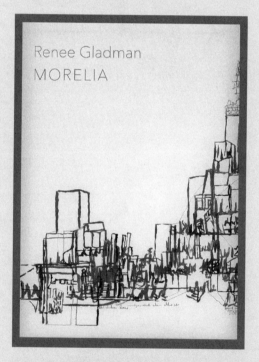

Submit work January 1–31, 2020 to the 18th annual

IOWA REVIEW AWARDS

guest judged by

NONFICTION

Leslie Jamison

FICTION

Lan Samantha Chang

POETRY

Stephanie Burt

$1500 to each winner
$750 to each runner-up

iowareview.org/rules

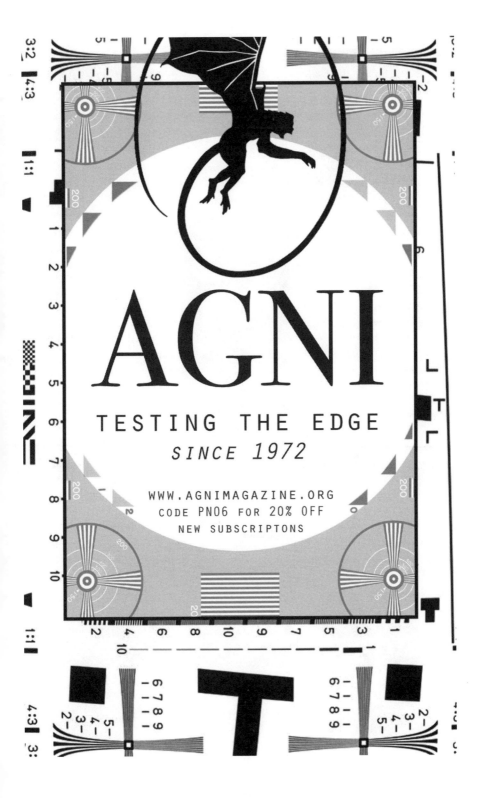

AGNI

TESTING THE EDGE

SINCE 1972

WWW.AGNIMAGAZINE.ORG
CODE PN06 FOR 20% OFF
NEW SUBSCRIPTONS

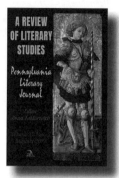

ANAPHORA
LITERARY PRESS

*Publisher of fiction,
poetry and non-fiction*
anaphoraliterary.com

PENNSYLVANIA
LITERARY JOURNAL

ISSN#: 2151-3066;
6X9", $15/iss: is a
printed journal that runs
critical essays, book-
reviews, short stories,
interviews, photographs,
art, and poetry. Also
available from EBSCO
and ProQuest. One PLJ
article won the 2015
CCCC Lavender Rhetoric
Award for Excellence in
Queer Scholarship. PLJ
published *New York Times*
bestselling and major
award-winning writers
such as Larry Niven,
Mary Jo Putney, Bob Van
Laerhoven and Geraldine
Brooks.

CINEMATIC CODES
REVIEW

ISSN 2473-3385 (print);
ISSN 2473-3377 (online);
6X9", $15/iss: features
work in and about all au-
dio/visual genres, including
music videos, feature films,
documentaries, photog-
raphy, or just about any
other mode or genre of
art beyond the realm of
"literature."

DISTRIBUTION:
• In full-text on
EBSCO Academic
Complete and
ProQuest databases.
• On sale as single
issues on Amazon,
Barnes and Noble.
• YBP/ Coutts
distribution
• Annual Subscription:
$45: shipping
included, 3 issues/
year. No extra fees
with electronic or
paper checks. 4.8% for
PayPal.
• Free excerpts of
reviews and interviews
with best-sellers are
publicly available on
the Anaphora website.

Unsolicited submissions
to both journals (scholarship, reviews, interviews)
and for Anaphora books are
always warmly welcomed
at director@
anaphoraliterary.com, Anna
Faktorovich PhD.

One of my favourite
magazines.
— Ben Lerner

IN BRICK 103

Michael Ondaatje
Amitava Kumar
Fanny Howe
Caryl Pagel
Pura López Colomé
Laurie Anderson
Hebe Uhart
Karen Solie

ORDER YOURS AT
BRICKMAG.COM

DONATE TO *CONJUNCTIONS*

Publishers Circle ($5,000+)

Jay Hanus   Hy Abady   Lawrence Bank

Benefactors Circle ($2,000–$4,999)

Barbara Grossman and Michael Gross

Friends Circle ($500–$1,999)

Beth L. Herstein   Cole Swensen
Peter Straub   Nancy Leonard
Theresa Fadul,   Jackie Douglas
in memory of William F. S. Orner James Jaffe
Motoyuki Shibata   Anonymous (3)

Supporters Circle (up to $499)

William Mascioli	Margaret Shuhala	Michèle Dominy
Catherine Imbriglio,	Angelica J. Smith	Shane Ryan Bailey
in memory of	Mary Caponegro &	Thomas Wild
Reginald Shepherd	Michael Ives	Michael J. Maresca
& C. D. Wright	Mark Cohen	Richard Murphy
Christopher Sorrentino	Rachel Blau DuPlessis	Hope Polidoro
Henry Dunow	William L. Evans	David A. Poole
Andi & Lance Olsen	Elizabeth Ely &	Jacob Wegelin
Margaret Fisher &	Jonathan Greenburg	Kristina Una Amadeus
Robert Hughes	Chris Kearin	Jennifer Breen
James B. Westine,	David G. Perry	Susan Love Brown
in memory of	Karen Russell	Leslie Bumstead
Peggy Brady	Laurence Ryan	Tyson Duffy
Rachel Tzvia Back	Michael Sheehan	Cecelia Shalini Dsouza
Mary Jo Bang	Enrique Urueta	Sharon Johnson
Jay Cantor	Amy Holman	Megan Kincheloe
Kathryn Davis	Tim Horvath	Byron N. Landry
Forrest Gander	Henry Ledwith	Roseanne Giannini Quinn
Frieda Gardner	Peter McCabe	Jane Rosenthal
Brandon Hobson	Kelly McKisson	James B. Stewart
Jared Killeen	Michael Parker,	Karen Burnham
Alison & John Lankenau	*in honor of*	Stephen E. Myers
Literary Hub	*Micaela Morrissette*	Rebecca Thomas
Debra Pemstein	Eleni Sikelianos	Anonymous (22)
	Jeffrey Wertheimer	

Please help *Conjunctions* continue to make reading dangerously and writing fearlessly possible! Be an activist reader and lover of literature, and donate today at http://annandaleonline.org/supportconjunctions. For questions about donating or to give by mail with a check or credit card, contact our managing editor at conjunctions@bard.edu or (845) 758-7054.

This project is supported in part by an award from the National Endowment for the Arts and from the New York State Council on the Arts with the support of Governor Andrew M. Cuomo and the New York State Legislature.

NATIONAL ENDOWMENT for ARTS
arts.gov

NEW YORK STATE OF OPPORTUNITY. | Council on the Arts

CONJUNCTIONS.COM

700 groundbreaking fictions,
poems, narrative essays,
interviews, translations,
artworks, and digital creations—
online only.

Recordings of author readings,
exclusive to *Conjunctions*.

Full-text selections from our
vast archive of print issues.

All free on our website.

 *Read dangerously.*

@_conjunctions